Human health and disease

Heinemann Educational Publishers
Halley Court, Jordan Hill, Oxford OX2 8EJ
A Division of Reed Educational & Professional Publishing Ltd

OXFORD MELBOURNE AUCKLAND
JOHANNESBURG BLANTYRE GABORONE
IBADAN PORTSMOUTH (NH) USA CHICAGO

First published 1998

ISBN 0 435 57091 9

01 00 99
10 9 8 7 6 5 4 3 2

Edited by Ruth Holmes

Designed and typeset by Gecko Ltd, Bicester, Oxon

Illustrated by Jane Bottomley and Gecko Ltd

Cover design by Gecko Ltd, Bicester, Oxon

Cover photo by Getty Image and inset Science Photo Library

Printed and bound in Spain by Mateu Cromo

Photo research by Thelma Gilbert

Acknowledgements
The authors and publishers would like to thank the following for permission
to use photographs:

p2: Science Photo Library; **p4 and contents:** Science Photo Library; **p6 middle:** Sally & Richard Greenhill; **bottom right:** Sally & Richard Greenhill; **left:** Sally & Richard Greenhill, **top right:** Sally & Richard Greenhill; **p8:** P.A.News; **p9:** Science Photo Library; **p10 and contents:** Mirror Syndication; **p11:** Science Photo Library; **p12:** Science Photo Library; **p13:** Science Photo Library; **p14:** Science Photo Library; **p19:** (× 5) Science Photo Library; **p20:** Beechams; **p23:** National Medical Slide Bank; **p24:** Science Photo Library; **p26:** Science Photo Library; **p28:** Science Photo Library; **p35 left:** Roger Scruton; **right:** Anthony Blake; **p36:** Science Photo Library; **p39:** (× 3) Mary Evans Picture Library; **p40:** Science Photo Library; **p42:** Ann Fullick; **p43:** Hulton Getty Pictures; **p45:** Panos Pictures/R.Gilling; **p46:** Science Photo Library; **p49:** Science Photo Library; **p55 middle:** Still Pictures; **top:** Ace Photos; **bottom:** Roger Scruton; **p57:** P.A.News; **p58:** Roger Scruton; **p59 top:** Sally & Richard Greenhill; **bottom:** Panos Pictures/R.Gilling; **p63 top:** Panos Pictures/P.Tweedie; **bottom left:** BBC; **bottom right:** Science Photo Library; **p65:** Roger Scruton; **p66 left:** Panos Pictures/T.Page; **right:** Panos Pictures/M.McEvery; **p67 top:** Mirror Syndication; **middle:** Mirror Syndication; **bottom:** Mirror Syndication; **p74 left:** Science Photo Library; **right:** Peter Gould; **p78:** Science Photo Library; **p81 top and contents:** Sally & Richard Greenhill; **bottom:** Sally & Richard Greenhill; **p83:** Science Photo Library; **p86:** Mary Evans Picture Library; **p87 and contents:** Mary Evans Picture Library; **p89:** P.A.News; **p90:** Science Photo Library; **p92 top:** Biophoto Associates; **bottom:** Health Education Authority; **p94:** Sally & Richard Greenhill; **p95 middle:** Colorsport; **right:** Action Plus; **left:** Roger Scruton; **p99:** Mary Evans Picture Library; **p100:** Science Photo Library; **p102:** Katz Pictures/G.Steinmetz; **p103:** Dept of Transport; **p105:** Network Photographers; **p106:** Mirror Syndication; **p107:** Network Photographers; **p108:** Mirror Syndication; **p111:** Popperfoto; **p117:** Science Photo Library; **p119:** Biophoto Associates; **p121:** Roger Scruton; **p122:** Sally & Richard Greenhill; **p124 and contents:** Science Photo Library; **p127:** Science Photo Library; **p133:** Science Photo Library; **p136 top:** Ace Photos; **middle:** J.Allan Cash; **bottom and contents:** Sally & Richard Greenhill; **p137:** Biophoto Associates; **p143:** Biophoto Associates; **p145:** Science Photo Library; **p147:** Mirror Syndication; **p150 top left:** Mirror Syndication; **top right:** Popperfoto; **bottom left:** Mirror Syndication; **bottom right:** Mirror Syndication; **p157:** Biophoto Associates; **p159:** Science Photo Library.

The author and publishers would like to thank the following for permission to reproduce copyright material:

map on p.5: World Health Organisation, *Programme on AIDS*, 1996: **bar chart p.7 and graph p.8:** Libra Pharma, *Common Diseases*, J Fry and G Sandler, published by Kluwer Academic, 1993; **bar charts p.15:** OPCS, *Health of Nations*, U205 Open University, 1985; **bar chart p.16:** SIMEP Editions, *Postgraduate Medical Journal* 57, Age, sex, ethnic origin and hospital admission for heart attack and stroke, Beevers and Cruickshank, 1981 p.764; **pie charts p.16:** OPCS, *Social Trends* 27, 1997, Office for National Statistics, and WHO based on *New England Journal of Medicine*, Selective Primary Health Care, K Walsh and KS Warren, 1979; **bar charts p.17:** HMSO, *DHSS Inequalities in Health (The Black Report)*, 1980; **bar charts p.27, graph p.43, graph p.47 and p.48 right, and graph p.50 and p48 left:** Blackwell Science Publishing, *Infectious Diseases*, Bannister, Begg and Gillespie, 1996; **bar charts p.63:** John Murray (Publishers) Ltd, *SATIS World of Science*, Fullick et al, 1996; **bar chart p.68:** British Heart Foundation, *Coronary Heart Disease Statistics*, 1997; **graph p.73:** Libra Pharma, *Common Diseases*, J Fry and G Sandler, published by Kluwer Academic, 1993; **bar charts p.81 and graph p.82:** John Murray (Publishers) Ltd, *SATIS World of Science*, Fullick et al, 1996; **poster p.103:** Alcohol Concern; **diagrams p.123:** Open University, *Human Health and Disease: An Evolutionary Approach*; **diagram p.128:** McGraw-Hill, *Biology*, Wessels and Hopson, 1988, published by Random House, NY; **graph p.131:** WHO Regional Office for Europe, Copenhagen, *WHO Regional Publications, European series, no. 38*; **bar chart p.140:** *Journal of Applied Physiology, Vol 55 pp. 191-5*, CTM Davies and K Young, 1983; **table p.146:** HMSO, Registrar-General Statistics, 1960 and 1991; **bar charts p.148-9:** Mercantile and General Reinsurance, *Long-term Care Insurance*.

The author and publishers would like to thank the following Examination Boards for permission to reproduce their material:
Northern Examinations and Assessment Board, Oxford & Cambridge Examinations & Assessment Council, Southern Examining Group, and University of Cambridge Local Examinations Syndicate for questions on pages 152 to 159.

The publishers have made every effort to trace the copyright holders, but if they have inadvertently overlooked any, they will be pleased to make the necessary arrangements at the first opportunity.

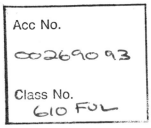

HOW TO USE THIS BOOK

Heinemann Advanced Science: Human Health and Disease has been written to accompany your advanced level biology or human biology course and contains all the syllabus material you will need during your period of study of Human Health and Disease. At the beginning of the book an introduction explores the real-life context of an area of the science which follows. You may use this to whet your appetite for the chapters to come, or read it when you have made some progress with the science to emphasise the relevance of what you are doing. However you use it, I hope it will make you want to read on!

In addition to the main text, the chapters of the book contain two types of boxes. The grey *information boxes* contain basic facts or techniques which you need to know. This often includes key facts you will have met at GCSE – the boxes then carry these ideas forward to A level. Information boxes are sometimes referred to in the main text, and can be read either as you meet them or when you have finished reading the chapter. The pink headed *extension boxes* contain more advanced information which is not referred to in the main text. You do not need to address the contents of these extension boxes until you have got to grips with the rest of the material in the chapter.

When you have completed the work in a chapter of the book there are questions to help you find out how much of the material you have understood and to help you with your revision. Summaries at the end of each chapter provide further help with revision. At the end of the book there is a selection of A level questions.

Throughout the book the Institute of Biology's recommendations on biological nomenclature have been followed.

This book has been written to be an accessible, clear and exciting guide to Human Health and Disease at A level. I hope that it will help to maintain your interest in the subject you have chosen and that it will play a valuable role in developing your knowledge of human biology – and with it give an increased understanding of health, disease and the social implications of our growing ability to intervene and control both the causes and the symptoms of disease.

Acknowledgements

Many people have been extremely generous with both their time and their expertise whilst I have been writing this book. In particular Dr Bill Inge has been of immense help in checking both the veracity and relevance of the text. Of course, as author I accept full responsibility for the final content of the book.

I should like to thank Clare Farley and my publisher Lindsey Charles for their hard work and persistence in ensuring that this book made it into print. My copy editor Ruth Holmes deserves special mention for without her the book would undoubtedly be poorer.

Finally I would like to thank my husband Patrick who has, as always, provided invaluable help, support and encouragement, and my mother who has given freely of her time to make the project possible.

Dedication

For William, Thomas, James and Edward

Ann Fullick, 1998

CONTENTS

INTRODUCTION

Old plague, new plague 2

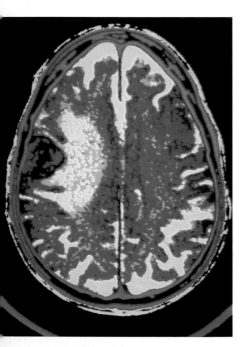

1 HEALTH AND DISEASE

Defining health and disease 6
Aetiology – the causes of disease 8
Detecting disease 10
Studying disease 14
Summary 18
Questions 18

2 INFECTIOUS DISEASES

Types of pathogen 19
Passing it on 24
Natural defences 27
The pathogens fight back 33
Controlling disease 36
A closer look at some infectious diseases 49
Summary 52
Questions 54

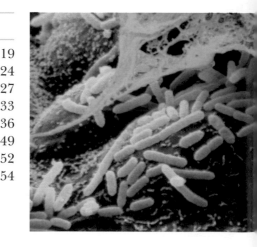

3 LIFESTYLE DISEASES

Diet and disease 55
Diseases of the respiratory system 69
Diseases of the cardiovascular system 74
Cancer – the last word 82
Summary 83
Questions 85

4 DRUGS, HEALTH AND DISEASE

What is a drug?	86
Legal drugs: caffeine and nicotine	88
Legal drugs: alcohol	96
Illegal drugs	105
Summary	108
Questions	110

5 REPRODUCTIVE HEALTH AND GENETIC DISEASES

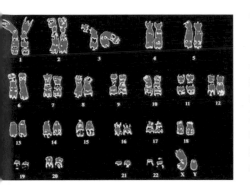

Sexually transmitted dieases	111
Contraception	112
Infertility	117
Genetic diseases	121
Summary	134
Questions	135

6 AGEING AND DEATH

Theories of ageing	136
Observing ageing	137
Dying and death	146
Summary	150
Questions	151

EXAM QUESTIONS   152

INDEX   160

INTRODUCTION

Old plague, new plague

For as long as people have been making written records, the occurrence and spread of human diseases, and diseases of their animals and crops, have been documented. From these records, we have a fairly clear picture of the pattern of development of some major diseases.

Malaria – an old plague...

Malaria has been around for centuries, and at present shows no signs of loosening its grip on the human race. The disease affects 267 million people over 103 countries, and results in around 107 million clinical cases and up to two million deaths each year. It is largely, but certainly not entirely, found in the developing world.

The *Plasmodium* parasite causes malaria. This parasite is a protozoan with a complex life cycle involving two hosts, the *Anopheles* mosquito and people. The mosquito, shown in

Figure 1 This scanning electron micrograph shows the mouthparts of the female *Anopheles* mosquito, the vector for malaria which kills over two million people each year.

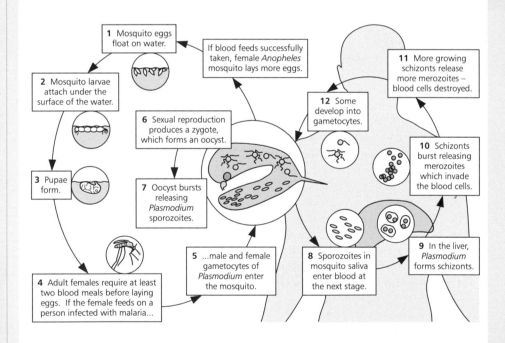

1 Mosquito eggs float on water.

2 Mosquito larvae attach under the surface of the water.

3 Pupae form.

4 Adult females require at least two blood meals before laying eggs. If the female feeds on a person infected with malaria...

5 ...male and female gametocytes of *Plasmodium* enter the mosquito.

6 Sexual reproduction produces a zygote, which forms an oocyst.

7 Oocyst bursts releasing *Plasmodium* sporozoites.

If blood feeds successfully taken, female *Anopheles* mosquito lays more eggs.

8 Sporozoites in mosquito saliva enter blood at the next stage.

9 In the liver, *Plasmodium* forms schizonts.

10 Schizonts burst releasing merozoites which invade the blood cells.

11 More growing schizonts release more merozoites – blood cells destroyed.

12 Some develop into gametocytes.

Figure 2 The symptoms of malaria coincide with the multiplication of the malarial parasites and the destruction of red blood cells. This may lead to long term weakness, anaemia and death.

figure 1, is the **vector** for the disease – it transmits it from one person to another. Only female mosquitoes bite people, because they need a blood meal before laying their eggs, and it is at this point that they pass on the protozoan.

Malaria begins with 'flu-like symptoms which develop 8–30 days after the infected bite, and the disease progresses to a regular cycle of severe fevers, shaking chills and drenching sweats. Figure 2 shows the life cycle of the *Plasmodium* parasite.

Malaria has always been associated with rivers and ponds, sources of water where the mosquito larvae can grow. But as millions of people flock to the shanty towns surrounding the new megacities of the developing world, fresh opportunities are arising for the mosquitoes. Strains are emerging that can breed rapidly in a tiny amount of water, such as a bottle top, a water-filled footprint or a blocked drain, threatening a new surge of the disease. Many people in Africa have become at least partly immune to malaria, carrying it but showing no symptoms. However, the increased exploitation of resources in areas such as the Amazon basin, Ethiopia, Madagascar and Sri Lanka has led to susceptible people moving into these areas and local epidemics occurring.

No really effective treatments against malaria have emerged so far. This is in part due to the nature of the organism involved, and partly because those countries most affected by malaria are also generally very poor. Potential profits for a company marketing a cure are limited, and so the investment in research has been limited too. There are no drugs to destroy the parasite once in people's bodies. Vaccines are extremely difficult and expensive to make because the protozoans keep changing their outer coats. Controlling the mosquito vectors has resulted in some success, by spraying waterways with DDT to kill the mosquito larvae, but the environmental effects can be grave. Controlling the environment by improving public and environmental health is an important factor. In Singapore, a law was passed making it illegal to have any standing water on property where mosquitoes might breed. People removed old tins, bottle tops, etc., and as a result the incidence of malaria has been substantially reduced. However, malaria is on the increase in the developed world as a result of climatic and social changes. Investment has increased and there is now the possibilty of a successful vaccine, based on a antibody to a vital *Plasmodium* protein. Malaria, the ancient scourge of the human race, may yet be defeated.

...and AIDS, a new one

In both the developed and developing worlds, a new disease is rapidly spreading, leaving millions infected and millions more dead. It is predicted that AIDS will overtake malaria as the disease that kills the most people worldwide by the beginning of the twenty-first century. The infective agent and the method of transmission from one individual to another are known (and described below), yet we have failed so far to halt the spread of the disease. Major research laboratories in many countries have been working to develop a cure or a vaccine, but as yet without complete success. In contrast with malaria, enormous amounts of research funding have gone towards understanding and curing AIDS because the potential financial rewards are great.

The emergence of AIDS

In 1981, doctors in America reported a new disease. It first became apparent in the homosexual community of Los Angeles, where unusually high numbers of young men developed a type of cancer, Kaposi's sarcoma, which was usually only seen in very elderly patients. Eventually a whole range of common symptoms (fevers, persistent diar-rhoea, loss in body mass, TB, a rare type of pneumonia, Kaposi's sarcoma and infections that rarely affect healthy people) were recognised as resulting from infection by one particular virus. The end result for those showing symptoms was usually death. This disease was **AIDS** (**acquired immune deficiency syndrome**), and the pathogen responsible is known as **HIV** (**human immunodeficiency virus**). Infection by HIV does not necessarily lead to AIDS. People infected by the virus who do not display the symptoms of AIDS are referred to as **HIV positive**. When tested, their blood shows the presence of HIV antibodies. **UNAIDS**, the Joint Nations Programme on HIV/AIDS, estimates that currently about 22 million people are living with HIV/AIDS, 90% of whom live in the developing world.

How is HIV transmitted?

The human immunodeficiency virus is very fragile and cannot survive in the air. It must be contained in human body fluids. HIV infection may come from either an individual who is HIV positive (who may be without symptoms and quite possibly unaware of their infection) or someone with AIDS. The virus can be transmitted from person to person in one of three ways, each of which involves contact between the body fluids of two individuals. The first and most common means of transmission is by sexual contact, between both homosexuals and heterosexuals. So far in the developed world homosexual sex has been more likely to transmit the disease, with relatively few cases of infection via heterosexual intercourse in the developed countries, but on a global scale heterosexual intercourse is responsible for over 70% of all HIV infections.

The second way in which HIV is spread is through infected blood. Intravenous drug users have appeared as a high risk group, due both to infection from shared needles and to the prostitution often undertaken to pay for the drugs. HIV has also been spread through the use of infected blood products. Haemophiliacs need transfusions of factor VIII to enable their blood to clot normally, and numbers of them, along with their families, became infected with the virus before the risk was recognised. In America and much of Europe, blood is now treated to destroy HIV before it is used for transfusions. However, in much of the developing world, blood for transfusions is bought from unscreened individuals and is frequently not treated in any way, so transmission through blood products continues.

Third, HIV can cross from a mother to her fetus in the early stages of pregnancy. Infection of the baby may also occur during birth, and the virus has been shown to be present in breast milk, so infants may be born free from HIV but become infected through breast feeding.

How does HIV cause AIDS?

Most of the clinical symptoms of AIDS are the result of the profound effect HIV has on the immune system of the body. It leaves individuals vulnerable to a whole range of infections which might be trivial in a healthy person but which, in an AIDS sufferer, may mean death. The immune system, which is described in

Figure 4 The effect of HIV on the immune system cascade

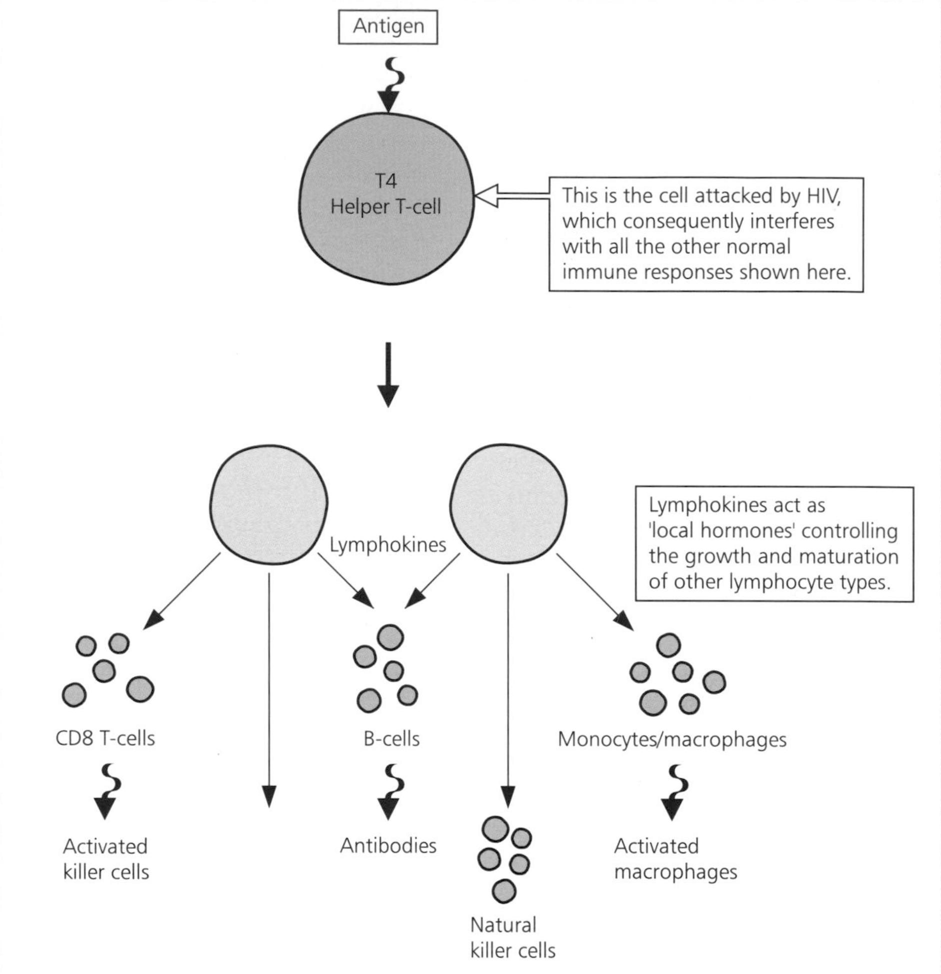

Antigen

T4 Helper T-cell

This is the cell attacked by HIV, which consequently interferes with all the other normal immune responses shown here.

Lymphokines

Lymphokines act as 'local hormones' controlling the growth and maturation of other lymphocyte types.

CD8 T-cells

B-cells

Monocytes/macrophages

Activated killer cells

Antibodies

Natural killer cells

Activated macrophages

chapter 2, has evolved to destroy and eliminate invading pathogens such as HIV, but it doesn't produce sufficient antibodies to overwhelm the virus because of the action of the virus itself. An important part of the immune system is a group of cells known as **T4** or **helper T-cells**. They have been termed 'the leaders of the immunological orchestra' because of their central role in the immune response. Helper T-cells support and amplify the response of other cells within the immune system, in particular the killer T-cells and some B-cells. Their role is outlined in figure 4.

However, on the surface of the cell membranes of the helper T-cells is a specific glycoprotein called CD4. This is recognised by HIV, and the viruses attach to the CD4, after which they can infect the helper T-cells. As a result of the HIV infection, the normal functioning of the helper T-cells is lost or impaired. This undermines the ability of the entire immune system to react to the invasion of the body by other pathogens.

Can AIDS be cured?

At the moment AIDS is still an incurable disease. A variety of methods of attack are currently under investigation and perhaps the most important of these is the attempt to limit the spread of the disease. As can be seen from figure 5,

Figure 3 A scanning electron micrograph showing the AIDS virus (red) attacking a helper T-cell

there are now millions of AIDS and HIV positive individuals throughout the world. Whilst the problem was first identified in America, there are now high numbers of affected people in the African and Asian continents. Education programmes have been set up to help people to understand the ways in which HIV is spread, and how to prevent it. Less promiscuous sex, the use of condoms to prevent internal contact between partners and the dangers of sharing needles in drug abuse are three of the main messages in the battle to contain this modern-day plague.

Many specialists feel that the development of an effective vaccine is crucial to the containment of the AIDS epidemic, but producing a vaccine against an organism whose target is actually part of the immune system is very difficult indeed.

Protection is needed against all strains of the virus, and HIV is a very variable virus. So far, insufficient detail is known about the infective mechanism of HIV to decide which part of the virus should be used as the basis for a vaccine. Added to this, AIDS is a peculiarly human disease. Chimpanzees seem to be the only other animals that are susceptible to the virus, and so work on animals to develop vaccines is limited. An effective vaccine is still only a hope on which much research is currently focused, although in the late 1990s a vaccine emerged with sufficient potential for a number of American doctors to offer themselves as human guinea pigs in a clinical trial.

Finally, drug therapy has a role to play. Although a variety of drugs have been tried so far, none has been found to be truly effective in either preventing the shift from HIV positive status to full-blown AIDS, or in slowing the progress of AIDS once it begins. Antiviral drugs are largely ineffective in the treatment of AIDS, and although drugs to stimulate the immune system have produced a short-lived improvement in killer T-cell functions, this improvement has not as yet been maintained over a longer period of time. However, towards the end of the twentieth century, combined drug therapies (where three or more drugs are used in a cocktail) are beginning to offer hope. Patients are living longer and remaining more healthy. If the current progress continues, AIDS may become a treatable disease in the not too distant future.

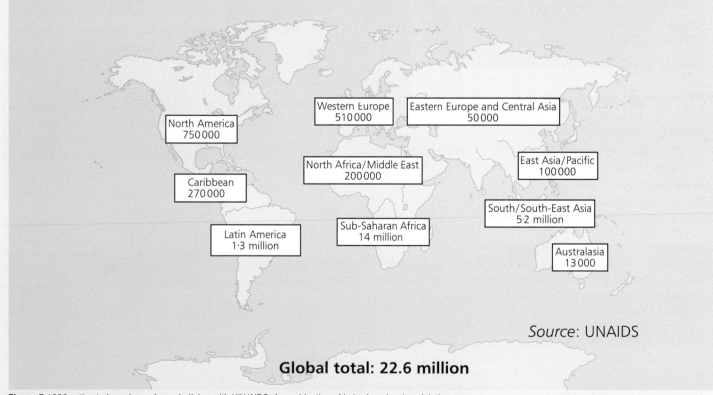

Figure 5 1996 estimated numbers of people living with HIV/AIDS. A combination of behavioural and social changes along with possible new vaccines and drugs may yet prevent HIV from becoming even more destructive than at present.

1 Health and disease

The state of our health is very important to us. 'How are you?' or its equivalent is the most common greeting in many languages. We also spend a great deal of time and money on our health – getting healthy, keeping healthy, returning to health. But what do we mean by 'health'? The World Health Organisation (WHO) defines health as *a state of complete physical, mental and social well-being which is more than just the absence of disease*. This is a relatively rare state which is also very subjective – for example, less than 10% of the British population claim to be completely healthy at any one time! Is health more than simply the absence of disease?

Figure 1.1 One of these people could have a mental illness, another be affected by parasitic worms and a third have a dietary deficiency disease. You cannot always tell by looking at people whether or not they are healthy.

DEFINING HEALTH AND DISEASE

Can you measure health?

Health is difficult to define and can be even more difficult to measure, either qualitatively or quantitatively. **Qualitative** measures (how people feel) are dependent on people's perceptions of their own health, and these are notoriously variable. Some people rarely if ever judge themselves as feeling healthy, even when they are perfectly well in a medical sense. Others who actually do suffer from medical problems may almost always describe themselves as feeling well. Perceptions of health also depend on the social context in which they occur. If you wake up with a slight headache on a school day you may feel so unwell that you stay in bed. A similar sensation at a weekend or during a holiday might be ignored!

Quantitative descriptions of health, involving precise measurements, are no easier to define. If someone feels well, they are unlikely to look for signs of ill health. Similarly, if someone feels ill, it is very hard to convince them that they are in fact healthy, and all the quantitative data in the world are unlikely to do this. Fortunately, although health is very difficult to measure, 'non-health' is rather easier to quantify. The opposite of health must be lack of health or non-health, usually referred to as dis-ease of the body, or **disease**.

There are different levels of disease, ranging from a general feeling of dissatisfaction with life, through **sickness**, when we feel something is wrong and treat it ourselves, into **illness**, when we feel unwell enough to seek help from a qualified health professional. This will often be a doctor, but it may be a nurse, a physiotherapist or a chiropodist. Increasingly, people are also consulting practitioners of alternative medicine such as a chiropractor or acupuncturist. A **disease** is a diagnostic label given to a set of signs and symptoms by a health professional. The **symptoms** of the disease we notice ourselves make us decide to visit our doctor, but there are often clinical **signs** unknown to us which the doctor will look for to aid diagnosis. For example, the symptoms of measles that we notice are the fever, irritability, cough and rash. But a doctor will look for Koplik's spots, white lesions inside the mouth, a clinical sign which confirms the diagnosis.

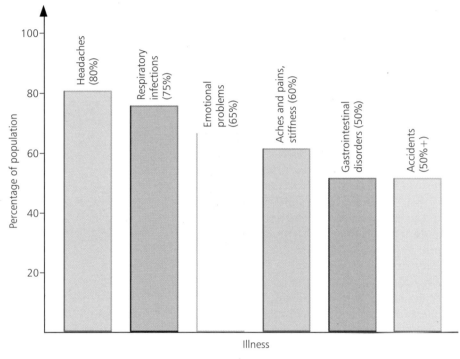

Figure 1.2 The proportions of adults suffering from minor illnesses in a single year in the UK

Types of disease

Physical illness

A **physical illness** affects the body, with symptoms either associated with a particular organ system or more generally spread throughout the body. **Coronary heart disease** is an example of a physical illness, and so is **osteoarthritis**. The majority of patients in a doctor's waiting room will be suffering from physical illnesses. Such illnesses vary in severity from trivial to those that are likely to cause death. A disease may have different effects depending on the reaction of the patient to it, or where in the world it is experienced. In many developed countries such as Britain and the USA, **measles** is an unpleasant childhood disease which very occasionally causes serious side-effects or even death (see figure 1.3 overleaf). Yet in parts of the developing world, measles is a regular killer disease of children – there is an Arab proverb which roughly translates as 'Don't count your children until they have had measles'. The range of ways in which your body can be affected by physical disease is too large to describe in one chapter, or indeed one book, but much of this and the following chapters will look at just some aspects of different types of physical disease. Many diseases will be mentioned in passing in this chapter, but will be examined in more detail later in the book.

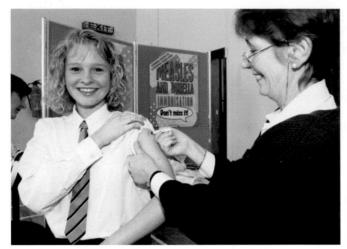

Figure 1.3 In recent years, the incidence of measles in many developed countries has been greatly reduced by vaccination programmes. A measles epidemic was predicted in Britain in 1994 which, because of the size of the population likely to catch it, would have killed a number of children. Mass vaccination of virtually all school children was introduced by the Government and as a result the epidemic did not materialise.

Mental illness

Mental illness affects the ability of the mind to function within a normally accepted range of behaviours. Some such illnesses arise when people find their circumstances difficult or very unsatisfying, and the reaction of the body is to rebel by producing a range of nervous and emotional reactions. Other mental illnesses seem to arise more as a result of inherited information, biochemical disturbances in the body and the physical processes of ageing. Like most health problems, mental illnesses (also referred to as **psychiatric disorders**) range from relatively common conditions like **depression** through to much rarer diseases such as **schizophrenia** and **manic depression**. Perhaps surprisingly, mental illness can cause death. This may occur through behaviour directly resulting from the condition – for example, people suffering from severe depression may, on rare occasions, commit suicide. On the other hand, in mental illnesses associated with ageing, the mental deterioration of **dementia** may prevent sufferers from taking proper care of themselves, so they may not eat properly and their physical systems deteriorate along with their mental capacity, leading eventually to death.

Twice as many women as men consult their GPs in any one year with psychiatric problems, yet many more men than women commit suicide. This might suggest that women are generally more willing to see a doctor about mental health problems, rather than being more prone to suffering from mental illnesses.

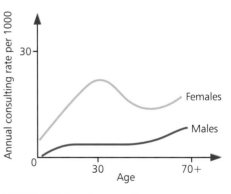

Figure 1.4 Whatever the reason, there are many more women than men consulting British GPs about mental health problems. It is also interesting to note the effect of age on the prevalence of psychiatric disorders. What factors might be causing this?

AETIOLOGY – THE CAUSES OF DISEASE

What causes disease? People have sought the answer to this question for thousands of years. Earliest records of modern human beings show evidence of attempts at medical care. In more recent years, our understanding of the causes of disease has developed greatly, yet there are still illnesses whose causes we do not know or do not fully understand. However, most human diseases can be described as either **infectious** or **non-infectious**. We shall look at each of these main groups in more detail.

Infectious diseases

An infectious disease is caused by the invasion of a **pathogen**. A pathogen is an organism capable of invading our bodies and causing disease. We are host to a huge number of microorganisms which have colonised the outside or inside of our bodies. These **normal flora** do not cause disease; in fact they often benefit

us by competing with potential pathogens for sites on our bodies and for nutrients, and even in some cases by producing chemical substances which are toxic to pathogens. Pathogens, in contrast, cause tissue damage as they rapidly reproduce themselves in or on the body. They are often microorganisms such as **bacteria**. By definition, an infectious disease must obviously also be **infectious** – in other words, it must be possible to pass the pathogen from one individual to another. Infectious diseases include **colds**, **influenza** ('flu), **cholera** and **measles**.

Parasitic diseases are a subset of infectious diseases. A **parasite** is an organism which lives on or in another organism, gaining benefit from it and causing it harm. Not all parasites harm their hosts seriously – in fact, a successful parasite does the minimum damage to its host whilst gaining maximum benefit itself – but many parasites do cause serious diseases. Disease-causing bacteria are parasitic, but the diseases they cause, such as tonsillitis, are not usually referred to as parasitic diseases. The term is usually reserved for conditions such as **schistosomiasis** and **threadworms**, which are caused by relatively large multicellular organisms.

Another subset of infectious diseases are described politely as **social diseases**. These are sexually transmitted diseases such as **syphilis**, **chlamydia** and **AIDS**. Caused by a variety of bacteria and viruses, sexually transmitted diseases are so called because the method of transmission of the pathogen from one person to another is usually by sexual activity.

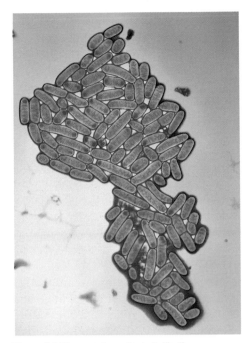

Figure 1.5 We can only see bacteria like these *Escherichia coli* in detail with the aid of electron microscopy. Pathogenic bacteria cause disease, suffering and death to millions of people the world over.

Non-infectious diseases

Not all diseases are caused by pathogens. A substantial number of the diseases that affect the population of the world are not caused by microorganisms but by lifestyle, ageing, starvation or genetics.

Degenerative diseases often, but not always, affect people as they get older. Common examples of degenerative diseases include **osteoporosis**, **osteoarthritis** and **Alzheimer's disease**. Such diseases are frequently seen as the result of ageing. However, research into these diseases, particularly when they occur in younger people, suggests that many of them are caused by the failure of particular biochemical pathways. Whilst this failure may be a result of ageing, it can also be triggered by genetic information, or a particular type of lifestyle behaviour, or even an infection.

At the moment of conception when a sperm fuses with an ovum, a new genetic individual is formed. Our genetic information gives the blueprint for an individual who is different from everyone else in the arrangement of our physical features, the colour of our hair and aspects of our personality and intelligence. Less obviously, most of us will have hidden in our genes a tendency to develop some diseases more readily than others. For example, some children will need ten different triggers in place before they get breathless with the symptoms of asthma, whilst others only need one trigger before they begin to wheeze.

Some people's genetic combination causes them to suffer from an **inherited** or **genetic disease**. These include conditions such as **Down's syndrome**, **Tay-Sachs disease** and **cystic fibrosis**. Genetic diseases are part of the fundamental nature of every cell in the body of an individual, so there are no cures for such diseases – yet. However, the relatively new science of genetic engineering does offer some hope for genetic diseases that affect only part of the metabolism.

Another group of non-infectious diseases is the **deficiency diseases**, which result from dietary deficiencies. Lack of certain vitamins or minerals, or a long-term imbalance in the diet, can lead to disease and ultimately death if the deficiency is not made up. Examples of such diseases include **rickets**,

beri beri and **scurvy**. The term 'deficiency disease' tends to conjure up images of starving children or adults in the developing countries of the world. However, deficiency diseases are reappearing in developed countries, particularly among individuals who eat large amounts of highly processed food.

A final category of non-infectious diseases is those diseases which are **self inflicted**. These include diseases related to alcohol and illegal drug abuse, along with food disorders such as **anorexia** and **bulimia**. This category is growing as research continues to reveal lifestyle factors in a wide range of diseases. The role of smoking in the development of lung cancer and heart disease is now well known, so it is possible to argue that in smokers these diseases are at least partially self inflicted. There are interesting social implications for the future as it becomes increasing likely that many of the major diseases affecting the developed world may have an environmental element in their aetiology.

What about cancer?

One of the most common and feared diseases in the developed world is **cancer**, yet apart from a mention of lung cancer it does not appear in any of our categories. This is because there does not seem to be a single 'cause' for cancer. Certain changes in the metabolism of cells are typical of all cancers, but the cause of those changes is not always known. In some cancers, virus infection seems to play a part – can we say these cancers are infectious? In other cancers, substances we take into our bodies, such as cigarette smoke or alcoholic drinks, seem to be major triggers. Are these cancers therefore self-inflicted diseases? Yet other cancers seem to occur mainly in ageing cells in older people. Is cancer a degenerative disease? The answer is that cancer is all of these things, but none of them describes the disease fully. There are many different types of cancers, and as yet there is no simple answer to what causes them.

DETECTING DISEASE

There are many occasions when we have no difficulty in detecting and diagnosing our own diseases – for example, the runny nose and headache of a cold are easy to recognise. However, detecting disease is not always so simple. A set of symptoms can have a variety of causes, and it is obviously vitally important that the right disease is treated. A simple example is vomiting. When people are sick, it may be the result of a 'stomach bug' – bacteria or more probably viruses infecting the gut and irritating the stomach, causing the vomiting. However, the same symptoms can be the result of poisoning, drinking too much alcohol or pregnancy. Poisoning requires very specialist medical treatment; drunk patients need careful monitoring to make sure they do not become unconscious and drown in their own vomit; and a pregnant woman should not be given anti-sickness drugs without careful checking that they will not harm her developing baby. In some cases, it is important not only to detect the cause of the symptoms, but to do so quickly – with problems such as heart disease and a wide range of cancers, early detection can mean the difference between life and death.

The first and most important link in the detection of disease is the relationship between the patient and doctor. A doctor has been through long training at medical school along with experience of diagnosis in practice, and when a patient turns up with a range of symptoms, the doctor uses a variety of tools to help detect the cause.

Figure 1.6 If it is possible to inflict disease on yourself, is it also possible to inflict health? These people working hard to increase their fitness and decrease their body fat obviously hope so!

Listening and looking

Listening to patients describing their symptoms, watching them during consultation and carrying out physical examinations are the oldest tools in the diagnostic kit bag. During this process a skilled doctor will be forming a mental diagnosis, or a list of possible diagnoses, and then looking for evidence to confirm the presence or absence of a particular disease. A surprising amount of evidence can be gathered simply by this process of observation and examination, but if more detail is needed then other methods are available.

Biochemical testing

Disease often results in biochemical changes within the body, which cannot always be detected by simple observation and examination. The need for biochemical testing was recognised long ago – urine from pregnant women was used on toads, which laid eggs if the woman was pregnant, and more adventurous doctors used to taste the urine of patients with suspected diabetes to see if it tasted sweet! Things have come a long way since then.

If a patient is breaking down protein as an energy source, the breath may have a distinctive smell of pear drops from the ketones formed in the process. A good doctor would notice this. However, there are a variety of causes for this symptom, one of the most common being untreated diabetes. A simple biochemical test helps in the diagnosis, without anybody having to taste urine!

Normally our bodies conserve glucose. The hormone **insulin** is secreted by the islets of Langerhans in the pancreas, in response to a high level of glucose in the blood. Insulin lowers the blood glucose level by causing the liver to convert glucose to glycogen, by stimulating fat cells to convert glucose to fat and by stimulating muscle and other tissues to absorb and respire glucose. In an undiagnosed diabetic, insufficient insulin is produced. This means that the level of glucose in the blood climbs higher and higher.

In the kidney, glucose is first filtered out of the blood into the filtrate and is then returned to the blood by an active transport system, so that no glucose normally appears in the urine. In an untreated diabetic, the concentration of glucose in the blood becomes so high that in the kidney, no further glucose can be reabsorbed into the blood. This means that increasing amounts of glucose appear in the urine, providing a useful diagnostic tool. The biochemical test for diabetes therefore detects the level of glucose in the urine. A small stick tipped with an indicator is dipped into a sample of the patient's urine. The tip changes colour, registering not only the presence or absence of glucose in the urine but also the concentration of glucose present (see figure 1.7).

Biochemical testing is now relatively common, with tests available for a wide range of diseases from PKU (phenylketonuria) in newborn babies to prostate cancer in older men.

Enzyme-linked immunosorbent assay (ELISA)

There are many variations on ELISA, all of them diagnostic techniques based around the same principles. They depend on the reaction between an antibody and an antigen (see page 30). Either the antibody or the antigen is bound to a solid phase, usually the wall of the vessel that contains the reaction mixture. When a sample from a patient is added, any relevant antigen or antibody will bind to its opposite on the solid phase. Then another molecule is added which in turn binds to the molecule from the patient. This last molecule is labelled with an enzyme. The final stage is for the plates to be washed with a substrate for the enzyme, and the enzyme–substrate reaction causes a colour change. This colour change indicates a positive test result. The process is illustrated in figure 1.8. ELISAs have many advantages:

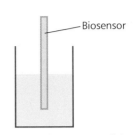

— Biosensor

Plastic stick coated with a mixture of the enzymes **glucose oxidase** and **peroxidase** and a blue **chromogen dye** is dipped into a urine sample collected from the patient.

If there is no glucose in the urine the dye stays blue.
If there is glucose in the urine, the glucose oxidase breaks it down in the presence of oxygen and water (both in urine):

Glucose + oxygen + water $\xrightarrow{\text{glucose oxidase}}$ gluconic acid + hydrogen peroxide

The blue chromogen dye is oxidised by the hydrogen peroxide in a reaction catalysed by peroxidase. The dye turns from blue to green to brown depending on the amount of hydrogen peroxide present.

Blue chromogen dye + hydrogen peroxide $\xrightarrow{\text{peroxidase}}$ green-to-brown chromogen dye + water

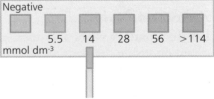

Comparing the colour of the test stick with a scale shows not only if glucose is present in the urine, but also at what concentration.

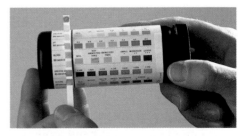

Figure 1.7 This simple, non-invasive biochemical test allows medical practitioners to detect early signs of diabetes. It also helps doctors, nurses and patients to check the effectiveness of any treatment for diabetes, which might be a carefully controlled diet, drugs or insulin injections.

- They use relatively cheap reagents.
- They do not need expensive detection systems.
- They can be automated easily.
- The reagents have long shelf lives and are easy to store.

As a result, ELISAs are widely used in the diagnosis of bacterial, viral and parasitic infections.

Figure 1.8 Using ELISA (enzyme-linked immunosorbent assay) to detect a particular antibody

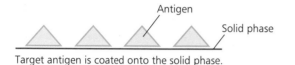

1 Coating

Antigen

Solid phase

Target antigen is coated onto the solid phase.

2 Specimen added

Antibody

The patient's serum is added and incubated. If the specific antibody is present it is captured by the antigen.

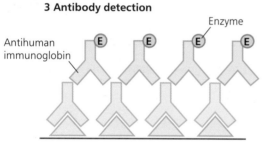

3 Antibody detection

Enzyme

Antihuman immunoglobin

Enzyme-labelled antihuman immunoglobin binds to the captured antibody.

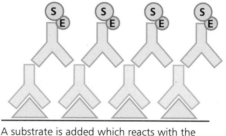

4 Substrate addition

S S S S
E E E E

A substrate is added which reacts with the enzyme label to produce colour.

5 Colour detection

The optical density is measured. This is proportional to the amount of antibody bound.

X-rays and scans

For thousands of years of human history, the only ways of knowing what was going on inside the body were to feel it from the outside or to cut it open to see inside. The latter was a particularly traumatic procedure in the days before effective anaesthetics became available. However, in 1895 Wilhelm Röntgen discovered X-rays by accident. Their penetrating power and their ability to blacken photographic emulsions led rapidly to their adoption by doctors for examining suspected internal injuries, especially broken bones (the skeleton shows up particularly clearly on X-ray photographs of the body).

X-ray radiation can knock electrons out of atoms, **ionising** them. This can damage many of the chemicals inside cells, including the DNA. The damage done to the body by the strongly ionising effects of X-rays was not recognised for many years. This led to quite inappropriate uses of X-rays – 40 years ago shoe shops had X-ray machines to take pictures of children's feet inside new shoes, to check that the shoes fitted properly and their feet were not being squashed! Later, doctors and nurses who had been exposed to significant doses of X-rays began to develop serious illnesses induced by the ionising radiation, and the dangers began to be recognised. There are strict regulations now governing both the operators of X-ray machines and the doses given to patients. This means the benefits of using X-rays to detect damage and disease can be enjoyed whilst keeping the health risks to a minimum.

The use of X-rays in the detection of disease has become very much more sophisticated in recent years. X-rays are used to detect internal infections as well as skeletal problems. In addition to the simple single-image X-ray like

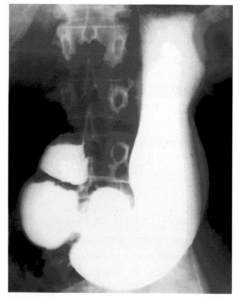

Figure 1.9 X-rays diagnose broken bones and skeletal problems such as arthritis, and are also used to identify problems in the heart and cancers in the lungs and other areas. In this X-ray of a patient after a barium meal, the stomach is clearly visible. The barium porridge is radio-opaque, and so shows up on the X-ray as the barium flows into various parts of the gut.

that in figure 1.9, **CAT** (computer-assisted tomography) scanners have been developed. These machines take a series of X-ray 'slices' through the body and then, with the aid of computer technology, produce images which detect disease hidden deep inside the body without resorting to surgery.

A further step in the diagnosis of disease has been the development of **MRI** (magnetic resonance imaging). Instead of X-rays, this uses radio waves in a strong magnetic field to produce images of the inside of the body. Because MRI does not use ionising radiation, it has safety benefits over CAT scanners, and provides clearer and more useful images for many types of diagnosis. However, both play a major role in the early diagnosis of many diseases, particularly cancers which can grow unnoticed within the cavity of the body giving few symptoms until the disease is widely spread. CAT scanners and MRI both also show the swelling that often accompanies internal injury or infection, allowing the appropriate treatments to be given rapidly.

Ultrasound monitoring and diagnosis

The use of ultrasound in the detection of disease has become very common in recent years. The technique is based on the same principles as echo-location in bats and depth sounders in submarines. Very high-pitched sound, above the level of human hearing, is directed into the body and the reflected sound from various organs is then converted into an image of the inside of the body.

One of the best known and most common uses of ultrasound technology is in the monitoring of the developing fetus during pregnancy. Until ultrasound scanning became possible, the growth of a developing fetus was monitored by external manipulation and measuring the size of the mother's 'bump'. This is not necessarily an accurate measure of the size of the fetus. The only way of actually 'seeing' the fetus and checking it was developing normally was to use potentially harmful X-rays, and so this was done as little as possible. Now ultrasound scans are carried out at least once during most pregnancies, and the accurate measurements produced make it easier to predict when the baby will be born. It is also possible to monitor the growth of the fetus if there is any concern about it, and also to check that the limbs, heart, brain and spine are forming properly. Some voices of concern have been raised about the absolute safety of using ultrasound during pregnancy, but at present the consensus of opinion among doctors and scientists is that the value of the information gained from at least one scan during a pregnancy far outweighs any possible risks.

Lights, camera, action!

All of the techniques described so far which are used to help medical professionals 'see' inside their patients give an image of the internal organs which usually needs expert interpretation. But techniques such as **endoscopy** allow doctors to literally see inside their living patients. A tiny fibre-optic light source and camera are fed directly into the body cavity being investigated, such as the gut. The patient is conscious but tranquillised to keep him or her relaxed, to make sure that the throat remains open and to help the endoscope tube to be swallowed down into the gut. A picture is relayed back onto a screen so that the doctor can see the living, moving gut. The technique is shown in figure 1.11. This technology not only allows ulcers, tumours and other problems to be seen directly, but also makes it possible to take samples of tissue at the same time. Variations of this technique enable different areas of the body to be investigated.

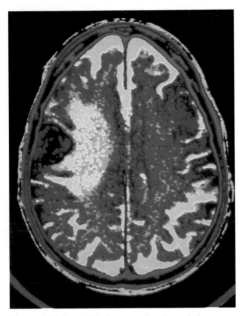

Figure 1.10 The ability to see a slice through the human body without resorting to the surgeon's knife has been a major step forward in the battle against disease. This CAT scan through the brain clearly shows a tumour (blue) on the left-hand side of the brain.

Surgery can be carried out using an endoscope without cutting into the patient, or through a very small incision just large enough to admit the camera unit. This is often referred to as keyhole surgery.

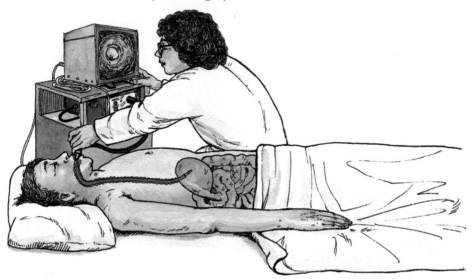

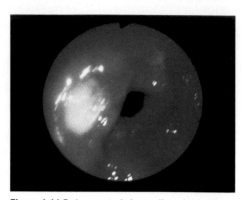

Figure 1.11 Endoscopy techniques allow pictures from inside the body to be seen directly. Because the patient is often conscious, some people actually see inside their own bodies! The photograph shows a stomach ulcer seen through an endoscope.

STUDYING DISEASE

As we saw on page 6, it is very difficult to measure health, or even to define it. Most of the information we have about health comes from studying disease. Diseases that cause easily defined and measured symptoms are much easier to quantify than the subjective feeling of being healthy.

The study of patterns of disease is known as **epidemiology**. There are three main questions that drive epidemiology:

1 Who gets ill? This is the major epidemiological question, answered by looking at the distribution of a particular disease within a population, a country or across the world.

2 Why do they get ill? This considers the **aetiology** (cause) of a disease. A classic example of this was the work done by Richard Doll who linked data on the prevalence of lung cancer with data on smoking habits and was the first to suggest a link between smoking and lung cancer.

3 How should they be treated? This aspect of epidemiology evaluates the effectiveness of different types of treatment.

Two main aspects of disease are recorded in epidemiological studies. One is the **morbidity** of the disease. This is the number of people who are made ill by the disease. Morbidity has to be carefully defined, as it is dependent on how the measurements are made. For example, measuring the number of hospital admissions for asthma would not necessarily give a clear picture of the number of people whose lives are affected by the condition. The other aspect of a disease that is measured is the **mortality** of the disease – that is the number of deaths resulting from it. Mortality is obviously easier to measure than morbidity, but can only be used for diseases that are severe enough to cause death. The information for epidemiological studies comes from analysing data from specific surveys, from doctor's surgeries, from hospital admissions, from registers of births and deaths and from sociological studies.

Epidemiological studies provide us with a wide range of information which can be used in a variety of ways for scientific, medical, financial (insurance) and political ends. Epidemiology provides explanations of disease which take both social and biological factors into account. However, there are limitations to these studies. There must be a strict definition of the disease or symptoms being investigated. A choice has to be made about which social and biological factors to focus on, and this choice will almost inevitably affect the eventual results of the study. Because there is a need to simplify the situation and only consider certain factors, an epidemiological study may fail to take account of multifactorial causes or of the interaction between factors. Finally, and in some ways most importantly, an association being identified between two factors does not necessarily mean that one causes the other, so the results must be looked at with great care.

There are several clearly defined factors which epidemiology has shown to be closely associated with the state of health or disease of the individual. These are age, gender, marital status, ethnic background, place of residence and social class and occupation. We shall briefly consider these in turn.

1   Age affects all sorts of areas of our health. An example is the data in figure 1.12 showing the relationship between cause of death and age in females in the UK.

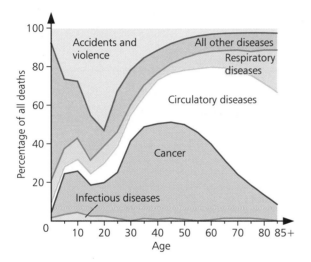

Figure 1.12 Causes of death for females in the UK, 1980

2   Health also varies with gender. On average, males die younger than females. Men are significantly more likely to die of coronary heart disease and cancer than women. Males are also more likely to suffer from genetic diseases caused by problems on the X chromosome. Epidemiology can help to decide how much this difference between males and females is due to intrinsic maleness, and how much to patterns of male behaviour common in different societies.

3   Marital status seems to affect health, although as more people live together in long term stable partnerships without becoming legally married, these differences may well appear to decline. For example, the effect of marital status on the incidence of mental disorders in the UK is quite striking, as shown in figure 1.13.

4   Ethnic origins can be used to identify groups particularly prone to certain diseases. However, as with all epidemiological evidence, these data need to be handled with care. Some classic research in 1981 showed patterns in the incidence of heart attacks and strokes in people of white European, Asian and West Indian background, as shown in figure 1.14.

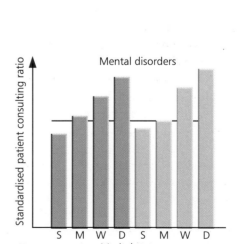

Figure 1.13 Mental disorders and marital status in the early 1980s

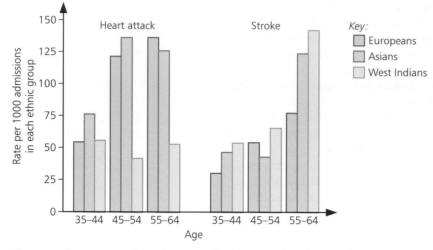

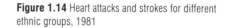

Figure 1.14 Heart attacks and strokes for different ethnic groups, 1981

The graph suggests that clear conclusions can be drawn about the ethnic groups and these particular diseases. But the data take no account of the social classes and occupations of the individuals, and therefore of the health status and health care received by individuals before attacks, or of the same ethnic groups living in other countries like the USA.

5   Where you live has a major influence on your projected health. The main causes of death in adults in England and Wales in 1982 are shown in figure 1.15, compared with the main causes of death in Africa, Asia and Latin America in 1978.

Infant mortality rates are a very good indicator of the state of health of a nation or a social group. The chances of a newborn baby surviving the first year of life varies enormously depending on where in the world it is born, as shown in table 1.1.

Country	Infant mortality rate per 1000 live births
Egypt	110
Kenya	92
Sierra Leone	215
Bolivia	138
Brazil	82
Cuba	22
Jamaica	30
USA	14
China	49
India	129
Japan	9
United Arab Emirates	57
Sweden	8
UK	14
Yugoslavia	35
New Zealand	14
Papua New Guinea	111

Table 1.1 Infant mortality rates in different countries, 1975–80

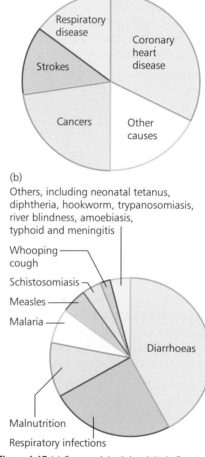

Figure 1.15 (a) Causes of death in adults in England and Wales, 1982 (b) Causes of death in developing nations, 1978

The same disease can have a very different impact in different parts of the world. For example, as mentioned on page 7, measles is a highly infectious and potentially dangerous disease, linked with severe and debilitating fevers, a high risk of secondary bacterial respiratory infections and post-measles encephalitis (inflammation of the brain). In most developed countries, measles is now a relatively rare disease thanks largely to intensive vaccination programmes aimed at young children, the most vulnerable members of the population. Even if children in a developed country do catch measles, improved health and hygiene conditions mean that the mortality ratio has fallen from one child dying in every 100 in 1940 to 0.02 dying in every 100 in 1989. This probably has many factors. Children tend to be older now when they catch measles because of the relatively isolated way they live in developed countries. Alongside this, drugs to control fever and antibiotics to fight secondary infections have improved beyond recognition. In the developing nations, measles is still one of the main causes of childhood death. Epidemics are common, and children tend to be very young when they contract the disease, often less than one year old. The extended families common in developing world communities mean that young infants and children spend considerable amounts of time together, giving rise to pools of infection. Many of these children already have their health challenged in other ways, for example by parasites, malaria or malnutrition, so the measles virus is devastating. In addition, neither the vaccine nor the antibiotics to treat secondary infections are widely available or affordable. Thus on a global scale, measles is now largely a disease of the developing world, although it is difficult to eradicate completely even in the developed world because it is so highly infectious.

6 Finally, social class and occupation are very important in determining health. The graphs in figure 1.16 show the relationship between social class and mortality for a range of conditions in the UK from stillbirths to diseases of the digestive system. The graphs reveal how the dice are loaded against those born into the poorest groups in society. Epidemiological data such as these may be used to argue for social change in an attempt to improve the living conditions and thus the health of those in our society least able to help themselves.

Figure 1.16 Incidence of stillbirths, deaths in the first year of life and diseases of the respiratory system, the circulatory system and the digestive system related to social class

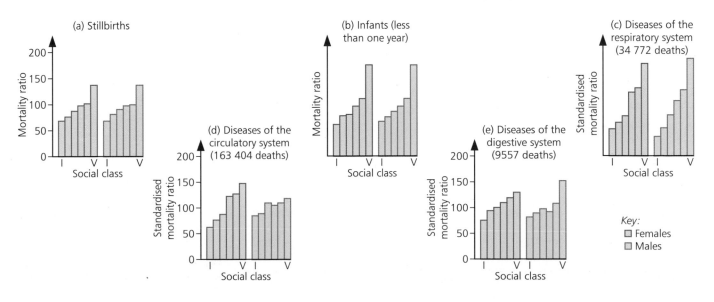

Mortality ratios and social classes

Statistics on mortality often refer to the number of deaths per 1000 people. However, sometimes that is not the most useful measure and a **mortality ratio** is used instead. A mortality ratio compares the number of people in a particular group who have died of a particular cause with the total number of deaths from that cause. For example, in figure 1.16(a) the figures show the total number of stillbirths of girls or boys which occurred in each social class. Age is not a factor, as stillbirth can only happen at one particular stage of life. However, when looking at other diseases age is one of the variables. Therefore if we are concentrating on a variable other than age – in this case, social class – the data are **age standardised**. This means the total number of deaths from the disease across the age range is used – there is no age selection.

Social class is a way of dividing people into groups based on their socioeconomic status. Thus people in social class I are the wealthiest and those in social class V are the poorest. People in social classes I and II are generally well educated and have professional jobs, while those in class V have few qualifications and may have a very low paid job or no job at all. The divisions are quite artificial, but they are used by epidemiologists and social scientists to investigate the effects of different ways of life on health.

SUMMARY

- **Health** is a state of physical, mental and social well-being which is more than just the absence of disease. This is very difficult to measure. A **disease** is a label given to a particular set of symptoms. A **physical** illness affects the body, while a **mental** illness affects the ability of the mind to function within the normally accepted range of behaviours.

- An **infectious disease** is caused by an organism (a **pathogen**) that invades the body and causes the symptoms of the disease. The pathogen can be passed from one person to another. Infectious diseases include those caused by bacteria and viruses, and also the **parasitic diseases** caused by larger multicellular organisms.

- **Non-infectious diseases** are not caused by pathogens but by lifestyle (such as coronary heart disease), ageing (**degenerative diseases**), starvation (**deficiency diseases**) or genetics (**inherited diseases**).

- The detection of disease may involve physical examination, biochemical tests such as the ELISA technique, X-rays, CAT or MRI scans, ultrasound scans and endoscopy.

- **Epidemiology** is the study of patterns of disease. The distribution of a disease is studied, the **aetiology** (cause) of the disease suggested and the effectiveness of different treatments assessed. The **morbidity** of a disease is the number of people made ill by the disease, and the **mortality** of the disease is the number of deaths it causes. There are many social as well as biological factors that determine whether someone is likely to suffer from a particular disease.

QUESTIONS

1 a What is meant by the term 'health' and why is it so difficult to measure?
 b What is meant by the term 'disease'?
 c Make a table summarising the main types of disease with their causes, giving a specific example of each type of disease.

2 Explain the use of the following techniques in the diagnosis of disease:
 a observation
 b X-rays and ultrasound
 c ELISA
 d biosensors.

3 Epidemiology is a relatively new science. What is it, and how is it useful to our understanding of diseases and their causes?

Infectious diseases

As we have seen in chapter 1, **infectious diseases** are diseases that can be transmitted from one person to another. They are caused by invading microorganisms known as **pathogens** which do not belong to the normal body flora. The invading microorganisms often cause tissue damage, though in some cases they produce a toxin and it is this that causes the symptoms of disease, rather than the microorganisms themselves. Infectious diseases range from being so mild we hardly notice them to those that may cause death. So what are the pathogens that cause disease?

TYPES OF PATHOGEN

There are five main groups of pathogens: viruses, bacteria, fungi, protozoans and larger organisms such as parasitic worms. Examples of each of these are shown in figure 2.1.

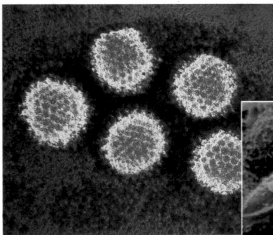

These adenoviruses cause infections of the respiratory tract such as the common cold (×24 000)

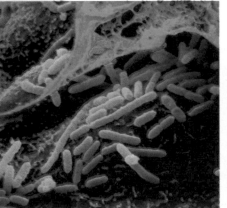

Haemophilus influenzae bacteria also infect the respiratory tract but cause diseases such as pneumonia, bronchitis and even meningitis (×5000)

Viruses

Viruses are very small with such a simple structure that there is dispute about whether or not they are living. They are made up of a piece of genetic material which may be DNA or RNA, some enzymes that are needed for replication and an outer case of structural protein (see figure 2.3 on page 21). This protein is often very regular and geometric in shape. Viruses can last for years in the air, but they are incapable of replication unless they are inside a host cell. Once inside a cell, the virus takes over the cellular biochemistry and uses it to produce new viruses until the host cell structure completely breaks down, releasing the new viruses to infect other cells. This gives rise to the symptoms of viral disease. All known viruses cause disease in living organisms. Examples of human viral diseases include **polio**, **influenza** and **AIDS** (acquired immune deficiency syndrome).

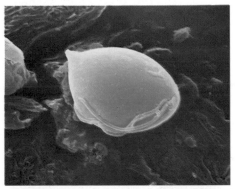

Trichomonas vaginalis, a protozoan that causes a sexually transmitted disease (×2400)

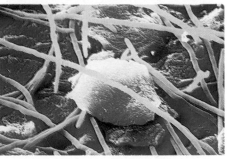

This fungus causes athlete's foot (×1300)

These parasitic worms cause schistosomiasis (×10)

Figure 2.1 Examples of the five main groups of pathogen

Influenza – a viral killer

Influenza – more commonly referred to as 'flu – is a relatively common respiratory disease which can be a killer. It is highly infectious and has a very short incubation period. These two factors mean it can cause huge **epidemics** (affecting many people in one country at one time) and even extensive **pandemics** (affecting people in many countries at the same time). Three 'flu pandemics have been recorded in the twentieth century alone, in 1918, 1957 and 1968. The 1918 pandemic, hitting populations exhausted by the rigours of the First World War, caused more deaths in a few months than had occurred throughout the whole of the war.

There are three strains of the influenza virus – influenza A, B and C. Strain A in particular causes severe disease. Influenza infects the ciliated epithelial cells of the respiratory system (see page 70), killing them. This leaves the airways open to infection, and many of the deaths associated with 'flu are from severe secondary bacterial infections on top of the original viral invasion. The people most likely to die of 'flu are the elderly and anyone who is prone to asthma or heart disease. During 'flu epidemics, there is a marked increase in deaths from respiratory disease – for example, during the 1989/90 epidemic in England and Wales there were about 26 000 more deaths than would have been expected in that period of time. Between 80 and 90% of the 'extra deaths' were of people aged 65 or over, and the great majority were due to respiratory problems.

Each year the 'flu virus is subtly different, as the antigenic proteins (see page 30) on the surface of the virus change. The change is usually quite small, so having 'flu one year leaves you with some immunity against infection for the next year. But every so often there is a major change in the surface antigens, and this heralds a 'flu epidemic or pandemic as no one has any 'almost right' antibodies ready.

Symptoms

The symptoms of 'flu include fever, often accompanied by shivering and sweating; feeling very unwell and unable to do anything; loss of appetite, aching muscles and painful joints. In addition, many people suffer from severe headaches, sore throats and shortness of breath. If no secondary infection sets in, the disease lasts for about 5–7 days before the fever goes down and convalescence begins. The lungs and the heart can both be severely infected.

The exhaustion that follows a bout of 'flu can last 6–12 weeks, even in patients without secondary infections.

Treatment

Rest, warmth, plenty of fluids to avoid dehydrating and mild painkillers are used. No specific drug will help treat the viral infection. If secondary bacterial infections set in, then antibiotics can be used to combat them.

Control

There are 'flu vaccines, but because of the changing nature of the virus, the vaccine has to be changed each year. A cocktail is made up of the A and B strains thought most likely to cause disease in any one year, and this vaccine is then made available to people in high risk groups.

One of the reasons 'flu spreads so rapidly is that people tend to carry on working and going about their daily routines as long as possible when they feel ill. Laudable as it may seem to battle on, it exposes many others to the virus via droplet infection. One employee in a meeting with early 'flu symptoms can lead to an empty conference table in a surprisingly short time! People would do better to nurse their symptoms at home, and by giving their immune system the opportunity to concentrate on recovery, would probably get over the virus more rapidly too.

Figure 2.2 Many proprietary medicines containing painkillers and decongestants are sold to help relieve the symptoms of 'flu, but they do not reduce the replication of the 'flu viruses.

Bacteria

Bacteria are single-celled **prokaryotic** organisms. Their cells are less highly organised than those of **eukaryotic** organisms, such as animals, plants, protozoans and fungi. Bacterial cells have a main circular strand of DNA, and may also have one or more smaller circular DNA **plasmids** which can code for antibiotic resistance or toxin production. Bacteria may have **flagellae** for movement, and protein rods called **pili** on their surface which are used for attaching to a host cell. The structure of a bacterial cell is shown in figure 2.3. They can live and replicate independently of any other cell, and there are many types of bacteria that do not cause disease; some are beneficial to humans and other life forms. Examples of bacterial diseases include **tuberculosis**, **salmonellosis** (*Salmonella* food poisoning) and **cholera**.

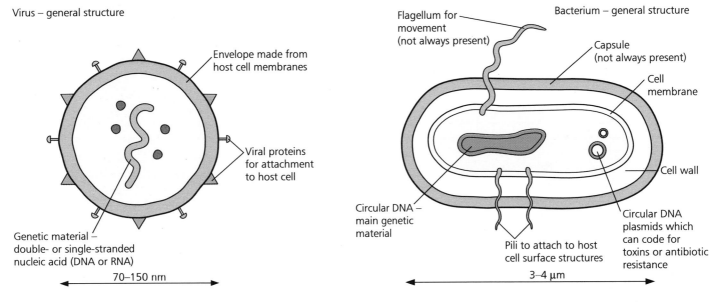

Virus – general structure

Envelope made from host cell membranes

Viral proteins for attachment to host cell

Genetic material – double- or single-stranded nucleic acid (DNA or RNA)

70–150 nm

Bacterium – general structure

Flagellum for movement (not always present)

Capsule (not always present)

Cell membrane

Cell wall

Circular DNA – main genetic material

Pili to attach to host cell surface structures

Circular DNA plasmids which can code for toxins or antibiotic resistance

3–4 µm

Figure 2.3 Bacteria and viruses have caused more human suffering and death than anything else in our evolutionary history.

Salmonella and friends

There are about 2200 different types of *Salmonella* bacteria which infect animals, and most of them are capable of causing disease in humans. Poultry is the most common source of human salmonellosis, as up to 60% of poultry meat is contaminated with the bacterium, and so are many egg shells and the contents of some eggs. Relatively large numbers of the *Salmonella* bacterium need to be ingested to cause symptoms (in contrast to a disease such as typhoid, where only a very small number of infective organisms can cause disease). The disease is usually spread either by eating infected food which has not been properly cooked, or by eating cooked food which has been contaminated after cooking, during storage or preparation. If contaminated food is stored without refrigeration, the microorganisms multiply until their numbers are high enough to cause disease. Salmonellosis usually occurs in small outbreaks, either within a single household or within a group of people who have all attended the same party, wedding or other function and eaten the same food. In 1995/6, 50 people in Britain died of salmonella food poisoning.

Symptoms

There is an incubation period of 18–36 hours after the infected food is eaten, and the severity of the disease that follows is very variable. Typical symptoms include feeling unwell, nausea, vomiting and often a fever followed by diarrhoea. This is the main symptom of the disease and can continue for some time after the other symptoms have gone. Elderly people can be particularly at risk in *Salmonella* infections as they cannot cope easily with dehydration.

Treatment

In (relatively) mild cases, rehydration fluids are given whilst the diarrhoea lasts, and occasionally these need to be given intravenously. Most patients recover on their own, but if the symptoms continue for several days, antibiotic treatment may be used. A major problem with antibiotic treatment is that *Salmonella* bacteria are common in farm animals as well as people, and they have developed resistance to many of the antibiotics used by vets, farmers and doctors. There is a very limited selection of effective antibiotics to choose from.

Control

Careful management of food hygiene both in the home and in commercial kitchens are the main features of *Salmonella* control. After an attack of salmonellosis, an individual will excrete *Salmonella* bacteria in the faeces for up to four weeks. Although the numbers of the microorganism in the faeces are too low to cause a high risk of infection, infected children cannot return to school until they have shown three consecutive clear faeces samples, and the same applies to any adult whose work involves the handling of food.

STATUTORY INSTRUMENTS

1995 No. 1763
FOOD
The Food Safety (General Food Hygiene) Regulations 1995

Chapter IX
Provisions applicable to foodstuffs

1. No raw materials or ingredients shall be accepted by a food business if they are known to be, or might reasonably be expected to be, so contaminated with parasites, pathogenic microorganisms, or toxic, decomposed or foreign substances, that after normal sorting and/or preparatory or processing procedures hygienically applied by food businesses, they would still be unfit for human consumption.

2. Raw materials and ingredients stored in the establishment shall be kept in appropriate conditions designed to prevent harmful deterioration and to protect them from contamination.

3. All food which is handled, stored, packaged, displayed and transported, shall be protected against any contamination likely to render the food unfit for human consumption, injurious to health or contaminated in such a way that it would be unreasonable to expect it to be consumed in that state. In particular, food must be so placed and/or protected as to minimize any risk of contamination. Adequate procedures must be in place to ensure pests are controlled.

4. Hazardous and/or inedible substances, including animal feedstuffs, shall be adequately labelled and stored in separate and secure containers.

Figure 2.4 Health regulations such as these are designed to avoid the spread of food poisoning such as salmonellosis. Health inspectors regularly check workplaces where food is prepared, sold or served to the public.

Fungi

Fungi are eukaryotic organisms which are not major human pathogens. They are frequently multicellular and are **heterotrophic**, which means they digest food extracellularly and then absorb it. Many fungi have a body structure made up of tangled threads forming a **mycelium**; some, like the yeasts, are unicellular. The fungi that cause human disease tend to be **dermophytes**, infecting the skin, hair and nails, although they can also cause systemic (within the body) diseases in areas such as the lungs, and give severe problems to patients such as AIDS sufferers whose immune systems are not functioning properly. Examples of fungal diseases include **athlete's foot** and **farmer's lung**.

Athlete's foot

Athlete's foot is a fungal infection of the feet. In the developed world, human fungal infections are generally fairly superficial, affecting the skin, hair or nails. They tend to cause local inflammation and damage at the site of the invading mycelium. Athlete's foot is a common fungal infection, often found on the warm, often slightly sweaty skin between the toes. Fungal spores are picked up from the air or the floor, and they germinate and thrive in these warm moist conditions. The fungus penetrates and digests the outer layers of the skin. These layers die and slough off, leaving the skin underneath raw and vulnerable to further attack.

Treatment of athlete's foot is usually by a topical (local) antifungal drug. A cream which can be bought over the counter at a pharmacy is rubbed into the infected area. If the infection is very entrenched in the skin, a course of oral antifungal drugs may be prescribed by a doctor so that the drug is within the system and the fungus is attacked from all sides.

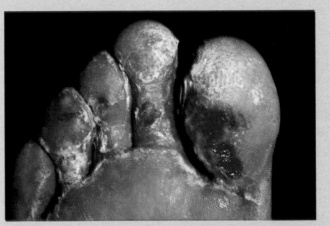

Figure 2.5 For most sufferers athlete's foot is itchy and perhaps sore at times. It is only after a long period of neglect that athlete's foot looks like this.

A common fungal disease of the skin is caused by the fungus *Candida albicans*. Known as **thrush**, it can affect the mouths of babies and small children as well as adults. It is also commonly found infecting the skin of the genitalia and anus. The fungus is almost always present on the skin but it only causes problems if the skin is compromised in some way. For example, if the skin is damaged or sore or if the normal skin bacteria are destroyed by the use of antibiotics, a thrush infection may well develop with its tell-tale patches of red or white inflamed skin and increasing itchiness and soreness. Antifungal drugs threat the fungus very effectively.

Protozoans

Protozoans are single-celled eukaryotic organisms. There are several different types of protozoans, and many of them have life cycles involving a number of different hosts and environments, and also **vectors**, which transmit the protozoan from one host to another. The vectors are often insects. Diseases caused by protozoans include **malaria** (see pages 2–3), **toxoplasmosis** and **giardiasis**.

Amoebic dysentery

The parasitic amoeba known as *Entamoeba histolytica* causes disease in many parts of the world, particularly where sanitation is poor. Amoebic dysentery is spread by eating contaminated food, especially raw vegetables which have been watered with or washed in contaminated water, or using contaminated water for drinking or washing. Even in the UK, with a relatively sophisticated water purification system, around 1000 cases of amoebic dysentery are reported each year. Amoebic cysts are passed out in the faeces of infected individuals. If these reach the gut of another person, they attach themselves to the lining of the large intestine and the amoebae reproduce and damage the mucosa of the large intestine.

Symptoms

The incubation period varies from a few days to several weeks. The main symptom is watery diarrhoea which quickly becomes full of mucus and blood. The patient develops a fever and suffers griping colicky pain, which becomes constant as the disease goes on. The disease is very debilitating due to fluid and blood loss. If the intestine becomes perforated, it may lead to death.

Treatment

A drug called metronidazole is used to give immediate relief, as well as painkillers and rehydration treatment. Patients will continue to excrete infectious cysts unless they are treated with an intestinal amoebicide.

Control

The most important factors in the control of amoebic dysentery are the careful disposal of human sewage and the provision of clean, filtered water for drinking and washing. Carriers of the disease need to be meticulous about hand-washing after defecation, but in the circumstances in which many live this is very difficult. Travellers need to avoid unwashed fruit and vegetables and to drink only treated water – bottled water is safest.

Multicellular parasites

Multicellular parasites are animals with organ systems of their own. They are usually **helminthes** or worms that are internal parasites. They may be roundworms or flatworms. People are the only hosts for some of these parasitic worms, but others have complicated life cycles in which humans are only part of the story. Helminthic diseases range from relatively mild problems such as **threadworms** in the large intestine (see figure 2.6) which are common throughout the world through to some of the most debilitating diseases of the developing world such as **schistosomiasis** caused by blood flukes and **river blindness** caused by a parasitic worm.

Figure 2.6 Parasitic worms can inhabit many areas of the body. They damage tissues and debilitate the patient, and there is also a risk of a blockage of the gut, the blood vessels or the lymphatic system, which can lead to very dramatic symptoms.

PASSING IT ON

Will it spread?

All pathogens *can* cause disease, but that is not to say they always will. Infectious diseases are **communicable** – the infection is spread from one person to another. The likelihood of any particular infectious disease being passed from one person to another will depend on the **pathogen**, the **host** and the **environment**.

- The **virulence** of a particular pathogen can vary. Virulence is the power of the pathogen to cause severe disease. An example of variable virulence is shown by the influenza virus. The virus is constantly changing slightly, producing different strains of 'flu, some of which are relatively mild but others which are highly virulent, causing severe disease and death. Also, different pathogens adapt to new environmental conditions and respond to drugs and the body's immune response with varying levels of success.

- The behaviour and general health of potential hosts will also affect the likelihood of disease being passed on. Travelling to countries where particular diseases are common obviously increases the risk of infection, as does irresponsible sexual behaviour. Some occupations, especially those in the field of medicine, also increase the risk. Crowded living conditions, poor hygiene, poor nutrition and existing disease all increase the risk of infection. Conversely, previous immunity, from either a full infection or vaccination, can reduce the risk of a new infection.

- Many disease-causing organisms have to withstand a period of time outside their hosts in order to be communicated from one person to another. This transmission time varies in duration, but it is always a vulnerable time for the pathogen. Environmental factors such as temperature, dust and humidity levels, the availability of water and the use of antibiotics and pesticides can all affect the ability of a pathogen to survive outside its host.

How does it spread?

Diseases can spread in many different ways. They can spread **horizontally** through the members of the same population, or **vertically** from one generation to the next, as an infection passes from a mother to her child during pregnancy and birth. In some cases an animal disease can spread to humans. Such a disease is called a **zoonosis**. People like farmers and vets who work with animals are particularly at risk of catching these diseases, as to a lesser extent are people who breed birds or simply have a houseful of pets.

Table 2.1 outlines the main transmission methods. An understanding of the way a disease is transmitted from one individual to another is extremely important in helping to prevent the spread of the disease through a community.

Outbreaks of disease

Many diseases occur at low levels within a population all the time. Sometimes, there is a sudden increase in the incidence of a particular disease. At a localised level, such an increase is called an **outbreak**. On a national level, an increased incidence of a disease is known as an **epidemic**. On very rare occasions, an epidemic will affect many of the countries of the world at the same time. This situation is known as a **pandemic**. Only four infectious diseases are known to have caused pandemics – influenza, cholera, plague and acquired immune deficiency syndrome (AIDS). Some diseases are common in the population all the time, for example, malaria in West Africa, and these are referred to as **endemic**.

An outbreak of disease can start in several ways.

1 There may be a single **point source** of infection, and a group of people are exposed to it at one time. For example, if some food at a party is infected with *Salmonella*, everyone who ate that food will develop the symptoms of food poisoning within a few days of each other.

2 There may be a **common-source outbreak**, involving a source of infection to which several individuals are exposed over a period of time. For example, if an ear- and body-piercing establishment used contaminated equipment which was not sterilised properly between clients, then many people going there could be infected with the same disease.

3 Many outbreaks of disease are simply the result of **person-to-person contact**. There is a chain of transmission from one person to another, with apparent gaps in the chain caused by the incubation period. An outbreak of chickenpox in a primary school is a good example of this, with waves of children becoming spotty as the infection sweeps through the classes.

Type of transmission	How transmission occurs	Examples of diseases
Vectors 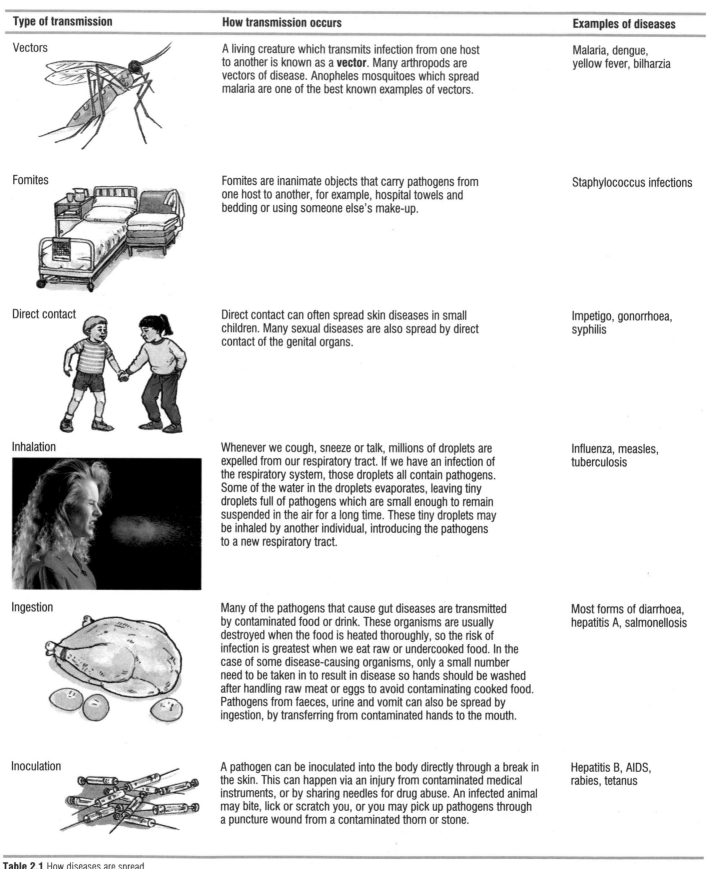	A living creature which transmits infection from one host to another is known as a **vector**. Many arthropods are vectors of disease. Anopheles mosquitoes which spread malaria are one of the best known examples of vectors.	Malaria, dengue, yellow fever, bilharzia
Fomites	Fomites are inanimate objects that carry pathogens from one host to another, for example, hospital towels and bedding or using someone else's make-up.	Staphylococcus infections
Direct contact	Direct contact can often spread skin diseases in small children. Many sexual diseases are also spread by direct contact of the genital organs.	Impetigo, gonorrhoea, syphilis
Inhalation	Whenever we cough, sneeze or talk, millions of droplets are expelled from our respiratory tract. If we have an infection of the respiratory system, those droplets all contain pathogens. Some of the water in the droplets evaporates, leaving tiny droplets full of pathogens which are small enough to remain suspended in the air for a long time. These tiny droplets may be inhaled by another individual, introducing the pathogens to a new respiratory tract.	Influenza, measles, tuberculosis
Ingestion	Many of the pathogens that cause gut diseases are transmitted by contaminated food or drink. These organisms are usually destroyed when the food is heated thoroughly, so the risk of infection is greatest when we eat raw or undercooked food. In the case of some disease-causing organisms, only a small number need to be taken in to result in disease so hands should be washed after handling raw meat or eggs to avoid contaminating cooked food. Pathogens from faeces, urine and vomit can also be spread by ingestion, by transferring from contaminated hands to the mouth.	Most forms of diarrhoea, hepatitis A, salmonellosis
Inoculation	A pathogen can be inoculated into the body directly through a break in the skin. This can happen via an injury from contaminated medical instruments, or by sharing needles for drug abuse. An infected animal may bite, lick or scratch you, or you may pick up pathogens through a puncture wound from a contaminated thorn or stone.	Hepatitis B, AIDS, rabies, tetanus

Table 2.1 How diseases are spread

Each of these different types of outbreak gives a different distribution pattern, as shown in figure 2.7.

NATURAL DEFENCES

The human body has a number of lines of defence against the invasion of pathogens. Our defences can be considered in two parts – the non-specific defences and the specific immune system.

Non-specific defences

Non-specific defences against disease are part of the normal functioning of the body. The first is the **skin**, which forms a natural barrier surrounding the body, preventing the entry of microorganisms to the body. The oily substance called **sebum** produced by the skin contains substances which inhibit the growth of microorganisms. The sebum does not harm the natural skin flora (the microorganisms which live on our skin without causing us any damage). These natural skin flora themselves play a role in preventing disease by competing successfully for position on the skin and also, in some cases, themselves producing substances which inhibit the growth of other microorganisms. The pharynx and the large intestine have protective coverings similar to the skin.

When we cut ourselves, we become vulnerable to infection by skin pathogens such as staphylococci or herpes viruses, and also to more invasive organisms such as *Clostridium tetani* which causes tetanus. Some organisms such as hookworms, ticks and biting insects can penetrate the unbroken skin for themselves, either causing disease directly or introducing disease-causing pathogens as in malaria. If the skin is damaged, the first response of the body is to seal the wound through the mechanism of **blood clotting**.

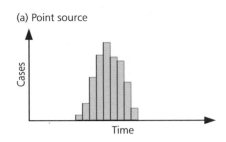
(a) Point source

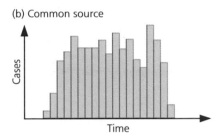
(b) Common source

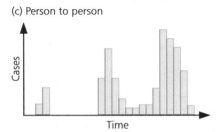
(c) Person to person

Figure 2.7 Recording case numbers over time gives these distinctive patterns of infection. Recognition of a disease as a point-source or common-source outbreak using this kind of analysis can help identify the source of the infection, preventing further outbreaks.

The blood as a damage limitation system

In theory a minor cut or scrape, or even a hard bang on the body surface, could endanger life due to loss of blood. In normal circumstances this does not happen because the body has a highly efficient damage limitation system in the **clotting mechanism** of the blood. It also seals the damaged vessels against the entry of pathogens into the blood.

When a blood vessel is damaged a semi-solid mass called a **clot** forms and seals the wound as a result of a complex sequence of events:
- Blood plasma, blood cells and platelets flow from a cut vessel.
- Contact between the platelets and some of the tissue components (for example collagen fibres) causes the platelets to break open in large numbers. They release several substances, two of which are particularly important. **Serotonin** causes the smooth muscle of the arterioles to contract and so narrows the vessels, cutting off the blood flow to the damaged area. **Thromboplastin** is an enzyme which sets in progress a cascade of events that lead to the formation of a clot.
- In the presence of sufficient levels of calcium ions, thromboplastin catalyses a large-scale conversion of the plasma protein **prothrombin** into the enzyme **thrombin**.
- Thrombin acts on another plasma protein called **fibrinogen**, converting it to **fibrin**. Fibrin consists of fibrous strands.

- Further platelets and blood cells pouring from the wound get trapped and tangled within the fibrin meshwork, forming a clot.
- Contractile proteins in the cytoskeleton of the platelets contract, pulling the clot into a tighter and tougher configuration.

These events are an example of a cascade system, where a relatively small event is **amplified** through a series of steps, as shown in figure 2.8. The speed and efficiency of clotting is effective in preventing blood loss. The difficulties of life without it are seen in the genetic condition of **haemophilia**, where normal life is impossible without regular injections of clotting factors.

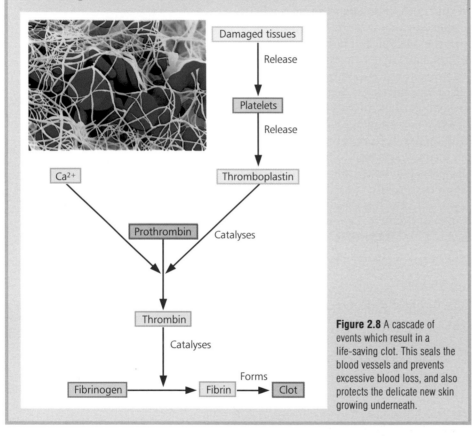

Figure 2.8 A cascade of events which result in a life-saving clot. This seals the blood vessels and prevents excessive blood loss, and also protects the delicate new skin growing underneath.

Following damage to the skin, the **inflammatory response** (see page 36) brings phagocytic white blood cells to the site of damage. They ingest any microorganisms that have entered the bloodstream.

The surfaces of our internal tubes and ducts are covered in epithelia which are much thinner than our skin and are not toughened with keratin. However, these epithelia often secrete substances which protect against invasion. Many produce mucus, a sticky substance which traps microorganisms. It also contains lysozymes, enzymes capable of destroying microbial cell walls. Phagocytic white blood cells which can engulf pathogens are often present on epithelial surfaces. In the respiratory system (see page 70), mucus is secreted and constantly swept upwards by cilia, either out of the body or down into the gut. The epithelium of the urinary system is constantly washed through with urine. These mechanisms are so successful that there are usually no bacteria in either the respiratory system or the urinary system, except for the areas nearest to the outside world. However, if microorganisms are present in sufficient numbers they may breach these defences, as the cold and influenza viruses often do.

The **gut** is an opening through which pathogens can enter. It has defensive mechanisms – the saliva in the mouth can kill some bacteria, and the acid in the stomach destroys the majority of ingested microorganisms. Throughout the gut, the natural flora usually competes successfully for both nutrients and attachment sites with any microorganisms that pass through the stomach, and like the skin flora the gut flora produces anti-microbial compounds.

There are large concentrations of phagocytic white blood cells at all the lymph nodes, and their task is to ensure that if one organ becomes infected, the infection does not spread throughout the body. This is one reason why your 'glands' become enlarged when you are unwell.

Should any pathogen manage to breach all these non-specific defences, it will then meet the system which has evolved specifically to deal with the invasion of disease-causing organisms: the immune system.

The immune system

The **immune system** provides a series of defensive responses to an invading pathogen. The immune response is brought about by various types of **leucocyte** (white blood cell). **Phagocytes** are one type of leucocyte which play several roles in the defence system of the body. They arise as **monocytes**, cells with a single large nucleus which are formed in the bone marrow of the long bones of the body. As they mature they become known as phagocytes. They can move in and

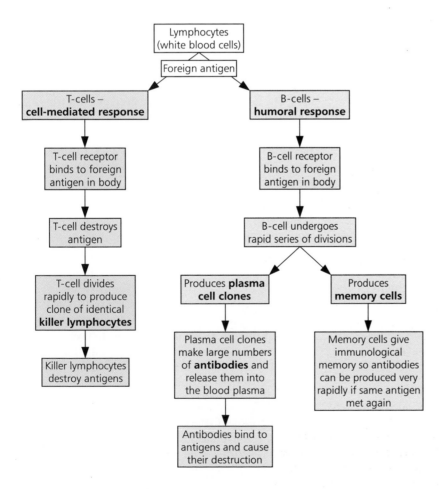

Figure 2.9 The cell-mediated response of the T-cells and the humoral response of the B-cells work together to destroy foreign material in the body.

out of capillaries and engulf dead cells or foreign material. **Lymphocytes** are another type of leucocyte – they are made in the lymph glands around the body, and there are two main types called **T-cells** and **B-cells**.

Once inside the body, a pathogen is recognised as foreign material because of its **antigens** – specific proteins on its outer surface. These antigens are recognised by T-cells which attach themselves to the antigen and destroy it. Phagocytes may then engulf and destroy the foreign material. In response to foreign antigens, the B-cells multiply to form large numbers of clones which secrete **antibodies**. These are proteins specific to a particular antigen, which bind to it and destroy it. The antigen–antibody complex can be engulfed by a phagocyte. These two immune responses are called the **cell-mediated response** and the **humoral response**, summarised in figure 2.9. It is thought that the phagocytes may also play a part in helping the lymphocytes to recognise foreign antigens.

Once the immune system has been activated, it usually destroys all the foreign material carrying those specific antigens that enters the body. Also, as part of the humoral response, **memory cells** are produced. These are specific B-cells which provide the body with a long-term **immunological memory**. As soon as you encounter the disease-causing antigen again, your body produces antibodies against it so quickly that the pathogens will all be destroyed before they have time to cause the symptoms of disease. This explains why you usually only get a disease such as chickenpox or measles once. However, some pathogenic organisms such as cold and 'flu viruses are constantly mutating and changing their antigens very subtly. This means that you can be reinfected with another strain of the same virus, because your body does not recognise its changed antigens.

How antibodies work

Antibodies are also known as **immunoglobulins**. Although antibodies are different, each being specific to one antigen, they all have the same basic structure. They are globular proteins made up of four polypeptide chains, two **light** or short chains and two **heavy** or long chains. The folding of these chains produces specifically shaped binding sites into which the antigen fits. Five different types of immunoglobulin have been isolated, each of which appears to have a slightly different function.

IgM is the first type of immunoglobulin to appear in the blood in response to an antigen. It is produced for a week or two and seems to be involved in the **primary response** of the body to an antigen – that is, they way it responds the first time it meets an antigen.

IgG is the main immunoglobulin type found circulating in the blood – it makes up about 80% of immunoglobulin. IgG is the workhorse of the immune system, conferring most of the benefits of immunity and being very heavily involved in the **secondary response** of the body to an antigen – the way it responds on repeated exposures to a particular antigen. IgG cannot be synthesised during the first couple of months of human life, and so newborn babies are dependent on immunoglobulins which they have received across the placenta and continue to receive through their mother's milk to protect them from a wide variety of diseases.

IgA is found in relatively low levels in the blood, but is the main immunoglobulin to be found in body secretions such as tears, saliva, nasal drippings, colostrum (the special antibody-rich form of milk produced during pregnancy and the first few days of lactation) and milk. The presence of IgA in colostrum and milk appears to be an important way of providing the infant with immunity to disease. IgA is one of the few proteins that can survive the pH conditions and enzymes of the stomach and intestines and be absorbed into the body with its biological activity intact.

IgD and **IgE** are found in relatively small amounts. The functions of these two immunoglobulins are not yet clearly understood. IgE seems to have a role in allergic reactions – see page 56.

Natural killer cells are another strand of the immune system. They do not need to be exposed to antigens – they bind to any infected or otherwise changed cells and activate the cell's own self-destruction mechanism.

The ABO system of blood groups

A specialised and unique aspect of the immune system is seen in the human blood. There is a variety of different **blood groups**, but the one most familiar to us and in most common usage is the **ABO system**. There are four possible blood groups within this system.

On the surface of the red blood cells of some individuals are molecules which act as antigens. They are substances known as **agglutinogens** and there are two different types, **A** and **B**. There are also two antibodies (**agglutinins**) that may occur in the blood plasma, called **a** and **b**. These antibodies are not made in direct response to an antigen as normal antibodies are – they are present regardless of any exposure to the antigen. If red blood cells carrying a particular agglutinogen come into contact with plasma containing the complementary agglutinin, the reaction between them causes the red blood cells to **agglutinate** (stick together). This means that they can no longer do their job and are likely to block capillaries or even larger vessels. Table 2.2 shows the agglutinogens and agglutinins present in the different blood groups.

Blood group	Agglutinogen (antigen on red blood cell)	Agglutinin (antibody in the plasma)
A	A	b
B	B	a
AB	A and B	–
O	–	a and b

Table 2.2 The ABO system of blood groups

In the UK group O is the most common blood group (46% of the population), with group A a close second (42%). Groups B (9%) and AB (3%) are much less common, although within specific ethnic groups the proportions may vary quite markedly.

For most of the population most of the time, blood groups have little importance. As long as your blood remains within your own body system and you avoid major blood loss or the need for surgery, it is quite possible that no one will know your blood group. But blood group information becomes vital when blood needs to be given from one person to another. Blood donors' blood groups are checked and the donated blood is clearly labelled. Before undergoing surgery or giving birth, or in any situation where the possibility of a blood transfusion arises, the blood group needs to be ascertained.

When a blood transfusion is given, it is the cells of the donated blood that will be affected by any adverse reaction. The blood of the recipient is usually present in much greater amounts and so any adverse reaction in the recipient's cells only effects a relatively small proportion of the total blood. But if the donated blood agglutinates as it flows into the recipient's system, then difficulties can arise.

Blood group O can be given to anybody in a transfusion. Because it carries no antigens on its red blood cells it cannot stimulate an agglutination reaction. It is often referred to as the **universal donor**. On the other hand, group AB blood cannot be given to anyone other than an AB recipient, because all the other blood groups contain antibodies in their plasma which would cause some level of agglutination. However, people with blood group AB can receive any type of blood as their plasma contains no antibodies – so group AB is known as the **universal recipient.**

Why does blood group matter?

Imagine an accident victim with blood group A who has haemorrhaged severely and needs several pints of blood. Figure 2.10 shows which blood groups are compatible. Blood from donors of groups B or AB cannot be given to the victim. Group A blood has the plasma antibody b. If this comes into contact with antigen B on the surface of donated red blood cells, the plasma would cause cell agglutination.

Donor \ Recipient	O (Antibodies a and b)	A (Antigen A, antibody b)	B (Antigen B, antibody a)	AB (Antigens A and B)
O (Antibodies a and b)	✓	✓	✓	✓
A (Antigen A, antibody b)	X	✓	X	✓
B (Antigen B, antibody a)	X	X	✓	✓
AB (Antigens A and B)	X	X	X	✓

Figure 2.10 Correct matching of the blood makes the difference between life and death when a blood transfusion is needed.

The rhesus factor

The **rhesus factor** is an agglutinogen (antigen) which is found on the surface of some red blood cells whatever their ABO grouping. In fact, 85% of us possess this particular feature of our red blood cells and are known as **rhesus positive**. The remainder, who do not have the agglutinogen, are **rhesus negative**. Normally neither rhesus positive nor rhesus negative blood possesses rhesus agglutinins in the plasma. Rhesus positive blood never forms rhesus agglutinins, otherwise it would coagulate itself. But in certain circumstances, rhesus negative blood will form plasma agglutinins, usually during pregnancy if a rhesus negative mother carries a fetus that is rhesus positive.

In theory this should not matter at all. Every fetus is genetically different from its mother. By some suspension of the immune system which we do not fully understand, this foreign genetic material is allowed to grow and thrive in the uterus for some 40 weeks without being attacked and destroyed. The placenta forms a barrier between the cells of the mother and the cells of the fetus so that an inappropriate immune response is not triggered. However, the placenta leaks. This leakage is usually only slight in the first pregnancy, but a few fetal red blood cells will get into the bloodstream of the mother. If they are of a different ABO blood group they will probably be destroyed. However, if mother and fetus have the same ABO group or a compatible one, the fetal blood cells will survive long enough to stimulate the production of rhesus antibodies in the mother's plasma.

In subsequent pregnancies the placenta gets progressively more leaky. The build-up of maternal agglutinins to any further rhesus positive fetal blood cells is much larger and more rapid. These agglutinins can cross the placenta. The red blood cells of the fetus are then attacked and agglutinated. In the past this led to many babies dying, either before they were born or shortly afterwards. In more recent years, once the rhesus incompatibility was recognised, affected babies were given transfusions as soon as they were born. Now blood transfusions are carried out whilst the fetus is still within the uterus.

It is worth noticing that rhesus incompatibility only matters in one direction – that is, if the mother makes antibodies against the fetus. If the developing baby is rhesus negative and the mother rhesus positive, the same thing will happen in reverse. But the amounts of antibodies the fetus makes against its mother's blood are so tiny that their effect is not noticed.

In order to prevent the necessity for intrauterine blood transfusions, women who are rhesus positive and have carried one rhesus negative child are usually given an injection shortly after the birth. This contains anti-rhesus agglutinins and is known as anti-D. It prevents the antibody-forming process, which means that a second fetus is at no higher risk than the first.

Transplants and the immune system

In recent years medical advances have highlighted the immune system in a new way. The development of the transplantation of organs and tissues from one person to another has led to much work being done on the immune system and its suppression. However closely the tissues of a donor organ – for example, a kidney – are matched to the tissues of the patient who is to receive the transplant, a perfect match is not possible unless the donor is an identical twin. This means that, to a greater or lesser extent, the immune system of the recipient will set out to destroy or **reject** the donated organ.

The problem is how to prevent the recipient from rejecting the transplanted organ without reducing the ability of the immune system to the extent that the patient dies from a succession of infections which the body cannot fight. Rejection is prevented by a cocktail of **immunosuppressant drugs** which endeavour to get the balance right. Transplant patients have to take these drugs for the rest of their lives.

The immune system is also capable of 'holding off' naturally. As we have already mentioned, during the development of the fetus the mother's immune system does not destroy this foreign genetic material. At an even earlier stage of reproduction, sperm are allowed to travel and live within the female reproductive tract for days at a time without triggering an immune reaction. Once scientists can understand how these suspension of the normal immune response are brought about, they may be in a position to develop a more specific and effective way of preventing rejection.

THE PATHOGENS FIGHT BACK

What makes a successful pathogen?

A successful pathogen exploits its host as effectively as possible. It is good at surviving and reproducing itself, and also at spreading to further hosts. In general, this does not mean killing the host, as a dead host is not very good at spreading pathogens! This ability of a pathogen to survive, spread and therefore cause disease is known as its **pathogenicity**. There are many adaptations of pathogens that help their success.

Surviving between hosts

A pathogen has to be able to survive in the environment between hosts. Many microorganisms are killed by drying, ultra-violet light and high or low temperatures. However, some strategies have evolved which overcome these difficulties. Many microorganisms form very resistant **spores** which withstand drying and changes in temperature for many years. For example, the Scottish island of Gruinard was infected with anthrax spores during an experiment on germ warfare early in the Second World War. It was to be 50 years before the island was passed as safe and free from the risk of infection.

Some pathogens are transferred from one host to another enclosed in droplets. Others, like the very delicate bacterium *Neisseria gonorrhoeae* which causes a sexually transmitted disease, cannot survive outside their host and are passed on directly through moist mucous membranes during sex.

Attaching to the host

Large pathogens like the helminthes often have very specialised body parts such as hooks, jaws or suckers which attach them to their host. Some bacteria also attach themselves to their host. A strain of *Escherichia coli* which causes urinary infections is not flushed out in the urine because it attaches itself to the epithelium of the urinary tract using pili (see figure 2.3, page 21).

Surviving the immune response

Microorganisms that can defend themselves against their host's immunological attack are likely to be very successful pathogens. Bacterial capsules can act as a defence against some host antibodies. Other microorganisms, such as *Mycobacterium tuberculosis*, actually colonise host phagocytes during their life cycle. Yet other microorganisms, such as *Toxoplasma gondii*, have specialised biochemistry which helps overcome the host reaction.

Changing surface antigens is an excellent way of beating the host immune system. By the time one set of antibodies is in place, new microorganisms are being reproduced with a different set of antigens. The *Plasmodia* that cause malaria produce individuals with new antigens every few days. The influenza virus changes its surface antigens less frequently than that, but new antigenic strains evolve regularly to which no one has immunity.

Some microorganisms have a high pathogenicity because they suppress the activity of the host immune system. They are then free to reproduce and invade host cells, and so are other infections as well, because the suppressed immune system cannot fight any new invading pathogen. African trypanosomiasis (sleeping sickness) and AIDS are both caused by such **immunosuppressant pathogens** – the patient is often attacked by other microorganisms whose pathogenicity is increased because of the suppressed immune system.

Producing toxins

The pathogenicity of many microorganisms depends on the **toxins** (poisonous substances) they produce. These toxins are usually produced as part of the microbial life cycle, and are frequently responsible for the symptoms of disease.

Botulism – the satan bug

When the bacterium *Clostridium botulinum* grows in anaerobic conditions, it produces a toxin which can cause paralysis and, if untreated, death. Botulism used to be more common than it is today, when people bottled and canned their own fruit and vegetables to preserve them for the winter. Now that most food is preserved commercially, outbreaks of botulism have become relatively rare. There is some suggestion that a form of botulism in very young babies may be one of the factors in cot deaths.

Symptoms

A mild feeling of a 'tummy bug' may precede the major symptom, which is paralysis. The paralysis spreads from the head downwards and is the result of the botulinum toxin blocking neuromuscular junctions. Once the paralysis has taken hold, it can last for several weeks. Breathing, blood pressure and the functioning of the gut can all be affected.

Treatment

The main treatment involves supporting the patient, usually with artificial ventilation and feeding, until the effects of the toxin wear off after a few weeks. Blood serum containing antibodies (antiserum) can be given, which protects the neuromuscular junctions and prevents the paralysis from spreading any further. This same antiserum can be given to anyone else who may have eaten the suspect food to prevent them from developing symptoms.

Control

The only effective control measures are the proper preservation and cooking of food – heat destroys the toxin.

Figure 2.11 Botulinum toxin had its 15 minutes of fame in the well known book by Alistair Maclean, in which the villain stole botulinum toxin from a top secret laboratory and planned to kill thousands of people with it. In reality, canned and home-bottled foods are the most common sources of botulism.

Symptoms of infectious diseases

The symptoms of infectious diseases are many and varied, but the human body responds to invading pathogens in certain ways which are common to many infections.

Fever

The first and most common response to infection is to develop a fever. Normal body temperature is maintained by the hypothalamus, a small area of the brain above the pituitary gland. The body temperature varies slightly throughout the day, being lowest in the early hours of the morning and highest at about 10 p.m. When a pathogen infects the body it causes the hypothalamus to reset to a higher body temperature, so that we become aware of 'running a temperature' – in other words, we have a fever. A raised temperature seems to help the body combat infection in two ways. First, many pathogens reproduce best at 37 °C or lower. Thus a raised temperature will reduce their ability to reproduce effectively, and so they cause less damage. Second, the immune system works better at higher temperatures, and so will be more successful at combating the infection even if the pathogen is unaffected by the raised temperature.

Although fevers can be beneficial, they can also be damaging and even fatal if they become too high. Some enzymes denature at a body temperature above 40 °C, and permanent tissue damage may occur. If the temperature is not lowered fairly quickly, death may result.

Inflammation

Inflammation is another common way in which our bodies respond to infection. It tends to occur when the infection is more localised. The local blood vessels vasodilate, causing heat and redness, and fluid is forced out of them causing swelling and often pain. Phagocytic white blood cells called neutrophils and macrophages accumulate at the site to engulf the invading pathogens, and can often be seen as pus. A third common response is a rash, which is a form of inflammation or tissue damage that particularly affects the skin. An example is shown in figure 2.12.

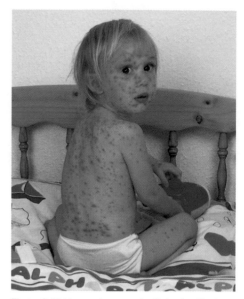

Figure 2.12 Many rashes are quite distinctive, like the chickenpox shown here, but general red rashes may accompany a wide range of bacterial and viral infections.

CONTROLLING DISEASE

The idea that diseases can be caused by microorganisms is central to our view of health and medical treatments, yet people have only known of the existence of bacteria, viruses and other microorganisms since the middle of the nineteenth century. Once the role of these organisms in causing disease was recognised, steps were taken to prevent their spread. For thousands of years people had used herbs, muds, prayers and infusions to try and overcome the ravages of disease and some of these methods had some success. But from the middle of the nineteenth century, in the developed world at least, the battle against disease became more focused. Today modern techniques such as monoclonal antibodies can identify specific pathogens, giving rapid and accurate diagnoses. As a result, appropriate treatments can be started quickly to maximise the chances of success. A chemical substance is usually used to prevent or treat a disease – this is called **chemotherapy**.

Monoclonal antibodies – medicine's magic bullets

In 1977 two research scientists at Cambridge University discovered a way of obtaining large amounts of a single known type of antibody. The Nobel prize-winning technique takes advantage of the special properties of two different types of cells.

A mouse is injected with a particular labelled antigen. **B-cells** (see page 30) that make the appropriate antibody are then removed from its spleen and fused with a **myeloma**, a type of cancer cell which divides very rapidly. The fused cell is known as a **hybridoma**. Each hybridoma can produce many antibody molecules specific to the antigen, and the hybridoma itself reproduces very rapidly to give millions of 'living factories'. The technique is outlined in figure 2.13.

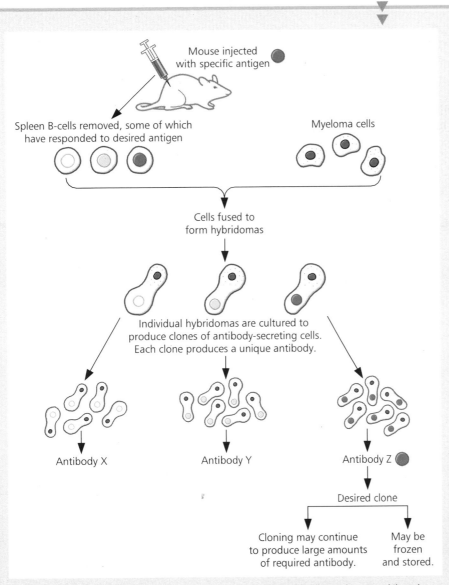

Figure 2.13 Monoclonal antibodies allow us to produce extremely specific diagnostic tests and therapies.

A large number of medical benefits have already resulted from this technology. Monoclonal antibodies tagged with radioactive or fluorescent labels can be used in medical research to identify specific cells and tissues. They have been used in research into areas such as hormone action, diabetes, cancer, heart disease, rheumatoid arthritis, allergies and the functioning of the brain. They can provide extremely sensitive diagnostic tests – for example, the many pregnancy tests on the market which can give an indication of pregnancy on the very day a woman is due to have her period rely on monoclonal antibodies. Monoclonal antibodies also provide an accurate diagnostic tool for specific viruses, bacteria, fungi and parasites. In some cases, monoclonal antibodies can provide an effective therapy. The possibilities of these 'magic bullets' continue to stretch ahead – it is hoped that in years to come many cancers and other diseases will be treated by these versatile fused cells.

Chemical control – antiseptics

Some of the earliest steps in the control of bacterial diseases are hard to believe nowadays. In 1847 Ignaz Semmelweiss substantially reduced the number of cases of childbed fever (infections which frequently killed women in the few days after giving birth) by encouraging doctors to wash their hands between deliveries!

Subsequently the use of **antiseptic** techniques and **disinfectant** solutions also began to reduce the number of deaths from infectious diseases. Surgery in those days was very much a last resort, usually to remove parts of the body that had become gangrenous in an attempt to stop the infection killing the patient. Such surgery was often ineffective. However, it was noticed that if a surgical wound was coated in coal tar it was less likely to become infected. The coal tar kept out the air, and any microorganisms present in it, and also contained an unrecognised antiseptic chemical, **phenol** (also known as carbolic acid). By 1860 the Scottish doctor Joseph Lister had started using pure phenol as an antiseptic during and after surgery. Doctors started to observe stricter codes of personal cleanliness, medical instruments were sterilised and antiseptics were used more. The number of deaths from infectious diseases began to fall, and medical intervention became much safer for the patient.

Phenol did have some drawbacks. It is an acidic compound, and while it prevented wounds from becoming infected, it could also prevent them healing because of its corrosive effects on the skin. Many modern antiseptics are phenol derivatives, but they are much more effective at destroying bacteria and kinder to human tissues. We now have a range of chemicals used to destroy bacteria – those used in the environment, for example to sterilise equipment, are usually referred to as **disinfectants**, while those used directly on people are **antiseptics**.

Chemical control – antimicrobial drugs

Although antiseptics were used during the nineteenth century to prevent the spread of infection, it was not until well into the twentieth century that drugs became available to treat a bacterial infection once it had taken hold. In 1935 Gerhard Domagk used a new drug called Prontosil on his youngest daughter, and prevented her dying from a severe streptococcal infection. In 1936 it was shown that the effective part of the drug was a chemical compound known as a sulphonamide. This interfered with the metabolism of the bacteria without disrupting human cells. All modern antimicrobial drugs have their effect because of this principle of **selective toxicity** – they interfere with the metabolism of the microorganism but cause minimal damage to the human host.

Types of antibiotic

The most commonly used and best known antimicrobial drugs are the **antibiotics**. These are antimicrobial compounds made by microorganisms, or similar compounds synthesised by chemists. Antibiotics can be used against both bacterial and fungal diseases. Alexander Fleming is usually credited with the discovery of penicillin, the first modern antibiotic. He noticed the *Penicillium* mould infecting his bacterial plates, and observed a clear area of agar jelly around the mould where it had destroyed the bacterial culture. However, it was not until 1940 that the Australian Howard Florey and the German Ernst Chain, working in England, developed penicillin as an antibiotic. This new drug had an almost magical effect, curing patients who were seriously ill with previously uncurable bacterial diseases. Many other antibiotics have been discovered since, but penicillin is still commonly used to

Figure 2.14 Alexander Fleming, Howard Florey and Ernst Chain were awarded a Nobel prize in 1945 for their work on the discovery of penicillin.

combat bacterial infections. The main classes of antimicrobial drug and the way they affect microorganisms are summarised in table 2.3.

Antimicrobial action	Examples
Antimetabolites interrupt the metabolic pathways of the microorganism, causing death.	Sulphonamides
Cell wall agents prevent the formation of cross-linking in bacterial cell walls. This weakens the cell walls so the bacteria are killed by lysis (bursting).	Beta-lactams, e.g. penicillins Glycopeptides, e.g. vancomycin
Protein synthesis inhibitors interrupt or prevent the transcription and/or translation of microbial genes, causing the genetic code to be misread and the wrong protein made in the bacterial cell.	Tetracyclines Chloramphenicol
DNA gyrase inhibitors damage the tertiary structure of bacterial DNA – they stop it coiling up so that it can no longer fit within the bacterial cell.	Quinolone

Table 2.3 Action of the main types of antimicrobial drug

Choosing the right antibiotic

The majority of antibiotics can be used to treat many different types of bacteria – they are known as **broad-spectrum antibiotics**. However, some antibiotic drugs are effective against only very few types of bacteria or even one particular type. These are known as **narrow-spectrum antibiotics**. When choosing an antibiotic, a doctor will consider carefully the pathogen likely to be causing the symptoms, and prescribe the cheapest antibiotic likely to be effective against it.

The effectiveness of any antimicrobial drug depends on a variety of factors. One such factor is the concentration of the drug in the area of the body infected. This depends on the dose, on how easily the drug can reach the tissue and on how quickly it is excreted. The effectiveness of the drug also depends on the pH in the body. Both the pathogen and the host tissue may destroy the antibiotic, which obviously makes the drug less effective. But one of the most important factors is the susceptibility of the pathogen to the particular antibiotic used. If the standard dose of a drug (in other words, what a doctor would normally prescribe) successfully destroys the pathogen and cures the disease, then the pathogen is **sensitive** to that antibiotic. If the standard dose is not completely successful but an increased dose of the antibiotic treats the disease, the pathogen is **moderately sensitive**. However, there are increasing numbers of cases where a particular microorganism is not affected by an antibiotic, sometimes even an antibiotic which has treated that disease successfully in the past. In these cases the microorganism has become **resistant** to the antibiotic.

Bacteriostatic or bactericidal?

An antibiotic may have one of two different effects on the pathogen. The drug, or the dose of the drug administered, may be **bacteriostatic**. This means that the antibiotic prevents the growth of the microorganism. This level of treatment is usually sufficient for the majority of everyday infections, because combined with the immune system it ensures that the pathogen is destroyed and removed. However, sometimes a particular drug, or the dose of the drug that is given, will be **bactericidal**. This means it will kill 99.9% of the pathogens present. This type of treatment is particularly important in severe and dangerous infections, and also for treating infections where the immune system is of limited use or suppressed through disease. The effect an antibiotic will have on a particular microorganism can be determined by a sensitivity test, as shown in figure 2.15.

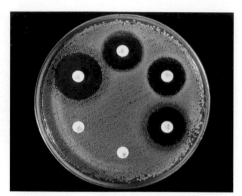

Figure 2.15 The sensitivity of a disease-causing organism to an antibiotic can be determined in experiments such as this. The discs contain known concentrations of antibiotics, and the inhibition of bacterial growth gives a measure of the effectiveness of the drug.

Superbugs – the drug-resistant strains

When the first antibiotic drugs were discovered, it must have seemed like the beginning of a brave new world in which dreaded infectious diseases would no longer kill thousands of people each year. In many ways, antibiotics have lived up to these hopes and expectations, at least in the developed world where they are readily available and affordable. But antibiotics are not the whole answer to bacterial diseases, and problems are now arising which result directly from the over-use of these valuable drugs.

Each antibiotic is only effective against certain bacteria. This is because the metabolic process or biochemical pathway with which it interferes does not occur in all bacteria, or because there is no binding site for the drug, or because some bacteria naturally produce enzymes that destroy the drug. This in itself is not a major problem, because many different antibiotics have been developed, so in theory there should be an antibiotic effective against every pathogen. However, antibiotics have been used widely and freely, exposing many pathogens to a wide range of our antibacterial weaponry. As a result, increasing numbers of pathogens are becoming resistant to the effects of many common antibiotics.

A microorganism becomes resistant through mutation. By chance, a mutated bacterium will come about that can withstand the antibiotic. It may become impermeable to the drug, or it may develop a new biochemical pathway, or most commonly it switches on or acquires a gene for the production of an antibiotic-destroying enzyme. This mutant will fairly rapidly become the main form, because non-resistant strains of the bacteria will be wiped out by antibiotic therapy, as shown in figure 2.16.

Some bacteria have become resistant to the effects of many different antibiotics. These are sometimes referred to as 'superbugs', and they can be killers. One of the more frightening aspects of this problem is that superbugs are most often found in hospitals, where drug use is at its highest. The only way to prevent this trend continuing is to use antibiotics only when strictly necessary, and to use as few different antibiotics as possible, holding some in reserve to treat diseases that have not responded to the usual drugs.

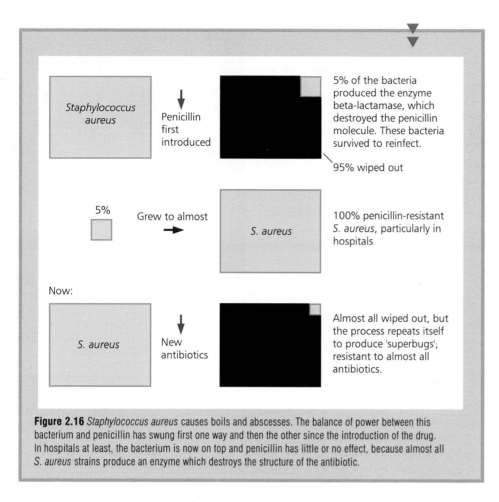

Figure 2.16 *Staphylococcus aureus* causes boils and abscesses. The balance of power between this bacterium and penicillin has swung first one way and then the other since the introduction of the drug. In hospitals at least, the bacterium is now on top and penicillin has little or no effect, because almost all *S. aureus* strains produce an enzyme which destroys the structure of the antibiotic.

Antiviral drugs – a long time coming

Whilst antibiotics have provided a vital weapon in the battle against bacteria, they are of no help at all in the viral war. Viruses are non-cellular, so how do we kill them? Because they do not have membranes or their own biochemistry, the problem of destroying the virus without harming the host becomes particularly acute. There are several lines of research which show promise, but there is still no group of antiviral drugs to treat the majority of everyday viral infections. Methods of attack which are showing promise include:

- **interfering with viral enzymes** – some viruses use host cell enzymes for reproduction; others cause the host cell to make viral enzymes. The latter type of virus can be attacked by drugs that inhibit viral enzymes, such as **acyclovir**. The drug is only activated in the presence of a viral enzyme, so it does not attack uninfected host cells. Once activated, it binds to DNA polymerase enzymes, making sure that the virus cannot replicate. Acyclovir is used against genital herpes, cold sores and shingles, and it is hoped that other antiviral drugs with a similar action will be developed soon.

- **interfering with viral genes** – this involves introducing complementary stretches of DNA or RNA into infected host cells, interfering with the viral genes and preventing them from being replicated or transcribed. Work is in progress on treatments based on this theory.

- **using interferons** – interferons are part of the body's natural defence system. They are glycoproteins that are made and released by virus-infected cells to make neighbouring cells resistant to infection by the virus. The prediction is that genetic engineering will enable bacteria to produce large quantities of interferons, and their use as drugs may then become practicable.

Vaccination

Prevention is better than cure

Drugs are used to treat microbial infections once they are present in the body. An alternative approach to breaking the cycle of disease is to prevent it happening in the first place. This is what vaccination programmes aim to do. The history of vaccination is long, going back to Edward Jenner in 1796 with his pioneering work on smallpox vaccination. Over 100 years later, Louis Pasteur moved vaccination forward again by demonstrating that a modified technique could provide protection against a variety of diseases, not just smallpox.

When we are exposed to a pathogen and suffer from a disease, we develop a natural immunity to that pathogen. Having dealt with the pathogen once, our immune systems can destroy it before it causes disease on a subsequent infection. Vaccination enables us to develop that immunity artificially, by exposing our immune systems to the pathogen in a safe way so that antibodies and memory cells can be prepared without us having the real disease.

Eradication, elimination and control

The aim of immunisation on a personal level is to protect individuals against diseases which might kill or harm them. However, immunisation also has a wider role in society. It is used to control diseases that cause large numbers of deaths, disabilities or illnesses within a population, and therefore place a strain on that society. Smallpox is the only disease that has been completely **eradicated** by vaccination. Eradication means that the organism is no longer found in people, in animals or anywhere in the environment. Once a disease has been eradicated, immunisation can stop. Smallpox was a very recognisable disease which had no long-term carriers, visible evidence of immunisation (see figure 2.17), no non-human hosts and a long incubation period. These features all helped make eradication possible.

Polio has many of the same infective features as smallpox, and the World Health Organisation hopes to have eradicated polio worldwide by the year 2000. However, for many other diseases – for example, where the pathogen survives in soil or water or animal hosts – eradication is not realistically possible. This is true for:

- measles, where infection is rapid, the incubation period short and the disease is not regarded as serious by many in the developed world
- tuberculosis, which is caused by airborne pathogens and can be present in a host without showing symptoms
- cholera, caused by a water-carried pathogen which is highly infectious and has a very short incubation period.

For such diseases, elimination or control have to be the aims of any immunisation programme. **Elimination** means that the disease has disappeared but the pathogen remains in animals, in the environment or in sub-clinical infections (without showing symptoms), and so immunisation must continue even when no clinical cases are being seen. A disease that is **controlled** still occurs, but not often enough to be a significant health problem. For some serious infectious diseases such as malaria, it has proved impossible to develop a vaccine that is effective against all the different forms of the pathogen, because it changes its antigens so rapidly.

Types of vaccine

Today, many different types of vaccine are available for use. **Live vaccines** use **attenuated** (weakened) strains of pathogens which can stimulate an immune response but are virtually incapable of causing active disease. A single dose of

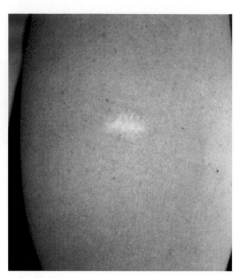

Figure 2.17 For years, people all over the world could prove they had been vaccinated against smallpox by showing the scar left by their body's reaction to the vaccine. But since 1979, children's arms have been scar free. Smallpox has been officially eradicated so worldwide immunisation is no longer necessary, as the smallpox virus only exists sealed up in two top security laboratories.

a live vaccine usually provides long-lasting immunity. Common examples of this type of vaccine include rubella, oral polio, measles and yellow fever.

The potential effectiveness of a vaccination programme is shown by data from the poliomyelitis vaccination programme in England and Wales from 1914 to 1992, shown in figure 2.18.

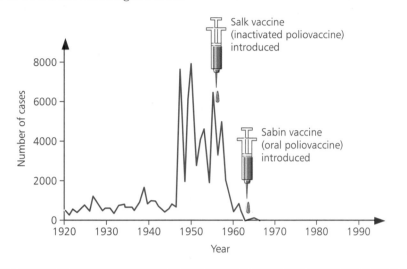

Figure 2.18 The graph shows cases of poliomyelitis in England and Wales that have caused paralysis, 1914–92. The vaccination programme has not completely eradicated polio. Because live vaccine is used, in rare cases infants develop the disease, and very occasionally adults have caught polio from changing the nappies of their recently vaccinated infants. However, the impact of the disease on the population as a whole has been reduced to a minimal level.

What is polio?

Polio is short for poliomyelitis, the disease caused by the poliovirus. The virus enters the body through the mouth. It infects and kills cells in the spinal cord, causing degeneration of the motor neurones and therefore paralysis. However, this only happens in about 10% of cases – in the other 90%, the disease is not apparent or gives mild 'flu-like symptoms or diarrhoea. Humans are the only known hosts of the virus, which is excreted in the saliva and faeces of an infected person, readily spreading the disease.

In poor and undeveloped areas of the world, the disease is often endemic – it is always present, particularly in young children, who pass it between themselves and rarely develop serious symptoms or paralysis. Polio causes problems when living conditions improve and the virus no longer passes freely between young children. When the infection occurs in older children and teenagers, it is much more likely to result in paralysis or even death.

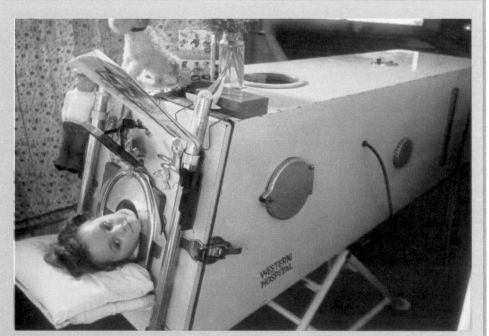

Figure 2.19 The poliovirus does not just paralyse the legs and arms. The muscles needed for breathing, and even for swallowing, can be affected too. Polio epidemics in the 1940s and 1950s left many young people confined to an 'iron lung' which artificially expanded and contracted their chests to enable them to breathe, and polio vaccines were developed in response to these human tragedies.

This is what happened in the USA, UK and many other countries in the 1940s and 1950s, as the peaks on figure 2.18 reflect.

Symptoms

The first symptoms of polio are fever, followed after 2–5 days by damage to the nervous system. The muscles may ache for the day or two before paralysis sets in, and using the muscles increases the likelihood of paralysis. The level of paralysis is very variable, and is generally worse the older the patient. Paralysis is largely irreversible, although very young children many regain some or all movement.

Treatment

The only treatment available is rest followed by physiotherapy, along with antibiotics for any secondary bacterial infections which may be set up.

Prevention

Live oral polio vaccine is the most commonly used preventive measure. It does not only give immunity to the recipient – the vaccine virus is passed out in the faeces for up to six weeks, so it can spread to and immunise close contacts. This means that a large proportion of the population can become immunised even if relatively few people have the vaccine. The main disadvantage is that because a live vaccine is used, about one in two million people who receive the vaccine will end up paralysed.

Polio remains endemic in Asia, but has been virtually eradicated in the developed world and in some developing countries, for example in South America. By introducing immunisation programmes wherever possible, the WHO is aiming for global elimination of polio by the year 2000.

Other vaccines are produced from killed virulent organisms, for example, the whooping cough (pertussis) vaccination. There is no risk of causing the disease, but the vaccination may have to be repeated, giving 'boosters' to top up the immune response from time to time. This is true for all vaccines that do not contain living pathogens.

Some pathogens cause disease as a result of a toxin they produce. In such cases, the vaccine may be a modified version of the toxin molecule, capable of stimulating an immune response without causing disease. The diphtheria vaccine is an example of this type.

In modern 'flu vaccines, the protein–polysaccharide antigens from the viral coat are separated and inoculated. Again there is no risk of developing the disease, but an effective immune response is stimulated.

Finally, genetically engineered bacteria can produce certain antigens which can then be used for vaccines. The vaccine against hepatitis B is produced in this way.

Dirty vaccines?

Vaccination sounds relatively simple – expose your immune system to a safe form of a nasty pathogen, and it will prepare appropriate antibodies in case it meets the real thing. The 'safe forms of a pathogen' are getting more and more sophisticated, with pieces of DNA or specific outer coat antigens being used to give immunity instead of whole organisms or toxins. However, this is not the whole story.

Vaccines based on whole viruses, like the oral polio vaccine, are all that is needed to stimulate the immune system. But as the pharmaceutical industries produced purer and purer vaccines, it became evident that the great majority of vaccines do not work effectively unless they contain an **adjuvant**. This adjuvant is not part of the safe pathogen, and could be any of a strange mixture of things – detergent, oil and water, dead bacteria which have nothing to do with the disease being immunised against, or even aluminium hydroxide! The role of these adjuvants seems to be to cause inflammation, and the worse the inflammation, the more effective the immune response to the vaccine. It is suggested that they alert the body to the presence of a foreign invader by mimicking a characteristic of the pathogen which is not present in the safe form used in the vaccine. It has even been shown using mice that the use of different adjuvants with the same vaccine can cause the stimulation of different parts of the immune system.

In the light of evidence like this, and in the quest to make vaccines that are as pure as possible yet as effective as possible, new adjuvants are being investigated and developed. The role of these 'added extras' in the vaccine mixture is being constantly evaluated to ensure that they continue to help without causing harm by bringing about too much inflammation.

Figure 2.20 Successful vaccination programmes around the world are reducing deaths from diseases such as polio and measles.

Vaccination programmes

For a vaccine to be effective in preventing epidemics of disease, a large proportion of the population needs to be vaccinated. Otherwise, a large pool of infection remains in the community and a drop in vaccination levels can lead to an epidemic. This is known as the **herd effect** – if enough of the 'herd' is protected by vaccination, the disease can only affect isolated individuals, and is unlikely even to do that. To try and achieve vaccination of a very large proportion of the population against the most common infectious diseases, many countries target small children for vaccination. This increases the likelihood of uptake, as parents are more likely to take their children for vaccinations and health checks than to have such vaccinations themselves. In the UK, the target coverage for childhood vaccines is 95% of all children at two years of age. Most of the vaccination programme is carried out at GP surgeries under the National Health Service, and in the 1990s there were financial rewards for surgeries that achieved the vaccination targets set by central Government. The childhood immunisation schedule in Britain in the mid-1990s was quite extensive, as can be seen from table 2.4. Some of the vaccines were delivered to pupils in schools, but the majority were for pre-school children.

It is interesting that not every vaccination given is needed by the individual concerned. For example, rubella (German measles) is a relatively mild infection accompanied by a rash and feeling slightly unwell. The disease often passes almost unnoticed, yet the aim is for the entire population of children to be vaccinated against it. This is because if a pregnant woman becomes infected by rubella in the early stages of her pregnancy, the developing embryo may become deaf, blind or possibly brain damaged. Immunising young children against rubella protects pregnant women, as it greatly reduces the pool of infection. Also, the vaccinated girls of today are the pregnant women of tomorrow, so they will already be immune to rubella long before they are likely to be carrying a fetus.

The whole population of children is targeted for vaccination, boys as well as girls. This benefits society by reducing the pool of rubella infection, but does it give any benefit to each male child as an individual? It can be argued that by reducing the likelihood that a future partner carrying his child will become infected by rubella, the boy is in fact receiving the same protection for his future children as girls. However, if *all* girls were immunised against rubella it

Age	Vaccines
2 months	Diphtheria/tetanus/pertussis (whooping cough) (**DTP**)
	Oral polio (**OPV**)
	Haemophilus influenzae (bacterial meningitis) (**Hib**)
3 months	DTP OPV Hib
4 months	DTP OPV Hib
12–15 months	Measles/mumps/rubella (**MMR**)
4–5 years	Diphtheria/tetanus OPV
10–14 years	Bacille Calmette-Guérin (tuberculosis) (**BCG**)
15–18 years	Tetanus/low dose diphtheria OPV

Table 2.4 British immunisation scheme, mid-1990s

should not in theory matter if boys were not immunised. Like any medical procedure, all vaccines carry an element of risk. Some individuals may be allergic to components of the vaccine, or show unexpected sensitivity to it and become ill. So this vaccination programme can be viewed as protecting society as a whole, rather than being for the good of the individual.

Immunisation programmes can also be used to prevent potential epidemics, and again individuals may be revaccinated with no value – and indeed an element of risk – to themselves for the good of society as a whole. A prime example of this was seen in the UK in 1994. It was predicted that a measles epidemic was likely in Britain which would potentially lead to the death of around 15 children, mostly teenagers who had not previously been vaccinated. As a result, a mass immunisation programme was put in place to immunise every school child in Britain. Many of the younger children had already been vaccinated against measles once, and in some cases twice (when the MMR was introduced). To convince people that their children should be vaccinated again, statistics were put out showing that up to 1 in 10 children would not have developed immunity to measles after their first vaccines. The risks of death and disability from measles were also given high-profile coverage.

Just before the vaccination programme started, certain sections of the British media published some of the risks allegedly associated with the vaccine. It is always extremely difficult to prove that a child's reaction following a vaccine is actually a response to that vaccine and not a coincidental alternative infection. However, some children were severely brain damaged by events immediately following vaccinations, and their parents were convinced that the vaccine was to blame. Their points of view were widely publicised, resulting in a great deal of agonising for many parents. The immunisation programme went through, a few people withdrew their children – and the great measles epidemic did not occur. However, after the media circus preceding the vaccination programme, there was very little media presentation of either the effectiveness of the campaign in preventing an epidemic or the damage done to children by the vaccine.

The parent's dilemma

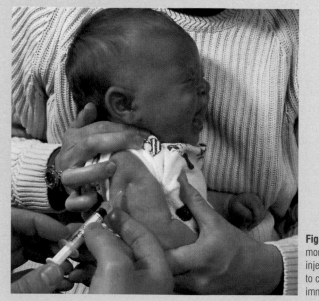

Figure 2.21 Apart from the momentary unpleasantness of the injection, there are serious issues to consider before deciding to immunise a child.

In countries such as the UK and the USA immunisation is widely believed to be a good thing. Parents generally bring their children along for vaccinations when they are advised to do so. However, in recent years people have become more aware that there are two sides to the debate. Increasing numbers of parents are weighing up the pros and cons of immunisation before going ahead with the vaccination programme.

By and large, the **pros** are very obvious.

● The child as an individual is protected against some of the more unpleasant infectious diseases.
● Society benefits as the potential pool of infection is reduced with every vaccinated child.
● The cost of treating serious diseases and caring for those left permanently damaged by them is kept to a minimum for a relatively small financial outlay (most common vaccines are relatively cheap).

The **cons** have, until recent years, been less well known.

● Some of the live, attenuated vaccines are cultured in eggs, to which a number of children may suffer a violent allergic reaction. Children with these sorts of allergies are advised not to have the vaccine.
● A tiny minority of children become very ill after a vaccination with what may be an extreme immune response. Some of these children may die; others have been left severely brain damaged but it is very difficult to prove a direct link between the vaccine and the damage to a child. In the case of the whooping cough vaccine, parents with any family history of epilepsy are advised not to proceed with vaccination.
● Some eminent scientists have suggested that mass vaccination programmes are linked to the massive rise in childhood asthma and allergies seen over the last few decades.
● Some vaccines, such as rubella for boys, are given more for the benefit of society than for the direct benefit of the child.

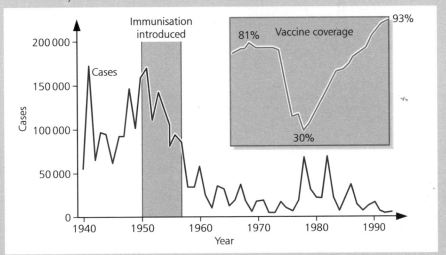

Figure 2.22 In the UK during the 1970s, a link was suggested between whooping cough vaccination and serious brain damage in some children. There was intense media coverage, and as a result the numbers of children vaccinated against the disease fell sharply. The effect on the numbers of recorded cases of whooping cough can be seen on the graph.

Many parents find the decision whether or not to vaccinate a very hard one to make. Most decide that the benefits outweigh the risk and go ahead with vaccination, but some parents feel the risks are too great, the benefits too uncertain and decide against it.

It is interesting that the safety and validity of immunisation has come into question in the generation of people who (perhaps largely as a result of immunisation programmes) have little or no personal experience of the diseases against which their children are to be vaccinated. In the developed world, few people of child-bearing age have seen anyone suffer with or die from diphtheria, polio, measles or whooping cough. The decision whether to vaccinate or not remains a luxury available only to those living in a society relatively free from major infectious diseases, yet for each individual involved it is a serious issue. How would you decide?

Change the world – prevent disease?

We tend to think of medical intervention (drugs, vaccines, etc.) as the main method of preventing and curing infectious diseases. Important as the medical developments of the late twentieth century certainly are, other changes are at least equally important in the prevention and even elimination of some infectious diseases. Data collected on the numbers dying of infectious diseases against which many of us have been immunised are shown in figure 2.23.

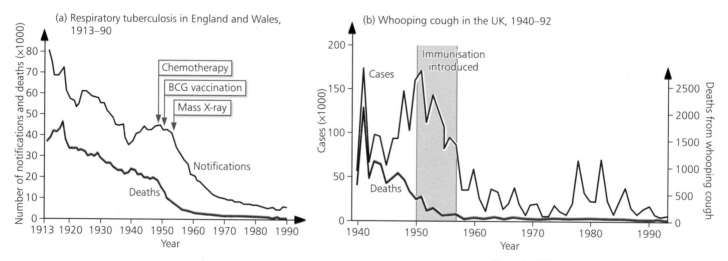

Figure 2.23 These data show that deaths from these major infectious diseases in the UK had started to fall substantially before the introduction of either antibiotics or immunisation programmes. What caused these large drops?

Over the last 150 years the population size, social structure, working conditions, affluence and health awareness of the general population of the British Isles have changed dramatically. Housing has improved, water supplies have been purified, sewage is removed and treated, diet has improved, children are no longer part of the workforce and health and safety regulations govern the working conditions in factories and other places of work. Add to this smaller average families, child welfare programmes and the Clean Air Act, and a whole range of reasons for the decline of many infectious diseases becomes apparent. For some diseases like smallpox, effective vaccination was almost the sole cause of its eradication. For most diseases, a drop in the death rate from the disease is due not to one specific reason but to a general improvement in nutrition and public health. Antibiotics and/or immunisation programmes can often be seen as the final piece of the jigsaw, reducing the levels of serious infections to a point where they no longer have a major impact on public health.

A CLOSER LOOK AT SOME INFECTIOUS DISEASES

We shall look at a few specific infectious diseases in more detail, giving us more insight into the problems surrounding their control, and also how their impact on individuals and populations may be lessened.

Tuberculosis (TB)

Tuberculosis is one of the most common human infections, with millions of people infected around the world. The majority of these cases are in the developing world, although TB ('consumption') used to be rampant in Europe and the UK. It is relatively rare in the western Pacific regions. In many developed countries, the number of cases of TB has fallen dramatically over the last 150 years due to a combination of social and medical reasons. However, the numbers are beginning to increase again, probably as a result of deteriorating social conditions, refugees, the spread of HIV and intravenous drug use.

TB comes in many forms, but it is most commonly caused by infections of *Mycobacterium tuberculosis*. It is transmitted by droplet infection and so crowded living or working conditions help it spread from person to person. The other common source of infection worldwide is from *Mycobacterium bovis*. This bacterium affects cattle, and people can become infected from drinking infected milk in areas where the disease has not been controlled in cattle and where milk is drunk unpasteurised.

Tuberculosis can affect many areas of the body, including the bones and the lymphatic system, but the most common forms of TB affect the respiratory system. The bacteria damage and destroy the lung tissue, and also suppress the action of the immune system, making the body less able to fight the disease.

Symptoms

Typical symptoms of TB are fever, night sweats, anorexia (inability to eat) and loss of weight. Coughing produces sputum from which *M. tuberculosis* can be cultured. However, in the developed world at least, the blood-stained phlegm of Victorian consumptives is rarely seen now as people are generally healthier and effective treatment is available. X-rays of the lungs give a picture typical of the disease – opaque areas and large, thick-walled cavities resulting from the bacterial damage, as shown in figure 2.24.

Treatment

The main treatment for tuberculosis is with antibiotics. For the first couple of months a cocktail of different antibiotics is used, to destroy any mycobacteria that are resistant to some of the drugs. This cocktail kills not only the rapidly reproducing microorganisms, but also those that are metabolising slowly, hidden in cysts or within the immune system. This initial treatment is followed by another four to seven months of treatment with just two drugs, rifampicin and isoniazid. Following this treatment regime, most patients will be completely free of TB in about nine months, but it can take a year to 18 months before all traces have gone, particularly if the TB has infected other tissues such as the joints or the kidneys as well as the lungs.

Although treatment is available, it is long term and expensive. It is therefore widely used in the developed world, but in countries like India where levels of TB are still very high, there is insufficient money to treat all the people who need it.

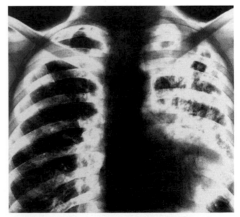

Figure 2.24 This X-ray of the lungs of a tubercular patient shows a shadowed area over the right-hand side of the chest where the disease has damaged the lung.

Control

The most effective ways of controlling TB relate to improved living standards. Less crowded housing and working conditions mean people are less likely to pass on the disease. Generally healthier and better fed people are less likely to develop debilitating TB even if they meet *M. tuberculosis*. Preventing and treating the disease in cattle and pasteurising or heating milk before it is drunk both prevent the spread of *M. bovis*.

A small but important factor in the control of TB in countries where it is rare is **contact tracing**. When a patient turns up with active TB, attempts are made to contact all the people who are in regular close contact with the patient so that they can be tested for TB and either immunised or treated as appropriate.

Immunisation has been very effective in the final reduction of the number of cases of TB in countries like the UK. The BCG (bacille Calmette-Guérin) vaccine is a live attenuated strain of the mycobacterium, given as a single injection. This is also more suitable for use in developing countries, as vaccines are much cheaper than treatment. In countries where TB is still very common, the vaccine is often given to very young babies. In the UK it is given to school children of 10–13 years old, and also to any adults in high-risk jobs such as teachers and health care workers. Before older children and adults are given the BCG, they are tested to see if they are already immune to or infected by tuberculosis. Between one and two per cent of all the children tested give a positive test and need further investigation.

Change society – or buy medicine?

The role of different factors in the control of tuberculosis are difficult to interpret from data, as shown in figure 2.25. There is understandably a great tendency to credit the development of drugs and vaccines with the control of disease, and to forget general social improvements that might also have an effect. It is also easier to fund a programme of medical aid than to attempt to improve the social conditions of large populations of people.

Information on death rates is often used as evidence to back up proposals for medical intervention.

However, by presenting the same data in different ways we can paint two different pictures of the role of modern interventions in the fall in the death rate from tuberculosis. Is the transition of TB in the developed world from a feared killer disease to a rare and treatable disease due to modern medical intervention or social factors? The same figures can be used to support an argument in either direction.

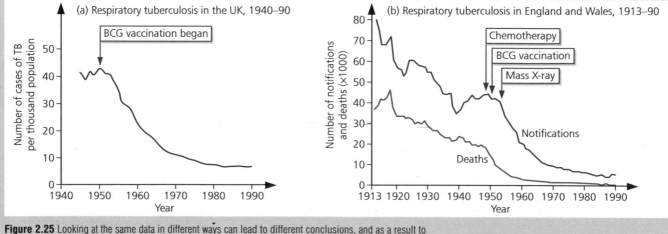

Figure 2.25 Looking at the same data in different ways can lead to different conclusions, and as a result to different emphases in health care programmes. Should social change or immunisation be the real priority for the eradication of TB?

Typhoid and cholera

Typhoid and cholera are both transmitted by drinking water contaminated by faeces, so they spread in conditions of poor sanitation. In previous centuries these diseases were found everywhere, thriving on the non-existent personal and public hygiene of the times. In the twentieth century both diseases have become rare in the developed world, with the development of extensive sewage treatment systems and better understanding of hygiene. But in the developing world, they are still epidemic. Whenever a society suffers trauma such as war, famine, earthquake or flood which disrupts normal living and forces people to live in crowded and makeshift camps, then typhoid and cholera claim lives and cause great suffering. In the slums of the megacities forming in some areas of the world, lack of proper sanitation again encourages the diseases to spread.

Typhoid is caused by the bacterium *Salmonella typhi*. Only a few bacteria need be ingested to cause infection, as they replicate very rapidly in the body. The incubation period is about two weeks, after which the disease starts like 'flu with high fever, headaches and feeling generally unwell. Diarrhoea does not start until a week to 10 days after the fever begins, but if the typhoid is not treated the diarrhoea becomes life threatening. It causes dehydration, and moreover the bacteria attack and damage the gut wall, causing bleeding and sometimes even perforating the gut. Typhoid can be treated by antibiotics taken over about two weeks to prevent a relapse, but it is important to begin treatment before serious damage to the gut lining has occurred.

Typhoid can be prevented by adequate sanitation, but without this it is necessary to avoid high risk foods like shellfish and drinking contaminated water. This advice may be fine for travellers, but is less useful to the indigenous population. Vaccines against typhoid are available, but they generally only offer protection for one to three years. Again, these are useful for travellers from developed countries, and can be provided in the wake of a natural disaster or a war, but they are less useful on a day-to-day basis in the countries most affected by typhoid.

Cholera is a disease caused by the response of the body to the toxin produced by a comma-shaped bacterium *Vibrio cholerae*. In the nineteenth century cholera was feared right across the world, but in the twentieth century it has, like typhoid, become common only in the poorer developing nations and travellers who visit these countries.

Cholera is spread mainly through drinking water contaminated with infected faeces or by eating raw or lightly cooked shellfish which have grown in contaminated water. It has a relatively short incubation period of just a few days before the victim begins to produce copious amounts of highly infectious diarrhoea. There are very few other symptoms. The diarrhoea has a typical appearance – pale fluid containing a little mucus and dead cells – and is known as 'rice water stools'. Rapid dehydration is the result which can lead to death if untreated.

V. cholerae do not damage the gut as typhoid does, so if patients can be given rehydration treatment (which is very cheap and becoming available all over the world), most will survive and recover after four or five days. Because of this, antibiotics are only used for the most seriously ill and vulnerable patients. There is a cholera vaccine but it only gives about 50% protection and only lasts about six months, so is of very limited use. Like typhoid, the best advice is to avoid taking in contaminated food and drink.

In this chapter we have had a brief look at some of the many infectious diseases in the world. Doctors now know how to reduce or eliminate many of these diseases, but in many areas of the world there is neither the will nor the resources to do so. In spite of all our advances in antimicrobial drugs and immunisation programmes, the sad fact is that one of the biggest killers in the world is diarrhoea. Simple gut infections causing diarrhoea still kill millions of people each year, many of them babies and young children who cannot cope with the rapid dehydration. Figure 2.26 shows the problem.

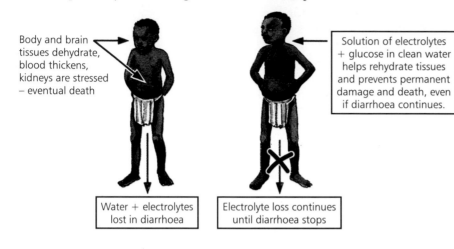

Body and brain tissues dehydrate, blood thickens, kidneys are stressed – eventual death

Solution of electrolytes + glucose in clean water helps rehydrate tissues and prevents permanent damage and death, even if diarrhoea continues.

Water + electrolytes lost in diarrhoea

Electrolyte loss continues until diarrhoea stops

Figure 2.26 The main cause of death due to diarrhoeal illnesses is the loss of body fluids and electrolytes (ions such as Na^+ and Cl^-). Keeping people hydrated through a diarrhoeal illness greatly increases their chances of complete recovery, and the manufacture and distribution of cheap rehydration packs is helping to reduce the impact of these diseases, still a major global cause of death in children.

In spite of some notable successes in the fight against infectious diseases in the developed world, on a global scale at the moment the pathogens are still winning.

SUMMARY

- There are five main groups of pathogen: viruses, bacteria, fungi, protozoans and larger multicellular organisms.
- **Viruses** consist only of genetic material, a protein coat and sometimes enzymes for replication. Viruses infect the host's cells and then take over the biochemistry of the cell to produce many more viruses. Viral diseases include polio, influenza and AIDS.
- **Bacteria** are single-celled prokaryotic organisms. They can live and replicate outside the host cell. Bacterial diseases include tuberculosis, salmonellosis and cholera.
- **Fungi** are eukaryotic organisms, frequently multicellular and heterotrophic. Most fungal infections affect the skin, hair and nails, though they can infect the lungs and other internal organs. Examples include athlete's foot and farmer's lung.
- **Protozoans** are single-celled eukaryotic organisms. Their life cycles can involve several hosts. A **vector** is an organism such as an insect that transmits the protozoan from one host to another. Examples of diseases caused by protozoans include malaria, amoebic dysentery and giardiasis.
- **Multicellular parasites** are usually **helminthes** (worms or flukes). Some have complex life cycles involving more than one host. Examples of diseases include schistosomiasis and river blindness.
- Infectious diseases are **communicable** (spread from one person to another). The likelihood of a disease spreading depends on the pathogen, the behaviour and general health of the potential host and environmental factors.

- Disease can spread **horizontally** through members of a population or **vertically** from one generation to the next. Animal diseases may spread to humans (**zoonosis**). Diseases may spread by:

  vectors – other organisms, such as the anopheles mosquito which transmits malaria
  fomites – objects such as towels and bedding
  direct contact – touching, also by sexual contact
  inhalation – breathing in droplets containing the microorganism
  ingestion – contaminated food or drink
  inoculation – through a break in the skin.

- A localised increase in the incidence of a disease is called an **outbreak**. An increase on a national level is an **epidemic**. An epidemic affecting many countries at the same time is a **pandemic**. A disease that is common in a particular population all the time is **endemic**.

- An outbreak of a disease can start from a single **point source**, and people exposed to the point source will develop the disease at the same time. There may be a **common source**, to which people are exposed over a period of time, or the disease may spread by **person-to-person contact**, where there is a chain of transmission with gaps while the disease incubates.

- The body is protected from pathogenic invasion by the skin, the blood-clotting mechanism, mucous membranes, phagocytic white blood cells, the acid in the stomach and competition from the natural flora (bacteria) on the skin and in the gut.

- The **immune response** enables the body to recognise and remove foreign material. The body recognises the material as foreign by its **antigens** – proteins on the cell surface membranes.

- **Lymphocytes** are white blood cells that each recognise one particular antigen. There are two types of lymphocytes – **T-cells** and **B-cells**.

- T-cells bring about the **cell-mediated response** to invasion by a foreign antigen. A T-cell binds to and destroys the antigen and then divides to produce a clone of **killer T-cells** which all destroy the same type of antigen.

- B-cells bring about the **humoral response** by producing **plasma cell clones** and **memory cells**. Plasma cell clones produce **antibodies**, proteins which bind to the antigens and destroy them. Memory cells convey **immunological memory** so that plasma clone cells are produced rapidly next time the antigen is met.

- The **ABO** system of **blood groups** classifies people onto four groups, A, B, AB, and O depending on the antigens (agglutinogens, A and B) and antibodies (agglutinins, a and b) that they have in their blood. These blood groups are important in blood transfusions, when the donated blood must be compatible with the recipient's blood group.

- The **pathogenicity** of a pathogen is its ability to survive, spread and cause disease. A successful pathogen needs to survive between hosts, attach to the host and survive the immune response. Some pathogens suppress the action of the host immune system.

- Common symptoms of infectious diseases include fever, inflammation and rash.

- Chemicals used to control the spread of disease include **antiseptics** (used on people) and **disinfectants** (used to sterilise equipment).

- **Antimicrobials** are drugs which are **selectively toxic** – they destroy bacteria inside the body without harming the human cells. **Broad-spectrum antibiotics** can be used to treat many types of bacteria; **narrow-spectrum antibiotics** are effective against a few or even just one type of bacterium. Bacteria may become **resistant** to an antibiotic, when they are no longer affected by it. **Bacteriostatic** antibiotics stop the microorganisms growing and multiplying; **bactericidal** antibiotics kill the microorganisms.

- **Vaccination** lets the body develop immunity to a pathogen without suffering the disease. **Live vaccines** use attenuated (weakened) strains of the pathogen. Other vaccines include killed pathogens, toxins or antigens from the viral coat.

- A disease has been **eradicated** when the organism is no longer found anywhere in hosts or the environment. It has been **eliminated** when people no longer suffer from the disease, but the organism is still around and so immunisation has to continue. A **controlled** disease still occurs, but not often enough to be a significant health risk.

QUESTIONS

1 Infectious diseases are caused by invading pathogens which may be viruses, bacteria, fungi, protoctista or multicellular organisms. Choose three of these groups of pathogens and for each describe:
   a one pathogen
   b the symptoms of the disease it causes
   c the treatment.

2 a Describe briefly the main body defences against disease.
   b How do pathogens attempt to overcome these defences?

3 Summarise the main methods of chemical control against disease and describe how they work.

4 For major diseases in the world, one of the main lines of research is usually for an effective vaccine.
   a What is vaccination and how does it work?
   b What are the main advantages of using vaccination programmes to control a disease?
   c What are the main disadvantages of vaccinations?

3 Lifestyle diseases

Many of the infectious disease we looked at in chapter 2 are at least in part the result of lifestyle. The poor living in slums in the developing world are exposed to many infectious diseases, and their inadequate diet may result in vitamin and mineral deficiency diseases. On the other hand, those living in relative prosperity in the USA or the UK have less risk of contracting an infectious disease causing severe illness or death. However, they are much more likely to suffer a disease related to their lifestyle, caused by overeating, unbalanced eating, lack of exercise, smoking, drinking or the effects of air pollution.

Some of the lifestyle factors that can cause disease, or at least increase the likelihood of suffering a particular disease, are under our control; others are not. Babies and small children have little choice about what they eat, yet the foundations of diet-related illnesses may well be laid in early childhood. You cannot change where you were born and the circumstances of your upbringing, and these early experiences help form many of your lifestyle habits. However, we in the more developed countries of the world are provided with knowledge with which to make lifestyle choices. If we know that exercise is important for a healthy heart, and yet sit slumped in front of the television during our leisure time, then we are choosing to increase our risk of disease. If, with knowledge of healthy eating, we choose to eat too much energy-rich refined carbohydrate and fat and refuse to eat fresh fruit and vegetables, then we cannot be surprised if we suffer ill-effects.

DIET AND DISEASE

Across the world, people eat an enormous variety of foods to obtain a balanced diet. It is becoming increasingly recognised that diet can affect our health in a number of ways.

Taking in problems

Lactose intolerance

The food we take into our bodies can cause health problems directly. For example, human infants almost all synthesise the enzyme **lactase** which is needed to break down lactose, the natural sugar in milk. Most mammals stop producing lactase once they are weaned, as they no longer drink milk. However, many human societies keep dairy herds and whilst no longer drinking human milk, many adults drink large quantities of cow's milk.

Some people suffer from severe stomach cramps, wind, diarrhoea and vomiting if they drink milk. They are said to be **lactose intolerant**. There is evidence that the ability of adult humans to digest milk has evolved within the last 5000 years or so, and only in those cultures that have traditionally kept dairy animals, such as in northern Africa, the Near East and Europe. Between 70% and 100% of individuals from these historical dairying regions produce lactase and can digest milk. In traditionally non-dairying regions, the situation is reversed and 70–100% of the population are lactose intolerant. Maintaining the ability to digest lactose must have been an advantage for children and young adults in areas where milk was a readily available source of food.

Figure 3.1 Wherever you live, your lifestyle contributes to your pattern of health and disease.

Figure 3.2 In many countries, people use cow's milk and its products as part of their diet. Sheep's milk, goat's milk and camel's milk are also used, and they all contain lactose.

Food allergies

Food allergies are another way in which the food taken into the body can cause a direct, and in some cases very serious, threat to health. **Mast cells** are small oval cells often found in connective tissue. They have immunoglobulin E on their surfaces, which responds to the presence of a foreign particle by stimulating the mast cell to secrete **histamine**. This causes local blood vessels to dilate and changes the permeability of the capillaries. As a result, plasma moves out into the surrounding tissues, causing them to swell. For many people this is a useful defence mechanism, helping them fight off invading infections. However, for increasing numbers of people (more than 35 million Americans alone) the mast cell system seems to be oversensitive, causing allergies to foods such as milk, eggs, wheat, peanuts, shellfish and various fruits. Allergic reactions range from mild breathlessness or a mild rash, through severe rashes and itching or sickness and diarrhoea, to severe wheezing and asthma and even, in extreme cases, death. The main treatment for any food allergy is to avoid the trigger food, but this is not easy as many processed foods contain traces of all sorts of substances which seem unrelated to the main ingredients. A mild allergy can be treated with antihistamine drugs, which counteract the histamine released by the mast cells. For more severe allergies, adrenaline has to be taken to counteract the state of shock which develops and to prevent the closing of the airways.

Food-borne infections

Finally, food can carry pathogenic microorganisms into the body. We have already mentioned salmonellosis, amoebic dysentery and botulism in chapter 2. Another food-borne disease is listeriosis, caused by *Listeria monocytogenes*. These bacteria may be found in soft ripened cheeses such as Brie and Camembert, in any cheeses made with unpasteurised milk and in pâtés. They have also been found in considerable numbers in prepared cooked and chilled meals which are reheated before eating, and in ready-to-eat poultry. In adults *Listeria* does not usually cause serious disease – mild fever and backache are the usual symptoms. Listeriosis is important because in pregnant women the bacteria can cross the placenta and reach the fetus. If a woman eats *Listeria*-infected food in the early stages of her pregnancy, the most likely outcome is that the fetus will miscarry (abort). If she becomes infected later in the pregnancy, the baby may be born severely ill and either die or be permanently damaged. Treatment with antibiotics can be very successful, but the bacteria do not always respond to the drugs as well as expected. The best policy is to avoid eating those foods that carry the highest risk during pregnancy.

E. coli *hits Scotland*

In the late autumn of 1996 there was a major outbreak of food poisoning in Scotland. Cooked meats and pies supplied by one butcher, John M Barr and Sons of Wishaw, who had been voted Scottish Butcher of the Year, were distributed around central Scotland. The meat products became contaminated by a strain of *E. coli* normally found in cattle guts, and which can be present in undercooked meat or cooked meat that has been in contact with raw meat. For example, the bacteria were found in gravy supplied by the butcher for a pensioners' lunch in Wishaw.

Figure 3.3 The butcher's shop where the fatal outbreak of *E. coli* food poisoning began

Several hundred people became ill. This infection is particularly dangerous as not only does it cause severe diarrhoea and sickness, but in around 25% of those infected it causes permanent kidney damage. Many sufferers were elderly, although people of all ages were admitted to hospital. Around 20 people died, making it one of the worst known outbreaks of food poisoning in the UK. Afterwards it was recognised that the outbreak had been very badly handled. The butcher had been warned about the products by health inspectors, but continued to sell them for several days. Once the outbreak was confirmed, the Scottish Agriculture, Environment and Fisheries Department prevented publication of the names of the known outlets, so that people continued to eat contaminated products and more became infected. With better management, substantially fewer people would probably have become ill or died. This is an example of the difficult marriage of commercial interests with the interests of public health, demonstrating the need for effective public health legislation.

The human diet

In many parts of the world, there is little choice over what food is eaten or how much is eaten. However, where there is sufficient food available for choices to be made, foods should be chosen in sensible combinations to provide a healthy balance of carbohydrates, fats and proteins as well as minerals, vitamins, plenty of water and fibre.

The detailed components of an ideal balanced diet for an individual change throughout the lifetime, particularly in the amount of protein and the total energy intake needed. However, there are other features of the diet which are important throughout life after weaning has taken place.

The components of a balanced diet

Carbohydrates provide energy – they are used largely in cellular respiration in the production of ATP, the body's energy source. Some carbohydrate is converted to glycogen, a storage carbohydrate found in the liver, muscles and brain. Any excess carbohydrate is converted to fat for storage.

Fats are also used to provide energy, and they are easily stored in readiness for times of food shortage. There are certain essential fatty acids which must be part of the diet if an individual is to remain healthy as they cannot be synthesised in the body. **Linoleic acid** and **gamma-linolenic acid** are needed both as precursors in the synthesis of other fatty acids not found in plants (for example, arachidonic acid) and as precursors in the formation of prostaglandins. These are hormone-like compounds which are very important in many physiological systems, including the reproductive system.

Proteins are used for body-building. They are broken down in digestion to their constituent amino acids and these are then rebuilt in the process of protein synthesis to form the appropriate proteins for that particular individual. Certain amino acids are vital if a diet is to be balanced because they cannot be synthesised in the body. These are called the **essential amino acids** and they include **isoleucine**, **leucine**, **phenylalanine**, **methionine**, **threonine** and **valine**. The essential amino acids are found mainly in animal proteins.

Mineral salts are generally needed in minute amounts, but lack of them in the diet can lead to a variety of unpleasant conditions, as described here.

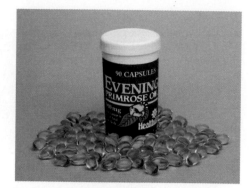

Figure 3.4 Oil of evening primrose capsules contain a rich mixture of essential fatty acids, which helps overcome dietary deficiencies.

- **Calcium** is found in dairy products and fish. It is needed for the effective working of some enzymes, for the formation of bones and teeth, for muscular contraction and the clotting of the blood. A diet deficient in calcium leads to poor bone growth and rickets in children, muscle spasms and delayed blood clotting.

- **Iron** is needed as part of the cytochromes of the respiratory chain. It activates the enzyme catalase and is needed for the formation of haemoglobin and myoglobin which carry oxygen in the blood and muscles. Iron is found in foods such as liver, red meats, eggs, dried apricots and cocoa powder. A lack of iron in the diet leads to anaemia.

- **Zinc** is essential for growth and repair of tissues and for sexual maturation. It is also important for enzyme activity and for the perception of taste. It is mainly found in dairy products, meat, eggs and fish as well as wholegrain cereals and pulses. It is rarely deficient, but if lacking in children can cause delayed puberty and retarded growth.

Vitamins are similarly required in very small amounts. They are organic substances which are capable of being absorbed directly into the bloodstream from the gut. If any particular vitamin is lacking from the diet in the long term it will result in a deficiency disease. These deficiency diseases can be remedied using vitamin supplements.

- **Vitamin A** is needed for vision in dim light as it is required for the formation of retinal, a chemical involved in vision in the rods. Vitamin A is also needed to maintain the mucous membranes and the skin, and for growth. It is found in dairy products, eggs, liver, oily fish, carrots, tomatoes and green vegetables. Deficiency leads to reduced night vision, lack of sight through deterioration of the cornea and lowered resistance to infection.

- **Vitamin D** promotes the absorption of calcium and phosphates through the gut, and is therefore essential for the formation and maintenance of healthy teeth and bones. It is found in margarine, oily fish, egg yolk, breakfast cereals and is made under the skin in sunlight. Lack of vitamin D can lead to failure of the bones to grow and calcify in children, and to osteomalacia, where the bones become weakened, in adults. Lack of vitamin D is becoming a problem in some immigrant communities in the UK because their protective skin pigment prevents vitamin D formation in the relatively weak British sun.

Water in biological systems is vital as a medium for the biochemical reactions within cells, as a solvent for food molecules, as a transport medium and in many other ways. Whereas the average person can survive with little or no food for days if not weeks, complete lack of water will bring about death in two to four days, depending on other conditions such as temperature.

Roughage or **fibre** cannot in fact be digested in the human gut, yet it is an essential part of the diet because it provides bulk for the intestinal muscles to work on and also holds water. With a diet low in roughage, peristalsis is sluggish and the food moves through the gut relatively slowly.

Energy requirements

One of the main purposes of the food in the diet is to provide an individual with sufficient energy to maintain basic body functions and also to carry out all the activities of daily life. The amount of energy needed varies from person to person, and also varies throughout life. The energy you need on a daily basis will depend on your **basal metabolic rate** (**BMR**) and how active you are. The BMR is measured when an individual is at complete rest. The BMR is proportionately higher in babies and young children than in adults as they use a great deal of energy in growth. The BMR is also related to the total body mass and the lean body mass. People with a high proportion of muscle will have a higher BMR as muscle tissue requires more energy for maintenance than fat does. This is one of the main reasons why men usually have higher BMRs than women, because they tend to have a higher proportion of muscle to fat. As people age, not only is their tissue replaced less often but they also tend to lose muscle and so the BMR tends to drop with age. The BMR makes up, on average, about 75% of the metabolic needs of the body.

The BMR is of relatively little use on its own in assessing the energy intake needed in a healthy diet. To make the measure more useful, the physical activity level must also be taken into account. By multiplying the BMR by a factor which reflects the **physical activity level** (**PAL**), we can obtain the **estimated average requirements** (**EAR**) for energy. A PAL of 1.4 is used for adults in the UK, reflecting the rather sedentary way of life most of us have. The energy EARs of people throughout life are shown in table 3.1. If we do not match our energy intakes to the requirements of our body then we will either gain weight (if we eat too much) or lose weight (if we eat too little).

Figure 3.5 During the last three months of pregnancy the daily energy requirements of women increase by about 200 kJ. They also need extra energy during breast feeding, but this depends on how much fat they have stored, the amount of milk they produce and for how long they breast feed – it takes a great deal more energy to produce enough milk to fully satisfy a five-month-old baby than it does for a five-week-old baby.

Age	EAR /kJ day^{-1} (males)	EAR /kJ day^{-1} (females)	Age	EAR /kJ day^{-1} (males)	EAR /kJ day^{-1} (females)
0–3 months	2280	2160	11–14 years	9270	7720
4–6 months	2890	2690	15–18 years	11510	8830
7–9 months	3440	3200	19–50 years	10600	8100
10–12 months	3850	3610	51–59 years	10600	8000
1–3 years	5150	4860	60–64 years	9930	7990
4–6 years	7160	6460	65–74 years	9710	7960
7–10 years	8240	7280	75+ years	8770	7610

Table 3.1 The estimated average requirements (EARs) for energy at different ages in the UK – the levels change quite dramatically with age.

Recommended nutritional guidelines

Although taking in sufficient energy is an important aspect of the diet, there are many other important factors. The major nutrients need to be taken in both in appropriate quantities and in the right balance with other aspects of the diet. To try and clarify which nutrients people need and in what quantities, **nutritional requirements** have been worked out and built up into recommended national guidelines for nutrition. Obviously these will vary from individual to individual depending on age and lifestyle, but estimates for groups of the population are based on advice given by the Committee on Medical Aspects of Food Policy (COMA). This committee reviews scientific evidence from research into diet and disease, and then uses this to advise the Government on policy. In 1991, the committee published a detailed report of the estimated nutritional requirements of different groups in the population. It included **dietary reference values** (**DRVs**) which indicate the range of requirements and appropriate intakes for the population, as illustrated in figure 3.6.

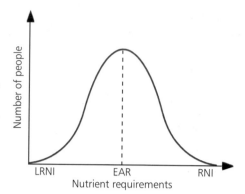

Figure 3.6 The distribution of nutrient requirements within a population

- The **estimated average requirement** (**EAR**) is an estimate of the average requirement for a particular nutrient. This means about 50% of the population will need less than this in their diet, and 50% will need more. If people are taking in adequate amounts, the intake will vary around the EAR.
- The **reference nutrient intake** (**RNI**) is the intake of a particular nutrient which will make sure that the needs of almost everyone in the population will be met. This used to be known as the RDA (recommended daily amount).
- The **lower reference nutrient intake** (**LRNI**) is enough for only a very small proportion of the population who have naturally low requirements.
- The **safe intake** is a DRV used when there is no precise scientific evidence to provide an RNI. The safe level is judged to be probably sufficient for everyone, and with no evidence that levels above this are beneficial.

The COMA report includes RNIs for protein, nine vitamins and eleven minerals, EARs for energy, safe intakes for four further vitamins and minerals and desired population intakes for fat and carbohydrates. Table 3.2 shows some of these data.

DRVs are useful in assessing the diet of a group of people. For example, if the average intake of a mineral of a group of people is close to the RNI it is unlikely that anyone will be deficient in that mineral. On the other hand, if the average intake of a group approaches the LRNI, then it is very likely that some people in the group are not getting adequate amounts of the mineral in their diet.

The requirements for different nutrients change throughout life, and this is clearly reflected in the DRVs. However, in some cases unusual output takes place and needs to be taken into account. For example, girls and women who have particularly heavy or frequent menstrual periods lose more iron than normal, and so they may need iron supplements to prevent themselves suffering from anaemia even if their dietary intake of iron is around the RNI.

The three nutrients that provide the energy in the diet are carbohydrates, proteins and fats, along with any alcohol which is also taken in. There is evidence that the proportion of energy-giving foods in the diet can increase or decrease the likelihood of problems such as heart disease developing. Thus a suggested balance of the energy-giving nutrients is suggested as part of the DRV. By comparing this with the average British diet (see figure 3.7) we can see that a number of changes need to be made if we are to become a healthier nation.

Table A Reference nutrient intakes for protein

Age	Reference nutrient intake /g day⁻¹	Age	Reference nutrient intake /g day⁻¹	
			Males	Females
0–3 months	12.5	11–14 years	42.1	41.2
4–6 months	12.7	15–18 years	55.2	45.0
7–9 months	13.7	19–50 years	55.5	45.0
10–12 months	14.9	50+ years	53.3	46.5
1–3 years	11.5	Pregnancy[a]		+6
4–6 years	19.7	Lactation[a]		
7–10 years	28.3	0–4 months		+11
		4+ months		+8

[a] To be added to adult requirement through all stages of pregnancy and lactation

Table B Reference nutrient intakes for vitamins

Age	Thiamin / mg day⁻¹	Riboflavin / mg day⁻¹	Niacin / mg day⁻¹	Vitamin B6 / mg day⁻¹	Vitamin B12 / mg day⁻¹	Folate / µg day⁻¹	Vitamin C / mg day⁻¹	Vitamin A / µg day⁻¹	Vitamin D / µg day⁻¹
0–3 months	0.2	0.4	3	0.2	0.3	50	25	350	8.5
4–6 months									
7–9 months			4	0.3	0.4				7
10–12 months	0.3		5	0.4				400	
1–3 years	0.5	0.6	8	0.7	0.5	70	30		–
4–6 years	0.7	0.8	11	0.9	0.8	100		500	
7–10 years		1.0	12	1.0	1.0	150			
Males									
11–14 years	0.9	1.2	15	1.2	1.2	200	35	600	–
15–18 years	1.1	1.3	18	1.5	1.5		40	700	
19–50 years	1.0		17						
51–64 years	0.9		16	1.4					10
65+ years									
Females									
11–14 years	0.7	1.1	12	1.0	1.2	200	35	600	–
15–18 years	0.8		14	1.2	1.5		40		
19–50 years			13						
50–64 years			12						10
65+ years									
Pregnancy	+0.1	+0.3	No increase	No increase	No increase	+100	+10	+100	+10
Lactation	+0.2	+0.5	+2	No increase	+0.5	+60	+30	+350	+10

Table C Reference nutrient intakes for selected minerals

Age	Calcium /mg day⁻¹	Iron /mg day⁻¹	Zinc /mg day⁻¹
4–6 months	525	4.3	4.0
7–10 years	550	8.7	7.0
Males			
11–14 years	1000	11.3	9.0
19–50 years	700	8.7	9.5
50+ years	700	8.7	9.5
Females			
11–14 years	800	14.8**	9.0
19–50 years	700	14.8**	7.0
50+ years	700	8.7	7.0
Pregnancy	*	*	*
Lactation			
0–4 months	+500	*	+6.0

*No increment required   **Insufficient for women with high menstrual losses where the most practical way of meeting iron requirements is to take iron supplements

Table 3.2 Tables like these are valuable in assessing whether the diet of a group within the population is adequate or not for any particular nutrient. They can also be used to show how the requirements for a particular nutrient change throughout the lifetime.

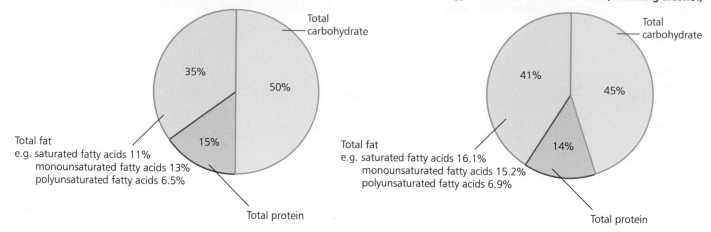

Figure 3.7 The recommended dietary make-up for the UK population differed from the actual energy gained from various nutrients in British households in several ways (1993 data). Most obviously, more fat and less carbohydrate were eaten than is recommended.

Fibre in the diet

Fibre is mainly the cellulose cell walls of plant material, along with other indigestible compounds. Plenty of fibre in the diet ensures that the food has sufficient bulk to stretch the walls of the gut and stimulate efficient peristalsis. This keeps the food moving steadily through the gut, ensuring a **throughput time** (the time for the remains of food taken in to reappear as faeces) of under 24 hours, which is desirable for several reasons. If there is insufficient fibre in the diet, the waste material spends a long time in the colon. Here water is removed from the waste, so a long throughput time means that more water is removed. This results in the hard, compacted faeces known as **constipation**. **Haemorrhoids** (piles) often accompany constipation – these are swollen veins in the wall of the rectum and anus. Constipation and haemorrhoids cause many people a great deal of discomfort and unhappiness, and make a large profit for the companies selling laxatives, yet a simple change of diet would solve the majority of such problems. However, a long throughput time can cause problems other than simple constipation.

Diverticulitis is a very painful condition which is particularly common in older, constipated patients. It involves pockets forming in the lining of the colon. These fill with compacted faeces and may become inflamed and extremely painful. If the lining of the pocket perforates, releasing the contents into the body cavity, the condition may cause death.

Much less serious, but still a problem to many people, is **irritable bowel syndrome**. This is also linked to a low-fibre diet, and is more common in women than in men. One symptom is pain, particularly in the lower abdomen but sometimes perceived as being higher up in the chest. Most sufferers have constipation, but they sometimes have diarrhoea. There is no major physical cause for the symptoms except lack of fibre in the diet, and it is thought that irritable bowel syndrome is linked with stress, and that it is partly a psychosomatic illness (involving both the mind and the body). Treated or untreated, the symptoms tend to lessen with age.

One of the most serious conditions currently linked to a low-fibre, high-fat diet is **cancer of the colon**. It is the most common type of gastrointestinal cancer in the developed world, yet it is seldom seen in developing countries. There may be genetic factors that make the disease more likely in some people, but the major cause seems to be a low-fibre diet leading to long retention of faecal material in the colon. This means that bacterial action takes place for longer, leading to the production of more toxic and possibly carcinogenic waste products which are kept in close contact with the lining of the colon. The constipation that results from a low-fibre diet makes any changes in the working of the bowel more difficult to notice, and so delays detection of the problem. Only 35% of people diagnosed with cancer of the colon will still be alive five years later, because symptoms are often not picked up until the cancer is far advanced. The possibility of screening for bowel cancer has been raised, and better education about dietary matters might also be useful in reducing the problem in years to come.

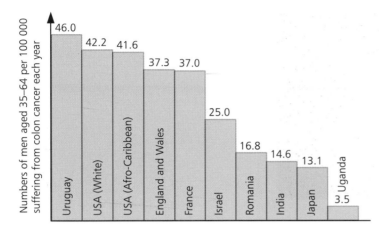

Figure 3.8 In many countries in the developing world, the diet is based largely around plant food, which is high in fibre and low in fat. It seems likely that this is the main reason for the low rates of colon cancer seen in such countries, and that highly refined diets are the biggest factor in the high levels of the disease in the developed world.

Ulcers – not a lifestyle disease after all

For many years gastric and duodenal ulcers were considered the ultimate lifestyle disease – no top executive was complete without one. They were seen as related to stress, which caused increased acid production in the stomach. This in turn caused the ulcer, an extremely painful eroded area on the lining of the gut. Treatment was with drugs to reduce the amount of acid produced by the stomach and/or neutralise it, allowing the ulcers to heal. However, when treatment stopped the ulcers often returned. This was thought to reflect the continued stressful lifestyle of the patient. Then in the 1980s an Australian, Dr Barry Marshall, found the bacterium *Helicobacter pylori* living in the stomach cells of patients suffering from gastric ulcers. The scientifically accepted view was that bacteria could not live in the acidic conditions of the stomach, so this find surprised Barry Marshall. He suspected the bacteria might be causing the stomach ulcers, and devised a series of tests to demonstrate whether this were true. Eventually he developed a treatment regime based on existing antibiotics. This cleared the ulcer symptoms in his patients, and because it destroyed the bacteria the ulcers did not return.

This cheap and simple treatment for the majority of ulcers met with a great deal of resistance among other doctors, particularly those who spent a great deal of their time treating chronic ulcer sufferers, and from the drugs companies. Drugs to relieve ulcer pain and block acid production have been among the best selling medicines in the world. It took ten years for around 10% of doctors to be convinced of the veracity of Marshall's work. Now the majority of physicians accept that *H. pylori* rather than stress is the major cause of ulcers. They test for the bacterium and treat accordingly when patients have painful ulcer symptoms. Barry Marshall went on to investigate a link between *H. pylori* and certain stomach cancers. Bacteria had never before been linked to cancer, but the WHO now classifies *H. pylori* as a class 1 carcinogen (cancer-causing agent).

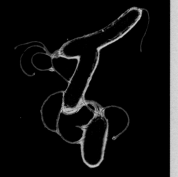

Figure 3.9 Australian doctor Barry Marshall and *Helicobacter pylori*, for many years the subject of controversy but now widely recognised as the cause of not only many ulcers but also of some stomach cancers.

Additives and E-numbers

For many hundreds of years people have preserved food against the decay caused by microorganisms. Food is kept usable for long periods of time by salting, smoking, pickling, canning, freezing and drying. During the twentieth century, we have gone further in the preservation, production and presentation of food. New chemical **additives** make food last longer, have a more reliable taste and look better on supermarket shelves. Chemicals have been introduced to make food production easier, and to make sure our food has a good texture.

In 1978 the Commission of the European Community issued a directive to member states requiring them to list food additives not only by category ('colour' or 'preservative'), but also by name or **E-number** (for example, 'tartrazine' or 'E102'). All colourings that are permitted to be used in foods in the EC have an E-number that identifies them.

Preservatives

Preservatives help to prevent food from decay. Many preservatives work as **antioxidants**. Fats are naturally oxidised, causing them to go rancid which affects both the appearance and the smell of the food. Antioxidants prevent this happening, and are used to extend the shelf life of a wide range of processed foods that contain fats. Examples of antioxidants added to foods include **ascorbic acid** (vitamin C) and **tocopherol** (vitamin E).

Colourings

Much of the processed food we buy is highly coloured. Home-prepared food generally looks less 'perfect' and the colours in home-made jams fade with time and exposure to light. Manufacturers want the food they sell always to look the same. Also, many processed foods would have an unappetising colour without a bit of help, so food labels often show lists of colourings. These colourings are some of the more controversial modern additions to processed food. Examples of synthetic colourings include **chocolate brown HT** (E155), **sunset yellow** (E110) and **indigo carmine** (E132), which are all coal tar dyes derived from the petrochemical industry. Permitted natural colourings include cochineal, which is made from an extract of crushed insects! There is evidence to suggest that some food colourings may have adverse effects on health. Some permitted coal tar dyes have been shown to be carcinogenic (cancer-causing) in laboratory animals. There is evidence to link other permitted colourings to hyperactivity, eczema and asthma in children, and even in some cases to fits.

There has been a wave of public reaction against the use of artificial colourings in food, and in response the food industry has reduced the number of colourings it uses, and switched to using more natural food colourings. In the Food Act 1974 in Britain, recommendations were made that colourings should not be added to food specifically targeted at babies and young children, and the food industry agreed to a voluntary ban on the use of additives in food for children of 18 months and under.

Flavourings

Flavourings are being used in increasing amounts as food manufacturers create more 'new' foods. For example, many desserts which are strawberry or raspberry or banana flavoured contain no real fruit at all – all the flavour comes from additives. Some flavourings are of natural origin, extracted from real fruit or herbs or spices, such as **quinine** and **menthol**. Many others are synthetic, straight from the chemistry laboratory. There is a whole industry making new flavourings for an enormous range of foods – how many different flavour crisps can you think of?

Flavour enhancers are used in foods that contain artificial flavourings and also in those with only natural flavourings. Probably the oldest known flavour enhancer is salt. Both salt and sugar have been added to foods for centuries, but they need to be used sparingly. Excess salt in the diet can lead to kidney problems and is linked to hypertension (high blood pressure). Excess sugar can lead to tooth decay and obesity. A more modern flavour enhancer is **monosodium glutamate**, which has been linked to hyperactivity in some children and to headaches, nausea and restlessness in adults who eat a lot of it.

Additives and hyperactivity

During the 1970s an American, Dr Feingold, became convinced that many of the hyperactive children he was seeing were being affected by food additives. He devised a diet free of foods containing certain additives, including monosodium glutamate, and although many of his peers criticised his thesis as unscientific and unproven, large numbers of parents with hyperactive children adopted the diet or simplified versions of it and felt that the behaviour of their children was substantially changed. The Feingold diet was taken up in America first, and then in Canada, Australia and New Zealand. In the late 1970s it began to be introduced in Britain, where the link between hyperactive behaviour and food additives is now taken more seriously by many health professionals.

In spite of increasing public awareness that food additives may cause some health problems, the overall consumption of additives continues to soar. The social changes in Britain during the 1980s and 1990s, with increasing numbers of people unemployed or on low wages, and with more women choosing or needing to work, have had an effect on shopping and eating habits. Pre-packed, ready-prepared meals of all sorts are popular, and these often contain large numbers of different additives. It has been estimated that an average British 12-year-old will have consumed around 250 g of additives!

Figure 3.10 Children love bright colours and strong flavours, so many foods targeted at them are high in additives to achieve the desired effect.

Malnutrition in the midst of plenty

Malnutrition is an inbalance between what someone eats and what is required to remain healthy. In the developed areas of the world, there are people who are starving or malnourished because of poverty – they simply cannot afford to buy enough of the right sorts of food to provide themselves and their families with a balanced diet. But there is another type of malnutrition in the developed world, which is spreading to developing countries as they become richer and adopt 'Western' ways of life. This malnutrition is self-imposed, and certainly does not involve lack of food, as illustrated in figure 3.11.

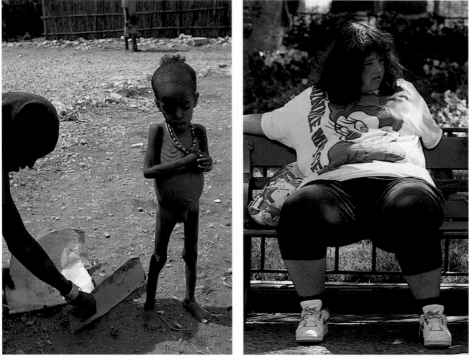

Figure 3.11 Whether you are forced by circumstances to eat too little or choose to eat too much, the wrong type of nutrition can seriously damage your health.

The most obvious effect of overeating is an increase in body fat, eventually resulting in obesity. The long-term effects of overeating are a shortened lifespan and poor health in old age. Longer, fitter lives result from eating just sufficient to supply the needs of the body. A large proportion of the adult population in countries such as Britain, France and America spend at least part of their lives on a weight loss diet, often driven by a desire to look younger and more fashionable rather than a conscious choice for health. Often the body weight aimed for by slimmers is unrealistic for a mature adult human, and the starvation levels needed to bring about the weight loss can lead to exactly the same problems of malnutrition as those experienced by people in the famine-struck areas of the developing world. Sadly for the millions of dieters across the world, recent evidence suggests that the weight of an organism is strongly governed by factors other than the amount of food eaten. There appears to be a **set point** rather like a thermostat, a genetically determined range for the body weight of each individual and in particular for the amount of fat stored. In most people tested, and in many other mammals, a large increase in energy content of the food eaten results in little weight gain above the upper level of the set point. The extra energy is burned off and lost as body heat unless the excess eaten becomes very large. Similarly, a lowering of food intake does not result in a large weight loss below the bottom level of the set point – the metabolism simply functions more efficiently. In order to adjust the set point, it is necessary to change the level of physical activity.

Long-term dieters may suffer from a range of dietary deficiency diseases, from vitamin and mineral deficiencies to problems caused by lack of protein in the diet. In the 1980s and 1990s there has been a trend towards very low-energy diets, often involving special 'milkshakes', soups or other foods. These diets do not help re-educate the slimmer to develop more sensible eating habits, so the weight lost is often regained rapidly after the dieting stops, because the energy intake goes up again. There is also a risk of damage to muscle tissue, even to the heart muscle, because the very low-energy intake sends the body into starvation mode and muscle protein may be broken down to supply the respiratory pathways. A lower fat, higher fibre diet is more likely to keep the dieter healthy and have a lasting effect.

The most severe cases of dietary deprivation are seen not in the ordinary dieter but in people suffering from food-related disorders such as **anorexia nervosa** and **bulimia**. These conditions arise from malfunctions of the normal appetite and feeding controls, and seem to have a strong psychological component. In anorexia, sufferers severely restrict their food intake. They reduce the food eaten to an absolute minimum, losing weight rapidly. They become secretive and manipulative, lying about when and where they have eaten to avoid having meals, secreting food off their plates to throw away later and vomiting food up again. They have a distorted body image – even if they are skeletally thin, anorexics still perceive themselves as overweight (see figure 3.13). Many anorexics are girls and young women, although increasing numbers of boys are suffering from the disease.

Figure 3.12 Reducing food intake and taking more exercise can result in quite dramatic weight loss, but the genetic set point will largely determine the level of body fat for most adults with fairly stable eating and exercise habits.

Treatment involves hospitalisation to try and restore a more normal body weight, and counselling and support to overcome the psychological problems which led to the anorexia in the first place. However, the disease remains potentially fatal – a number of people die from the disease every year in the UK and in many other countries. Anorexia may begin as normal dieting in response to social pressures to be 'slim', but the disease is thought to be psychologically much more deep-rooted. For many sufferers anorexia seems to be a way of exerting some control over their lives – perhaps of rebelling against over-dominant parents, or of denying the body changes that come with puberty, or a cry for help in coping with all the pressures placed on young people in their adolescent and early adult years.

Bulimia is a related disease, although it does not always lead to life-threatening weight loss. Bulimics 'comfort' themselves by **bingeing** – gorging on large amounts of food, often sweet food like chocolate and cakes or junk food like burgers and chips. Following the binge the bulimic will make her or himself vomit violently to get rid of all the excess food. For some this binge–vomit cycle occurs only rarely when they are under pressure; for others it can happen several times a day. This behaviour puts severe stresses on the physiology of the body. Like anorexia, bulimia is associated with low self-esteem and a need for psychological help. One of the most famous sufferers from bulimia was Diana, Princess of Wales.

The role of diet in heart disease

One of the biggest killers in the developed world is heart disease, and one of the major contributory risk factors appears to be the amount of fat, particularly saturated fat, taken in as part of the diet.

Eating too much saturated fat increases the risk of fatty deposits building up in the arteries (see page 78). Saturated fat is found in foods of animal origin, particularly meat and dairy products, and in foods cooked in animal fats. Some plant oils are also bad for the heart – many nut oils are as damaging as animal fats. However, other oils, particularly olive oil, seem to give positive

Figure 3.13 Anorexia involves starving the body over a long period of time, and results in devastating weight loss, although anorexics still see themselves as fat.

protection from heart disease. Figure 3.14 shows the annual death rates from heart disease in a number of countries. Countries such as Italy and Greece where large quantities of olive oil are a regular part of the diet show a significantly lower rate of death from heart disease than countries in the UK.

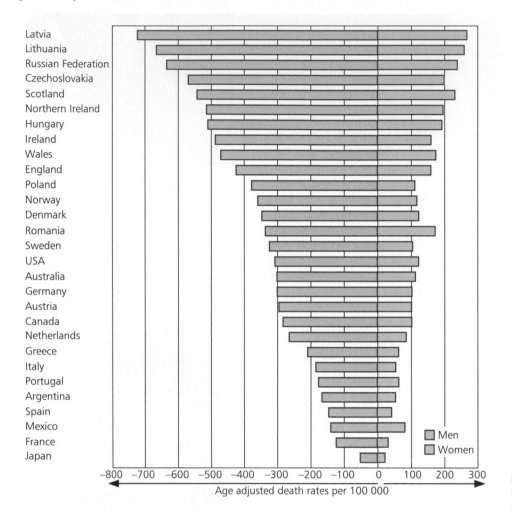

Figure 3.14 Deaths from heart disease in men and women aged 35–74 in different countries, 1991

Research done in the USA over ten years followed a group of middle-aged men with raised blood cholesterol levels. **Cholesterol** is a type of fat called a sterol, and it is the main constituent of fatty deposits in blood vessels. The research showed that the incidence of fatty deposits in the arteries, and of heart attacks and strokes that result from this, was lowered if the blood cholesterol level was decreased. In many patients, the blood cholesterol level could be lowered by careful management of the diet. Others needed to take cholesterol-lowering drugs. Diet is evidently a major influence on the risk of developing heart disease for most people. Eating a relatively low-fat diet in which much of the fat comes from foods such as olive oil and oily fish, which actually *lower* the blood cholesterol level, will reduce the likelihood of future heart disease and may even offer some protection against it. There is more information on cardiovascular health on pages 74–82.

DISEASES OF THE RESPIRATORY SYSTEM

The respiratory system takes in the oxygen the body needs for cellular respiration, and removes the waste carbon dioxide produced (see box overleaf).

Infectious diseases of the respiratory system can be life threatening – influenza and pneumonia are not infrequently cited on death certificates as the cause of death. However, in the developed world, infectious diseases of the respiratory system are becoming less of a threat, while respiratory diseases that result from our lifestyle and environment are becoming increasingly common.

Asthma

Asthma is one such condition. The number of cases of asthma is rising each year in the UK. Hundreds of thousands of asthma sufferers live completely normal lives, but around 2000 people die of the disease each year in the UK, many of them children and young people, in spite of improvements in both drug treatments and understanding of the management of the disease. Asthma occurs when the mast cells in the lining of the respiratory tract produce extra histamine (see page 56). This causes the lining to swell and the smooth muscle to contract, narrowing the bronchioles. There is a much increased resistance to air moving in and out of the lungs. This gives rise to the breathlessness and 'wheezing' sounds associated with asthma.

Asthma may be an inherited condition, with several family members suffering the disease. It may occur as an allergic reaction, often to house dust mites and their faeces, or to animals such as cats, dogs or horses. It may be a response to an irritant such as cigarette smoke or to an infection like the common cold. Everyone is capable of developing asthma, but some people are genetically programmed to be more sensitive than others, as we saw on page 9.

Management of asthma involves careful observations on how well the lungs are functioning. A machine measures the total volume of air breathed out over a complete exhalation, therefore showing the lung capacity available for use. These machines are usually found in hospitals or doctor's practices. A **peak flow meter** is more portable, and is used by most asthma patients. This is a simple device which is calibrated to give the **peak expiratory flow**, as figure 3.16 shows (page 71). By measuring this twice a day, asthma sufferers can see how their lungs are functioning and tailor their drug intake accordingly.

Another important aspect of asthma management is to remove as many triggers as possible. A home largely free from dust and dust mites, and with no pets, helps reduce the problem for many patients.

Drug treatments for asthma have come a very long way in the last 70 years. **Beta agonists** rapidly relax the smooth muscle of the respiratory tract, dilating the bronchioles and making breathing easier. They are usually taken as an aerosol using an inhaler which delivers a set dose. Beta agonists may be used regularly, or before exercise, or only at the onset of an attack, depending on how badly affected the sufferer is. **Sodium cromoglycate** is a preventive drug which stabilises the mast cells so they produce less histamine. It is particularly useful for allergy-induced asthma and for asthma triggered by exercise. For people who have more severe asthma, daily inhalation of **steroids** can help to prevent attacks.

Why is the incidence of asthma increasing? There is no single answer. Some feel that the disease is being diagnosed more often now that more is known and there are effective treatments. There is some evidence, certainly in adults, that the stress of modern life may play a part. Centrally heated and carpeted houses may provide the house dust mite with many more potential homes. There is evidence that increasing levels of air pollution from traffic may be a major contributor to what is sometimes referred to as 'the asthma epidemic'.

The lungs and gaseous exchange

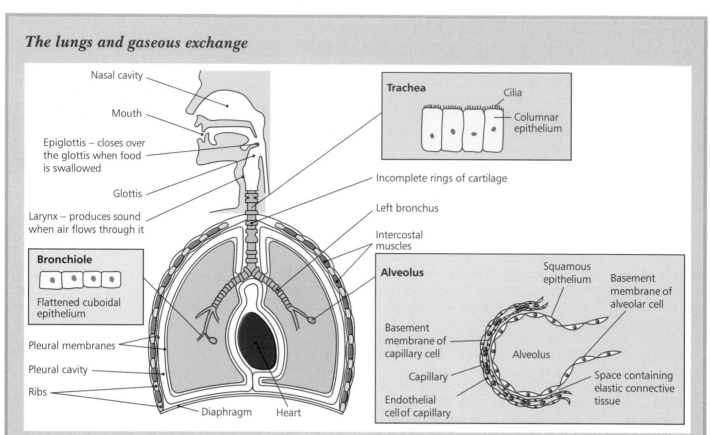

Figure 3.15 The human respiratory system

The human respiratory system has evolved to enable us to take in sufficient oxygen to supply the needs of all our cells. Air enters the system through the **mouth** or **nasal passages**. The nasal passages have a relatively large surface area and a good blood supply, which warms the incoming air. The epithelium secretes mucus and is covered in hairs. The hairs and mucus filter out much of the dust and small particles such as bacteria that are breathed in. The moist surfaces increase the level of water vapour in inspired air.

The **trachea** is the major airway leading down into the chest cavity. It is lined with **columnar epithelial cells** which have cilia that beat away from the lungs. **Goblet cells** secrete mucus, and the cilia waft the mucus with trapped particles and microorganisms upwards to be coughed or sneezed out, or to be swallowed into the stomach. The trachea is supported by incomplete rings of cartilage which prevent it collapsing. The trachea divides to form two **bronchi**, which are similar in structure to the trachea.

The bronchi divide repeatedly to form the **bronchioles**. Larger bronchioles have cartilage rings, but not those smaller than about 1 mm in diameter. As the bronchioles get smaller, the epithelium changes from columnar to **flattened cuboidal**, making diffusion of gases more likely.

The bronchioles end in sacs called **alveoli**, the main respiratory surface where most of the gaseous exchange takes place. Alveoli are made up of **squamous epithelial cells** which have a large surface area and are thin, so present a short distance for gases to travel through. The capillaries running close to the alveoli also have a wall that is only one cell thick. Between the capillary and the alveolus is a layer of elastic connective tissue which holds them together, and helps force air out of the lungs when they are stretched. This is called **elastic recoil**. Oxygen diffuses from the air in the alveolus to the blood, and carbon dioxide diffuses from the blood to the air in the alveolus.

The lungs are enclosed in the **pleural membranes**, between which is a lubricating fluid which allows the membranes to slide easily during breathing. The **ribs** form a protective bony cage around the respiratory system. Between them are the **intercostal muscles**, which contract to raise and lower the rib cage during breathing. The **diaphragm** is a broad sheet of muscle which forms the floor of the chest cavity and is also involved in breathing movements.

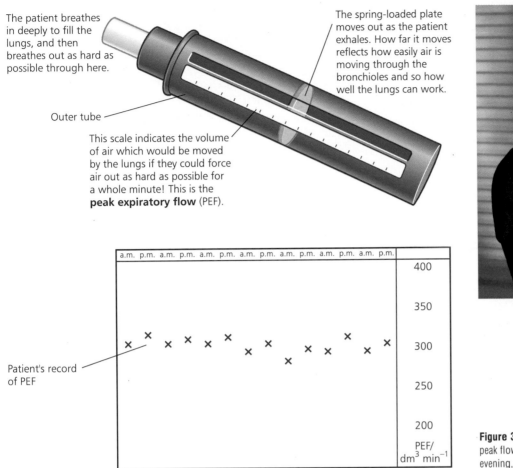

The patient breathes in deeply to fill the lungs, and then breathes out as hard as possible through here.

The spring-loaded plate moves out as the patient exhales. How far it moves reflects how easily air is moving through the bronchioles and so how well the lungs can work.

Outer tube

This scale indicates the volume of air which would be moved by the lungs if they could force air out as hard as possible for a whole minute! This is the **peak expiratory flow** (PEF).

Patient's record of PEF

Figure 3.16 The peak expiratory flow measured by the peak flow meter is usually lower in the morning than the evening, even in people who don't have asthma.

Pink puffers and blue bloaters

Bronchitis is another disease of the respiratory system that is closely linked with lifestyle and environmental factors. 'Bronchitis' is an umbrella term for a variety of chest conditions, and there are two distinct types. **Acute bronchitis** is an infectious disease which can affect anyone, although it is more common in smokers and their families, in people who work in environments containing irritant particles and in people living in areas of high air pollution. The word **acute** here describes an illness that comes on quickly and is short term. Acute chest infections are the largest group of serious diseases that turn up in doctors' waiting rooms, and even with modern treatments there is still a 2–3% mortality rate from them.

Chronic bronchitis is more closely linked with environmental factors, particularly smoking. The word **chronic** generally describes a disease that comes on gradually and may last a long time. Someone with chronic bronchitis secretes too much mucus in the airways, causing a persistent cough which does not respond to over-the-counter medicines. Because the airways are permanently irritated, they are vulnerable to infection, and so sufferers from chronic bronchitis are also likely to get infectious bronchitis. The mucus, irritation and frequent infections together cause narrowing of the bronchioles and so chronic shortness of breath. The lungs can be permanently damaged. The diagnosis of bronchitis is aided by measurements of the peak expiratory flow rate, and other lung volumes such as the **vital capacity** and the **expiratory reserve volume**.

Components of lung volume

A certain amount of air is always present in the respiratory system, simply filling up the spaces when no air is flowing. Other than this, the volume of air which is drawn in and out of the respiratory system can be very variable. There are different components of lung volume which have the following specific names for ease of reference:

(1) The **tidal volume** (V_T) is the volume of air that enters and leaves the lungs at each natural resting breath.

(2) The **inspiratory reserve volume** (**IRV**) is the volume of air that can be taken in by a maximum inspiratory effort, over and above the normal inspired tidal volume. In other words, this is the extra air that you can take in when you breathe in as deeply as possible after a normal inhalation.

(3) The **expiratory reserve volume** (**ERV**) is the volume of air that can be expelled by the most powerful expiratory effort, over and above the normal expired tidal volume. This is the extra air breathed out when you force the air out of your lungs as hard as possible after a normal exhalation.

(4) The **vital capacity** (**VC**) is the sum of the tidal volume and the inspiratory and expiratory reserves. It is the volume of air which can be breathed out by the most vigorous possible expiratory effort following the deepest possible inhalation.

(5) The **residual volume** (**RV**) is the volume of air left in the lungs after the strongest possible exhalation. It has to be measured indirectly.

(6) The **total lung capacity** (**TLC**) is the sum of the vital capacity and the residual volume.

(7) The **inspiratory capacity** (**IC**) is the volume that can be inspired from the end of a normal exhalation – in other words, the sum of the tidal volume and the inspiratory reserve volume.

Figure 3.17 illustrates these volumes.

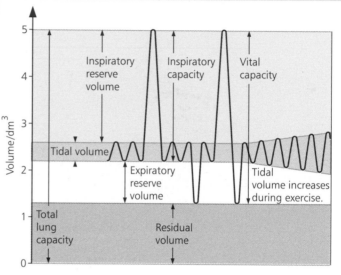

Figure 3.17 Different people's lung volumes vary – men usually have greater lung volumes than women, and athletes have larger lung volumes than non-athletes due to their training. This diagram gives the average figures.

Measuring the volume of inhaled or exhaled air

A piece of apparatus known as a **spirometer** is used to find out information such as the vital capacity of a person's lungs, or to measure the inspiratory or expiratory reserve volume. Spirometers come in a wide variety of shapes and sizes, but they all work in the same way, as shown in figure 3.18.

Figure 3.18 The volume of gas inhaled and exhaled under a variety of conditions can be measured using a spirometer.

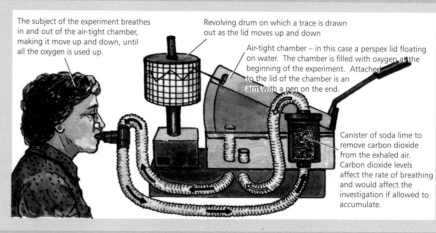

The likelihood of developing chronic bronchitis increases with age, and men are more likely to develop it than women, as figure 3.19 shows. British studies have shown that chronic bronchitis is also twice as common in urban dwellers as in rural dwellers. Social class affects the death rate from bronchitis

– unskilled labourers are four times more likely to die of chronic bronchitis than professional people. Genetic factors and exposure to dust in the workplace increase the risk of chronic bronchitis, but perhaps the major risk factor is smoking. Between 15 and 20 per cent of smokers will develop chronic bronchitis. If an affected smoker stops smoking, any permanent damage that has already occurred will remain, but further damage will be prevented.

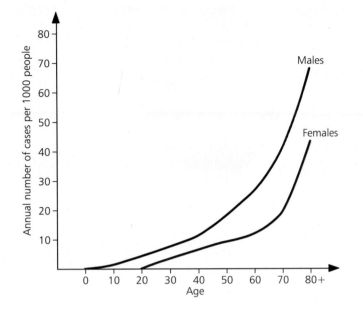

Figure 3.19 The occurrence of bronchitis at different ages in the UK

Chronic bronchitis can become severe, leading to **emphysema** (see figure 4.7, page 92). This condition is particularly common in heavy smokers and people exposed at work to chemicals or particles which irritate the lungs. In emphysema, the structure of the lungs begins to break down, and large air spaces develop which are not effective in gaseous exchange. Sufferers from emphysema breathe heavily and use voluntary actions such as hunching the shoulders to try and get more air into the lungs. The chest becomes barrel shaped and the noisy hyperventilation (fast breathing) often leads to a 'healthy' pink colour developing – hence the term 'pink puffers'.

The other major complication following chronic bronchitis is failure of the right ventricle of the heart. The heart beats rapidly and is substantially enlarged but does not function effectively, giving a bluish colour to the skin due to insufficient oxygen in the blood. This type of patient is often overweight and fluid builds up in the tissues causing swelling – the 'blue bloaters'. The breathing becomes very quiet and shallow.

Severely breathless bronchitics may be given oxygen supplies at home. Up to 15 hours of oxygen therapy is needed at a time. Smoking whilst using oxygen is obviously forbidden, but it is not unknown for heavy smokers to fit in their 40-a-day in the short time when they are not inhaling oxygen! If a patient with severe chronic bronchitis gets an infection, or continues to smoke, he or she runs the risk of total respiratory failure, low blood pressure and eventual circulatory collapse. This can lead rapidly to death, and about 35 000 people each year die from chronic bronchitis in the UK. Of those, 75% are over 65, and 80% are smokers.

DISEASES OF THE CARDIOVASCULAR SYSTEM

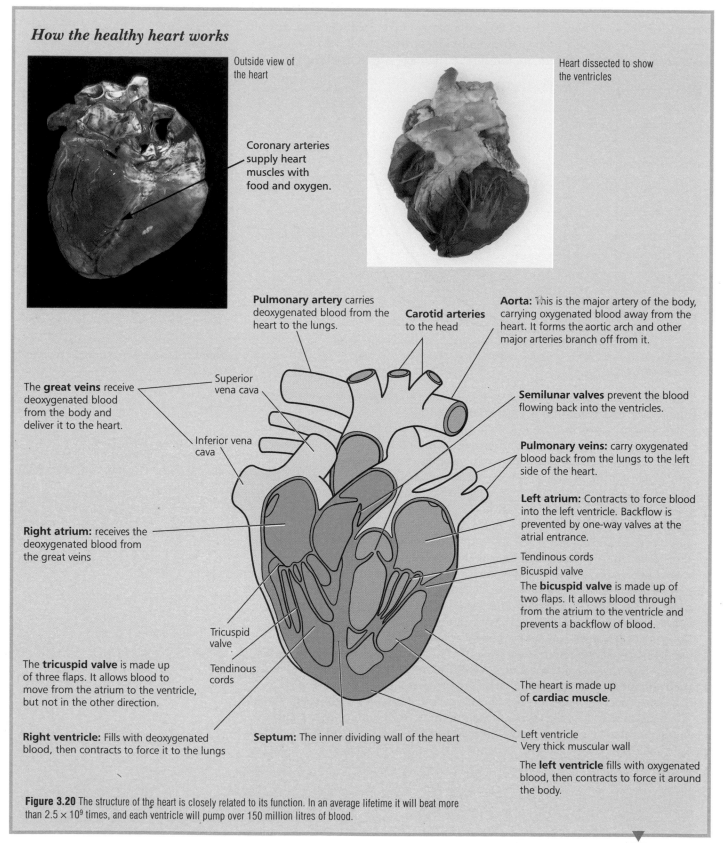

How the healthy heart works

Outside view of the heart

Heart dissected to show the ventricles

Coronary arteries supply heart muscles with food and oxygen.

Pulmonary artery carries deoxygenated blood from the heart to the lungs.

Carotid arteries to the head

Aorta: This is the major artery of the body, carrying oxygenated blood away from the heart. It forms the aortic arch and other major arteries branch off from it.

The **great veins** receive deoxygenated blood from the body and deliver it to the heart.

Superior vena cava

Semilunar valves prevent the blood flowing back into the ventricles.

Inferior vena cava

Pulmonary veins: carry oxygenated blood back from the lungs to the left side of the heart.

Left atrium: Contracts to force blood into the left ventricle. Backflow is prevented by one-way valves at the atrial entrance.

Right atrium: receives the deoxygenated blood from the great veins

Tendinous cords
Bicuspid valve

The **bicuspid valve** is made up of two flaps. It allows blood through from the atrium to the ventricle and prevents a backflow of blood.

Tricuspid valve

Tendinous cords

The **tricuspid valve** is made up of three flaps. It allows blood to move from the atrium to the ventricle, but not in the other direction.

The heart is made up of **cardiac muscle**.

Right ventricle: Fills with deoxygenated blood, then contracts to force it to the lungs

Septum: The inner dividing wall of the heart

Left ventricle
Very thick muscular wall

The **left ventricle** fills with oxygenated blood, then contracts to force it around the body.

Figure 3.20 The structure of the heart is closely related to its function. In an average lifetime it will beat more than 2.5×10^9 times, and each ventricle will pump over 150 million litres of blood.

A healthy adult heart beats about 70 times a minute, pumping the blood to the lungs to pick up oxygen and then on around the body. The right atrium receives deoxygenated blood from the great veins of the body, and both the atrium and the ventricle fill with blood. The right atrium contracts, forcing blood into the right ventricle and the bicuspid valve shuts to prevent backflow. Then the ventricle also contracts, forcing the deoxygenated blood into the capillaries of the lungs.

At the same time oxygenated blood from the lungs has filled the left atrium and ventricle. In the same way, the left atrium contracts followed closely by the left ventricle and oxygenated blood is forced out around the body. The muscle wall of the left ventricle is thicker than that of the right ventricle as it has to overcome the resistance of the blood vessels to the whole of the body rather than just the lungs.

The stage where the atria and ventricles are filling with blood is **diastole** and the stage where the atria and ventricles contract forcing blood out of the heart under pressure is **systole**.

The heartbeat sounds which can be heard through a stethoscope are made by the blood hitting the heart valves. The basic heart rate is controlled by electrical activity generated in the heart itself. The natural pacemaker region of the heart is known as the **sinoatrial node (SAN)**. Electrical activity generated here starts the contraction of the atria. The electrical activity spreads to the **atrioventricular node (AVN)** and then on through the centre of the heart in the **Purkyne tissue**, stimulating the cardiac muscle to contract. On top of this basic rhythm, the heartbeat is controlled by nerves which can slow down or speed up the heart, and it also responds to hormones such as adrenaline in the system. In this way the heart rate responds very sensitively to changes in the needs and circumstances of the body as a whole.

As we have already touched on (pages 67–68), the cardiovascular system is particularly vulnerable to diseases resulting from lifestyle factors such as diet, smoking and lack of physical fitness. Cardiovascular diseases, including heart attacks and strokes, kill more people than any other group of diseases in the developed world.

Hypertension – high blood pressure

How high is high?

One of the most common conditions of the cardiovascular system is **hypertension** (high blood pressure). This disease is unusual in that most sufferers are unaware of it because unless the blood pressure is very high, hypertension gives no symptoms.

Blood pressure

The blood travels through the arterial system at pressures which vary as the heart beats. The blood pressure reading is expressed as two figures, the first higher than the second. The most common way to take the blood pressure uses a **sphygmomanometer**. A cuff is connected to a mercury manometer (an instrument which measures pressure using the height of a column of mercury). The cuff is pleased around the upper arm and inflated until the blood supply to the lower arm is completely cut off.

A stethoscope is positioned over the blood vessels at the elbow. Air is slowly let out of the cuff. The pressure in the cuff at which blood sounds first reappear is recorded. The first blood to get through the vessels under the cuff is that under the highest pressure – in other words, when the heart is contracting strongly. The height of the mercury at this point gives the **systolic blood pressure**. The blood sounds return to normal when blood at the lowest pressure can get through the vessels under the cuff. The pressure in the cuff at this point gives the **diastolic blood pressure**. A systolic reading of 120 mm Hg and a diastolic reading of 80 mm Hg is regarded as 'normal'. The blood pressure is expressed as '120 over 80' or '120/80'.

Blood pressure is used as an indicator of the health of both the heart and the blood vessels. A weakened heart may produce a low blood pressure, whereas damaged blood vessels which are closing up or becoming less elastic will give a raised blood pressure.

When the blood pressure is measured, a result higher than the expected norm of around 120/80 reveals hypertension. It seems likely that blood pressure is naturally a variable characteristic rather like weight and height, so it is quite difficult to judge whether someone's blood pressure is in fact 'high'. If your blood pressure is naturally very low, then a reading at the high end of the normal range could mean you are suffering from mild hypertension. On the other hand, if your blood pressure is naturally on the high side, a reading just above the normal range could be quite normal for you. Blood pressure is usually higher in urban societies than in rural ones, and differs with ethnic groups – African and Japanese people generally have lower than average blood pressures, while Afro-Americans have higher than average values.

Systolic blood pressure can change rapidly in response to many things, including the stress of having your blood pressure taken. For many years this was regarded as relatively unimportant, although there is now evidence that raised systolic pressure figures should be treated with caution. Instead, a raised diastolic pressure has been taken to indicate hypertension. However, it has now been shown that diastolic pressure too can rise with stress, and 'white coat hypertension' – a raised blood pressure which only exists when a doctor or nurse is taking your blood pressure – is now a recognised state! The level of blood pressure regarded as mild hypertension needing treatment varies from country to country. In Britain it is 140/90, but the figures have been known to alter as different treatments become available.

Using the British figure, about 15% of the entire population have some level of hypertension. For people over 40 the figure rises to 20%, and about 40% of people over 70 have hypertension. The majority (85%) of these people will have only mild hypertension, with diastolic blood pressures of 90–109 mm Hg. These data raise the question whether the mild hypertension being treated is in fact just the higher end of the 'normal' range of blood pressure. The current thinking is moving away from treating these people purely on the strength of the blood pressure reading, as most probably do not need clinical treatment.

The problems of hypertension

The reason for anxiety over hypertension is the diseases associated with it. It can cause kidney damage and blindness, and the risk of a stroke is greatly increased, along with a significantly higher risk of heart disease. A stroke may result from a blocked artery supplying the brain due to atherosclerosis, as described on page 78. The artery may be blocked by a blood clot formed elsewhere in the circulatory system, or a stroke may be caused by a blood vessel rupturing, releasing blood into the brain. A stroke frequently leads to permanent brain damage, paralysis or death.

The role of lifestyle in hypertension

Raised blood pressure is usually due to a narrowing of the blood vessels, which may be the result of fatty deposits in the blood vessels, or of the artery walls losing elasticity, or a response to stress. Smoking causes damage to the endothelial linings of the blood vessels, making the build-up of plaque more likely. Being overweight means there are more capillary networks supplying the adipose tissue, and so increases the peripheral resistance of the circulatory system. Too much salt in the diet affects the water balance of the body, increasing the blood volume. Taking insufficient exercise results in narrowed blood vessels and therefore more resistance to the flow of blood. All of these factors make raised blood pressure more likely. Removing any one of these risk factors – giving up smoking, losing weight, reducing the salt in the diet or exercising more – is likely to lower the blood pressure.

Treatment

When preventive measures such as these fail, hypertension needs to be treated with drugs. There are several alternative approaches.

- **Diuretics** increase the excretion of salt and water in the urine, reducing the blood volume and thus the blood pressure.
- **Beta blockers** slow the heart rate and decrease its output, thus reducing the blood pressure as less blood is forced through the blood vessels (see box below).
- **Calcium antagonists** dilate arteries and arterioles by preventing calcium ions moving into smooth muscle cells. This reduces the resistance to blood flow.
- **Angiotensin-converting enzyme inhibitors** prevent the formation of the peptide hormone angiotensin II. This hormone acts to constrict the arteries, so the inhibitors prevent this constriction.
- A number of drugs dilate the arteries by decreasing sympathetic nervous system activity.

Many of these drugs have side-effects, but untreated high blood pressure increases the risk of cardiovascular disease, so their use is worthwhile. Diuretics and beta blockers are the most commonly used drugs in the battle against hypertension.

Beta blockers

The heart beats rhythmically as a whole organ because of the pacemaker region, as described on page 75. The rate and strength of the heartbeat sometimes need to change in response to changes in the body's needs, and these changes in heartbeat are brought about by nervous messages and hormones.

The sympathetic nervous system supplies the heart and releases adrenaline as a neurotransmitter. Adrenaline binds to a protein called a **beta receptor** on the surface of the cardiac muscle cells and stimulates them to contract both more quickly and more strongly, so speeding up the heart rate and increasing the force of pumping. The hormone adrenaline released by the adrenal glands in times of stress has the same effect.

Beta blockers such as propranalol have their effect by interacting with the adrenaline beta receptors. The molecules are a similar shape to adrenaline and fit the beta receptors of the cardiac muscle cells without having a stimulating effect on them. This reduces the number of

▼

receptor sites available for the adrenaline to bind to, and so reduces the effect of adrenaline on the heart. One result of this is a reduction in the force of the ventricular contraction, which is very important in the reduction of high blood pressure. Someone using beta blockers will not experience the heart pounding most of us feel when very nervous, and so these drugs are sometimes used to help people cope with extremely stressful situations.

One problem with using beta blockers in the control of high blood pressure is that they block the normal nervous messages carried by adrenaline, as well as the larger outflow of adrenaline during stress. As a result, patients using beta blockers may have impaired circulation to their hands and feet and feel very cold, because their heart rates are slowed and their blood pressure relatively low most of the time.

Low blood pressure

When discussing blood pressure problems, most people automatically think of raised blood pressure. However, lowered blood pressure is also a clinical problem, as the oxygen supply to major organs can become insufficient. Lowered blood pressure is usually the result of the heart either not beating strongly enough or beating too infrequently.

Atherosclerosis

Atherosclerosis (hardening of the arteries) is a build-up of yellowish fatty deposits (**plaque**) on the endothelium inside the arteries. A large abnormal mass of fatty material building up on the arterial wall is called an **atheroma**. Figure 3.21 shows how atherosclerosis develops. It may begin as early as late childhood, and continues throughout life. Plaque is particularly likely to form in the arteries of the heart (coronary arteries) and the arteries of the neck (carotid arteries). It may cause the wall of the artery to be severely weakened, which can lead to a balloon-shaped swelling of the artery called an **aneurysm**. This can burst, leading to massive internal bleeding. Aneurysms often happen in the brain or the aorta, and a ruptured aneurysm is usually fatal. More frequently, the plaque

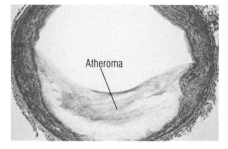
Atheroma

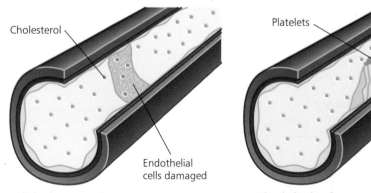
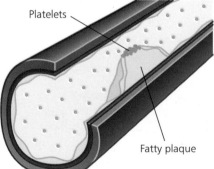
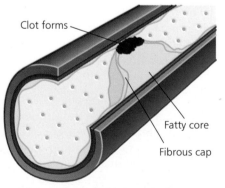

Cholesterol

Endothelial cells damaged

Slight damage to the endothelial cells can lead to an accumulation of lipids – the start of a plaque desposit.

Platelets

Fatty plaque

Blood platelets form a cap over the fatty plaque, narrowing the entire artery.

Clot forms

Fatty core

Fibrous cap

If the cap breaks, lipids from the fatty core can combine with clotting factors. A blood clot forms which can block the artery and lead to a stroke or a heart attack.

Figure 3.21 The development of atherosclerosis, which can begin in childhood

blocks the blood vessels, resulting in a blood clot called a **thrombosis**. A thrombosis in the coronary artery causes **coronary heart disease**. A thrombosis in an artery supplying the brain causes a **stroke** – part of the brain is damaged. In America alone, atherosclerosis accounts for half of all adult deaths each year.

Coronary heart disease

Coronary heart disease, the result of blocked or impeded coronary arteries, causes around 27% of all deaths in the countries of the developed world, which means around 160 000 deaths in the UK alone each year. The most common diseases of the heart are **angina** and **myocardial infarction** (heart attack).

Angina

Angina can be seen as a milder form of heart attack. To maintain regular contractions of the heart, the cardiac muscle needs glucose and oxygen, and these are supplied by the blood via the coronary arteries. Atherosclerosis often occurs in the coronary arteries, reducing the supply of blood to the heart. The symptoms become apparent initially during exercise, when the heart rate goes up and more blood is being pumped. The cardiac muscle is working harder and needs more oxygen, but the narrowed coronary arteries cannot supply it. This leads to a gripping pain in the chest, which can extend down into the arms, particularly the left one, and up into the jaw. This is angina. The symptoms subside once exercise stops, but the experience is painful and frightening. Most angina is relatively mild, but up to 20% of patients with severe angina are likely to die within five years. Management involves stopping smoking, a low-fat diet, regular exercise and losing weight. **Glyceryl trinitrate** is taken when symptoms occur, either as a tablet to put under the tongue or a spray. The drug causes rapid dilation of the blood vessels and so improves the supply of oxygen to the cardiac muscle.

If the blockage of the coronary arteries continues to get worse, so will the angina, until it can become impossible even to walk across a room without experiencing severe pain. Treatment then involves calcium antagonists to dilate the blood vessels and beta blockers to reduce the heart rate – these drugs were described on page 77 for the treatment of hypertension. Drugs cannot solve the problem of severe angina permanently, so at this stage, or earlier, heart bypass surgery may be carried out.

Heart attack

If a branch of the coronary artery becomes completely blocked, part of the heart muscle will be totally starved of oxygen and the patient will suffer a **myocardial infarction** or **heart attack**. The symptoms are pain in the same areas as angina, but much more severe. It does not go off once exercise stops, and indeed may start when sitting down or in bed. The pain lasts for several hours, and glyceryl nitrate does not help. Death may occur within a few minutes having felt no previous symptoms, or after a few hours of pain, or after several days of feeling 'tired' and suffering 'indigestion'. Anyone with a suspected heart attack needs to be admitted to hospital as quickly as possible, for intensive care and treatment with anti-clotting drugs. An **electrocardiogram** (ECG), a recording of the electrical activity of the heart, is taken to confirm a diagnosis of heart attack. Rapid treatment is needed following a heart attack, as up to 45% of heart attack victims will be dead within five years of their initial attack and most of those will die within a week of the initial attack. For patients who survive this first week after an acute attack, the outlook is much more positive – 75% can expect to be alive five years later.

Heart surgery – the bypass and the transplant

Bypass surgery

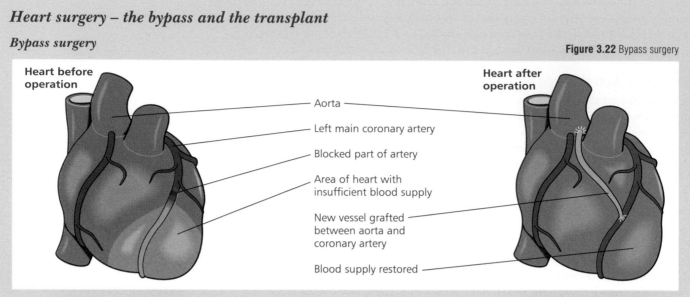

Figure 3.22 Bypass surgery

Heart before operation

Aorta

Left main coronary artery

Blocked part of artery

Area of heart with insufficient blood supply

New vessel grafted between aorta and coronary artery

Blood supply restored

Heart after operation

In patients with severe angina, the blood supply to the heart may become very restricted. To overcome this, **bypass surgery** may be carried out in which the diseased parts of the coronary arteries are 'bypassed' using pieces of blood vessels taken from elsewhere in the patient's body. This gives the cardiac muscle a much improved blood supply, and avoids the tissue being rejected. The symptoms of angina are relieved very rapidly and the quality of life is greatly improved.

Heart transplant

If a bypass operation is not suitable, or the heart has been severely damaged by a series of heart attacks, then the only remaining option may be a **heart transplant**. This technique was pioneered in the 1960s by the South African surgeon Christiaan Barnard. Now it is carried out regularly in many countries and most heart transplant patients can expect years rather than months or weeks of life ahead of them.

A heart transplant involves taking the diseased heart out of a patient's body and replacing it with the healthy heart of someone who has died, usually in an accident or from a brain haemorrhage. Once connected, the new heart will pump blood around the body, controlled by a pacemaker. The nervous connections have obviously been severed, so the overriding controls needed to stop the heart slowing down or speeding up have been lost. By imposing a rhythm, the artificial pacemaker overcomes these problems.

One of the major problems of heart transplants is rejection of the new organ by the body of the host. Once the body recognises the new heart as 'non-self' it will rapidly attack and destroy it. To prevent this, recipients have to take a cocktail of immunosuppressant drugs for the remainder of their lives, and this makes them vulnerable to attack by infectious diseases.

The heart transplant programme is hindered by lack of suitable donors. Accident victims who have registered to donate their organs are fewer than the patients needing transplants. Obviously the tissue match must be as close as possible, and there is no guarantee that an available heart will be of the right tissue type. More potential donors are needed, but future developments include the possibility of making entirely artificial hearts, or of using genetically engineered animals to produce 'human' hearts.

A change in lifestyle

Treatments such as bypass surgery and heart transplants raise certain dilemmas. Although some people with coronary heart disease are simply the victims of their own genetics, many patients have contributed to their own ill-health by various factors in their lifestyle. The most frequent contributory factor is smoking, along with eating a high-fat diet and not taking exercise. If a patient is treated without making lifestyle changes, the arteries supplying their cardiac muscle may once again become blocked, and further expensive surgery will be needed in future. In a health service where resources are always at a premium, do doctors have the right to demand that patients change their lifestyle before treatment is made available? Even if a patient does make changes before surgery, such as giving up smoking, old habits die hard and a reformed lifestyle cannot be imposed on an individual once the need for direct medical intervention is past.

Risk factors for cardiovascular disease

The risk factors involved in heart disease break down into two main groups – those we can't help and those we can do something about. There is a genetic tendency in some families to develop heart disease or hypertension which can bring about heart disease and this we cannot (at present) alter. Age is also an unalterable factor. As we get older, our blood vessels begin to lose their elasticity and to narrow slightly, making us more likely to suffer from heart disease. The final unalterable factor is our gender – men are more likely to suffer from heart disease than women. This difference is particularly marked before the female menopause, as the female hormone oestrogen appears to offer some protection against the build-up of plaque.

Other risk factors for heart disease are aspects of our lifestyles which can be changed, as illustrated in figure 3.23. We each have the power to change some or all of these things for ourselves. However, as a society we have less power to prevent heart disease – banning smoking or introducing compulsory exercise for all would be unlikely to win a politician many votes. Health education programmes aimed at all ages can help to make everyone aware of the choices they are making in their lifestyle, and the future implications of those choices. Schools can provide education in healthy eating and in the risks associated with smoking, poor diet and lack of exercise. In the final analysis, everybody has to weigh up the evidence, make their own choices and take their own risks.

Smoking increases the risk of heart disease by damaging the endothelial lining of the blood vessels and encouraging a build-up of plaque. Being overweight puts a greater strain of the heart because of increased peripheral resistance. Too much fat and/or cholesterol in the diet can raise the blood cholesterol level (see page 68), which in turn increases the likelihood of plaque in the arteries. However, blood cholesterol levels also depend on the genetically determined metabolism. Some individuals seem to be able to eat almost unlimited amounts of fatty food with no appreciable effect on their blood cholesterol, whilst others can eat a very low-fat diet and still have raised blood cholesterol levels. One of the most publicised ways of helping to avoid heart disease is physical fitness. Is it really effective against heart disease, and if so, why?

Physical fitness can be considered as 'the capacity to meet successfully the present and potential challenges of life'. This means that our body systems are in a condition that meets with the demands of our current way of life and also with any increased demands which may be put upon us. Most animals maintain physical fitness simply through their natural way of life. However, this is not always true for humans. In the developed world the average person lives a far more sedentary existence than our evolutionary ancestors, and so needs to make an effort to remain reasonably fit. Like any other muscle in the body, the heart develops with use. A fit heart is slightly larger than an unfit heart, and the muscle contracts more effectively, pumping more blood around the body with each contraction. As a result a fit person has a lower resting heart rate. Also, a fit person has enlarged and dilated blood vessels, so that the lumen is larger. This means the vessels are less likely to be blocked by plaque. Regular exercise reduces the likelihood of being overweight, another risk factor in heart disease, and fit people are also less likely to suffer from high blood pressure. Apart from the benefits to the heart, physical fitness leads to toned muscles, the ability to exercise longer without becoming breathless and better performance in sports and fitness activities. Exercise produces a feeling of physical well-being as chemicals known as endorphins are released in your brain. Being fit has positive benefits, making you look and feel healthy.

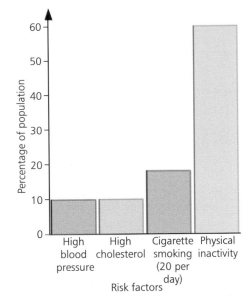

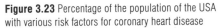

Figure 3.23 Percentage of the population of the USA with various risk factors for coronary heart disease

Figure 3.24 We make our lifestyle choices for many reasons and knowledge about causes of heart disease may not be enough to influence our decisions.

How much exercise is good for you?

It is generally agreed that exercise is good for us, and that few people take enough exercise. There is evidence to suggest that the amount of activity undertaken by a person depends on factors such as their age, economic status and gender. But what exactly is meant by exercise? If you never take exercise, walking to the shops might seem quite strenuous, but an active person might swim 3000 metres each morning before work or school. There is no universal agreement on how much exercise you need to do to benefit your health. However, studies indicate that a level of exercise which uses at least 31.5 kJ of energy per minute with an oxygen uptake of 1.5 litres per minute has a clear health benefit.

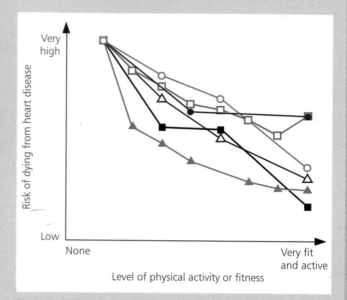

Figure 3.25 The graphs show the results of six different studies on the effect of exercise on the risk of dying of a heart attack.

In spite of evidence of this sort, very few people take regular vigorous exercise. However, an increasing body of research suggests that even quite gentle exercise such as walking two or three times a week can have positive health benefits.

Activity	Examples of 'vigorous exercise'
Keep fit	Aerobic exercises
Recreation	Swimming, tennis, dancing, sailing, climbing
Gardening	Digging, clearing scrub, planting bushes
DIY	Building in stone or brick, fencing
Getting around	Brisk walking, running, cycling
Climbing upstairs	500+ stairs daily
Other	Moving snow, heavy car repairs

Table 3.3 Some physical activities which use at least 31.5 kJ of energy per minute

CANCER – THE LAST WORD

The many causes of cancer

Cancer is one of the most common causes of death in the developed world. Cancer is a mass of abnormally growing cells (a **tumour**), which can appear in almost any part of the body. The cancer cells do not respond to the normal mechanisms which control cell growth, and they divide and invade the surrounding tissues. A tumour may split up, releasing small clumps of malignant cells into the blood or lymph systems where they circulate and then lodge in a different area of the body, continuing their uncontrolled division and forming a **secondary tumour**. Cancer is often fatal as it interferes with the functioning of vital organs, and modern medical treatments cannot guarantee a cure. Many of the factors that increase the likelihood of cancer developing are present in our individual environments as part of our lifestyle.

Some people have a genetic make-up programmed with particular genes called **oncogenes** or **protooncogenes** that make them more vulnerable than normal to cell changes, and they obviously have no control over this factor. As we age, our exposure to cancer-triggering stimuli becomes longer, and errors in DNA replication increase, raising the likelihood of a loss of control of cell growth. We cannot avoid ageing, but there are also behavioural factors that can increase our risk of developing certain cancers, including:
- smoking cigarettes
- drinking too much alcohol

- exposure to the ultra-violet light of the Sun
- not eating sufficient fibre and fruit
- promiscuous sex
- eating a diet of highly refined foods containing lots of additives.

These are all aspects of our lifestyle over which we have at least some control.

Figure 3.26 Regular breast checks and mammography are offered to women with a family history of breast cancer and to all women from the age of 50 onwards.

Screening – an early warning system

Screening means testing people who are apparently healthy to find any early symptoms of disease. We can check our own bodies for some diseases. Women should examine their breasts regularly for signs of a lump developing, which could turn out to be breast cancer. Men should check their testes regularly for any lumps or enlargements that might signal testicular cancer. Both of these cancers can be treated successfully if they are detected early enough. There are also national screening programmes for certain diseases. For example, in the UK all women are offered a regular cervical smear test to pick up precancerous changes in the cells of the cervix. It is then possible to treat the condition simply and cheaply before there is any major risk to health. Blood pressure measurements are taken at regular intervals in adults to screen for hypertension or for abnormally low blood pressure, and blood cholesterol levels are measured in anyone with a family history of heart problems. Considerable amounts of money are being spent on screening large sections of the population, with the assumption that this is cheaper long term than treating more advanced diseases and also paying sickness benefit and pensions to those who become severely ill or die, leaving dependents needing support. Only time will reveal how effective these screening programmes are.

A combination of knowledge, enabling informed choices about lifestyle which minimise the risk of disease, and screening, to pick up many serious diseases early on, may well lead to a society of healthier individuals.

SUMMARY

- Many non-infectious diseases are a result of the lifestyle people are either forced or choose to lead – for example, the diet they eat.

- Diseases caused directly by the food eaten include **lactose intolerance** (inability to digest the natural sugar in milk), **food allergies** and **food-borne infections** such as listeriosis.

- The balance of food in the diet plays an important role in maintaining health. Too much or too little fat, protein, carbohydrate, fibre, vitamins or minerals can cause disease. The energy content of the food taken in also affects health. The Recommended Guidelines for Nutrition highlight the nutritional requirements of the population.

- Eating insufficient fibre leads to a long throughput time (the time the food stays in the gut). This can cause **constipation** (hard compacted faeces), **haemorrhoids** (swollen veins in the wall of the anus and rectum), **diverticulitis** (pockets forming in the colon), **irritable bowel syndrome** (pain in the lower abdomen) and **cancer of the colon**.

- **Additives** are chemicals added to foods to preserve them or improve their texture or colour. **E-numbers** are numbers given to additives by the EC and listed on food labels. Additives include preservatives such as antioxidants, colourings, flavourings and flavour enhancers. There may be a link between food additives and hyperactivity in some children.

- **Malnutrition** is an imbalance between the food eaten and what is required to remain healthy. Malnutrition can take the form of deficiency diseases, or over-eating leading to obesity. Slimming diets can lead to deficiencies of vitamins, minerals or protein. Psychologically based food disorders are **anorexia nervosa** (sufferers starve themselves, perceiving themselves as fat) and **bulimia** (bulimics binge and vomit).

- Eating too much saturated fat in the diet is linked with heart disease, caused by a build-up of cholesterol deposits in the arteries. Some oils, such as olive oil and oily fish, appear to give protection against heart disease.

- Diseases of the respiratory system resulting from lifestyle include **asthma**, which can be triggered by an allergic reaction or an irritant such as cigarette smoke. Too much histamine is produced which causes the bronchioles to contract. This increases the resistance to air moving in and out of the lungs, resulting in breathlessness and wheezing. Asthma is treated with **beta agonists** which relax the smooth muscle and so open up the bronchioles, **sodium chromoglycate** which reduces histamine production and **steroids** which help prevent an attack.

- **Acute bronchitis** is an infection of the respiratory system. **Chronic bronchitis** is the secretion of too much mucus in the airways, leading to a persistent cough, narrowing of the airways and shortness of breath. Smokers and people exposed to irritant particles and traffic pollution are more likely to suffer from bronchitis. **Emphysema** (large air spaces in the lungs) may result from severe chronic bronchitis, as may failure of the right ventricle of the heart.

- **Hypertension** or high blood pressure can be caused by too much fat or salt in the diet, smoking, stress, obesity or insufficient exercise. It can be treated with **diuretics** to increase the excretion of salt and water in the urine, **beta blockers** to slow the heart rate, **calcium antagonists** to prevent constriction of the arteries or **enzyme inhibitors** to block the action of certain enzymes that constrict the arteries.

- **Atherosclerosis** is a build-up of **plaque**, fatty deposits in the arteries. It can lead to a swelling in the artery called an **aneurysm**, which may burst. Plaque can also encourage a clot or **thrombosis** to form, which can block the coronary artery, leading to **coronary heart disease**, or the arteries supplying the brain, leading to a **stroke**.

- Plaque in the coronary artery can cause **angina**, pain in the chest when exercising. The reduced blood supply to the heart muscle cannot supply it with enough glucose and oxygen. **Glyceryl trinitrate** causes dilation of the blood vessels and is taken during an angina attack.

- A **heart attack** or **myocardial infarction** results when the coronary artery is completely blocked by a thrombosis. Part of the heart muscle is starved of oxygen and dies. An **electrocardiogram** (ECG) records the electrical activity of the heart and anti-clotting drugs are given.

- Risk factors in coronary heart disease include smoking, eating too much saturated fat, being overweight and suffering high levels of stress. Regular exercise and physical fitness help reduce the risk of heart disease.

- **Cancer** or a **tumour** is a mass of cells which are dividing out of control. Cells may split off from the tumour and circulate to another part of the body, causing a **secondary tumour**. Some people have genes that make them more likely to develop cancer, but environmental factors include smoking, too much alcohol, ultra-violet light, insufficient fibre and fruit or too many additives in the diet, and promiscuous sex.

● **Screening** – checking all members of a population to find early signs of some diseases – means treatment can be effective at an early stage.

QUESTIONS

1 Many diseases have now been linked to the type of food we eat, or do not eat. Summarise the main ways in which diet and disease are linked.

2 **a** How does the human respiratory system work?
   b What causes asthma, and how does asthma affect the respiratory system?
   c What is bronchitis?

3 Produce a leaflet called 'A healthy heart – lifestyle choices for the future' designed to be placed in sixth form, university and college common rooms, as well as in waiting rooms at doctors' and dentists' surgeries. It should inform people in a lively and accessible way about how they can affect their own future health by the choices they make now. The leaflet needs to explain clearly the importance of cardiovascular health and the ways in which it can be compromised or damaged by lifestyle factors.

4

Drugs, health and disease

Drugs appear to have been used from the earliest times of human society. Drug use has always been divided into two main areas – medicinal treatments used to alleviate the symptoms of a disease or effect a cure, and recreational drugs used to enhance the experience of life.

WHAT IS A DRUG?

A **drug** is a substance that alters the functioning of the mind, the body or both. Some of the drugs developed by pharmaceutical companies to help in the battle against disease have already been mentioned, and more of these will be looked in subsequent chapters. This chapter looks at recreational drugs.

Within every society there are certain drugs that are used for pleasure. Some of these substances are socially acceptable and others are frowned upon or illegal. In many countries such as the UK and the USA, caffeine, nicotine and alcohol are the main legal recreational drugs. In some European countries like the Netherlands, drugs such as marijuana are also legally sold. In other parts of the world, such as the Arab states, alcohol is illegal. The social attitude towards a drug may be related to its effect, or it may be simply a result of the history of its usage. For example, alcohol is not only highly intoxicating, bringing about extremely anti-social behaviour, it is also poisonous. If it were a newly discovered substance being introduced as a leisure drug it would almost certainly be regarded as highly dangerous and banned. But because there is a history of alcohol use going back for centuries, the drug is widely accepted as part of normal social life.

Figure 4.1 As this painting shows, alcohol was a commonly used drug in the nineteenth century, and continues to be widely used today.

Some recreational drugs

Recreational drugs are usually taken because of their effect on the mind, although they may well affect the body too. Some body builders and athletes take testosterone and other anabolic steroids primarily to increase muscle mass, and in these cases the effect on the mind is an unwanted side-effect.

Drugs are usually categorised by the way they affect the mind. There are four main categories – sedatives, stimulants, hallucinogens and painkillers – and we shall look at each in turn.

Sedatives slow down the responses of the brain, making the user feel calm and sleepy. The most commonly used sedative drug is alcohol. Sedatives may be prescribed by doctors for people who are particularly anxious and highly strung, or for people who have difficulty sleeping. One group of sedative drugs, the **barbiturates**, are very powerful – one barbiturate drug is used as an anaesthetic. Barbiturates are highly addictive (see page 88), so they need to be prescribed with care. This fact went largely unrecognised or unacknowledged for a long time, and doctors used to prescribe barbiturates as sedatives (often for women) for years and years. During this time the patients became completely addicted, with confused behaviour and loss of memory and coordination. The risks are now well understood, and modern sedative drugs are much less addictive, and are also more carefully prescribed. However, barbiturates are also used illegally.

Stimulants are substances that speed up the activity of the brain, making the user more alert. They may be used medically to help people suffering from severe depression. Pills to provide 'energy' and to keep you awake and alert have been used in all sorts of ways over the years. Young people wanting help to cope with long periods of studying or partying have been known to use this kind of chemical stimulant to keep going. **Ecstasy** is an illegal stimulant drug but the legal (and much milder) stimulants caffeine and nicotine are used far more commonly on an everyday basis.

Hallucinogens are drugs that produce vivid waking dreams, where the user sees or hears things happening which are not really there, or has a distorted view of the world. Hallucinogens have been used by mystics, in religion and healing, for a large part of human history. Marijuana (cannabis, pot, hash) is a relatively mild hallucinogen, whilst LSD (lysergic acid diethylamide) has a much stronger effect on the brain. LSD was a popular drug with young people in the 1960s. However, it led to a number of young people leaping from high buildings in the mistaken belief that they could fly, which was quite an effective deterrent to other users. Although LSD is still around, it is no longer a fashionable drug.

Painkillers are the final category of drugs. Mild painkillers such as aspirin and paracetamol are commonly used for medical reasons, along with many other painkillers, but do not have recreational use. However, drugs such as heroin, opium and morphine suppress the part of the brain responsible for the sense of pain and they induce a sensation of great well-being and power. These drugs are all extracted from the opium poppy. Morphine is widely used medically for the relief of severe pain, although care is taken with patients who are likely to recover from their illness because of its addictive properties. Heroin and opium are used illegally purely for recreational use.

Figure 4.2 The effects of the opiates on the nervous system have been recognised for centuries. This picture shows opium use in China 150 years ago.

Producing effects

The effects of a drug depend on a number of factors as well as the nature of the chemical compound taken. The amount of the drug used is very important. Many drugs range from giving very mild experiences to being lethal poisons, depending on the dose taken. The past drug experience of the user also has an effect. For someone who has never used a recreational drug, the first experience may be quite terrifying, or mind-blowingly exciting. A more seasoned user knows what to expect, and how much drug is needed to achieve that effect.

The way in which a drug is taken will change its effect. Taking a drug orally, for example, allows some of the drug to be digested and gives a time delay while the drug is absorbed from the gut, whereas injecting substances directly into a vein gives an almost immediate effect. Finally, the circumstances in which a drug is taken can have a major influence. The place, the presence or absence of other people, the psychological and emotional stability of the user and the use of alcohol or other drugs at the same time can all change the perceived effects of a drug.

Addiction

Addiction means being unable to function properly without a drug. It may be **psychological**, when the drug becomes so central to someone's thoughts, emotions and activities that the need to keep using it becomes a craving or compulsion. Addiction may be a **physical** dependence, where the body has adapted to the presence of the drug and no longer works properly without it. Once addicted to a drug, a user cannot manage without it in the short term. What is more, ever-increasing doses are needed to keep the user feeling normal and in control. This is known as **drug tolerance** and happens in people who are addicted to legal drugs such as tobacco and alcohol as well as those addicted to illegal drugs such as heroin. This tolerance can drive people to use such high levels of drugs that they are effectively poisoning themselves.

When addicts try to stop using their drug, they feel very unwell, often experiencing combinations of aches and pains, shaking, sweating, fever, visual disturbances, headaches and cravings for the drug. These are known as **withdrawal symptoms**. Although the combination of symptoms will vary from individual to individual, and from drug to drug, withdrawal from all addictive drugs, from nicotine to heroin, causes problems.

LEGAL DRUGS: CAFFEINE AND NICOTINE

A cup of caffeine

The drug that is probably used the most commonly in modern society is taken at regular intervals every day by millions of adults and young people. Many people find it hard to get going in the morning without their first fix of caffeine – more commonly known as a cup of tea or coffee. Caffeine is a mild stimulant, which is why tea or coffee helps you to wake up in the morning or to keep going during the day if you feel sleepy. As well as stimulating the brain, it also has an effect on the body, increasing the heart rate and blood pressure. For most people this physical effect is of little consequence, but large amounts of caffeine can be damaging to people with heart disease or high blood pressure, who should cut down on the amounts of coffee and tea that they drink or change to decaffeinated brands. Also, as with most drugs, some people are more sensitive to caffeine than others and find that drinking coffee in the evening prevents them sleeping properly. Caffeine is legal, socially accepted and widely enjoyed, but like many other drugs it can be addictive, particularly if taken in large amounts. It is easy to drink lots of strong coffee to cope with extra pressure of work or a need to concentrate late at night. However, when coffee-drinking drops back to normal levels, feeling of tiredness and headaches may result – withdrawal symptoms brought on by an addiction to caffeine. If these symptoms are ignored the addiction is soon broken and the person feels normal again, but many people in this situation simply make another cup of coffee without thinking! Caffeine is not, in the amounts normally used, a dangerous drug and there are no health warnings on a pack of coffee. But the way it becomes a part of our lives, leaving a void if we try to give it up, gives us a working model of what happens when we use other, more damaging drugs.

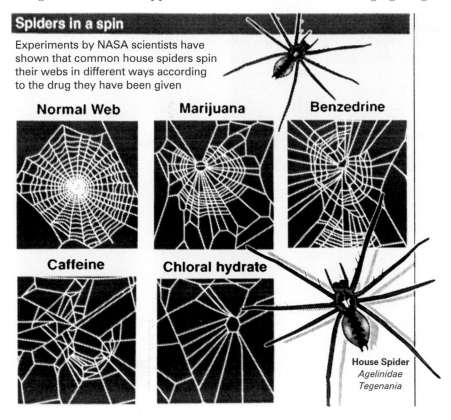

Spiders in a spin

Experiments by NASA scientists have shown that common house spiders spin their webs in different ways according to the drug they have been given

Normal Web　**Marijuana**　**Benzedrine**

Caffeine　**Chloral hydrate**

House Spider
*Agelinidae
Tegenania*

Figure 4.3 The action of caffeine on the web-spinning ability of a spider! In this experiment spiders were exposed to minute amounts of several different drugs and the effect on their nervous system was demonstrated by the disruption of the web. It is interesting to note that, for spiders, caffeine has a more disruptive effect than several other drugs.

Tobacco

Nicotine – the smoker's drug

Cigarettes contain tobacco leaves which burn to produce smoke, which is inhaled into the lungs. Here the drug **nicotine**, one component of that smoke, is absorbed into the bloodstream and then carried around the body to the brain, where it has its effect. Nicotine is a mild stimulant, although some of its effects are more like a sedative as it causes vasoconstriction (narrowing) of the peripheral blood vessels, as illustated in figure 4.4. The overall effect of the drug is to produce a sensation of calm well-being and 'being able to cope'. The heart rate is slightly raised by the drug, but the peripheral blood flow is reduced, so less blood flows to the skin and areas such as the hands. This in turn leads to a slight increase in blood pressure.

Nicotine is a physically addictive drug, which means there is a physical craving for the drug as the blood nicotine level drops. Also, increasingly high levels of the drug are needed over the years to maintain the same effect, so the number of cigarettes smoked tends to increase over the years. On giving up smoking, nicotine withdrawal symptoms include a craving for the drug (for a cigarette), irritability, difficulty in concentrating, restlessness, hunger and feelings of sadness or depression. In addition, there is a level of psychological addiction to smoking. Smoking gives smokers something to do with their hands and their mouths and it gives comfort and reassurance through a regular ritual. To give up the habit, smokers have to battle with both physical and mental addiction, and it is often the latter which drives them back to smoking months after any physical addiction has been lost.

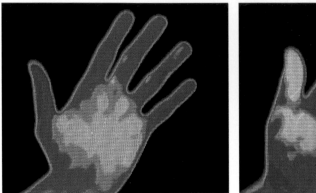

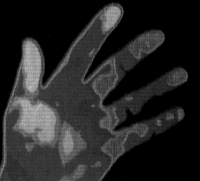

Figure 4.4 Pictures taken with a heat-sensitive camera show the effects of smoking on the temperature of the hands. The difference between the hand of the non-smoker (left) and the smoker (right) is the result of vasoconstriction caused by the drug nicotine. (Blue=cool, yellow=warm.)

Tobacco facts

- There are 1.1 billion smokers worldwide.
- In developed countries, on average, 41% of men and 21% of women smoke regularly.
- In developing countries, on average, 50% of men and 8% of women smoke regularly.
- The number of women who smoke is increasing in many countries, and so are the numbers of women with smoking-related diseases.
- Six thousand billion cigarettes are smoked each year.
- Three million deaths a year are a direct result of smoking, with 30% of these in the developing world. In other words, someone dies every 10 seconds as a direct result of smoking.
- If current smoking trends persist, in 30–40 years' time there will be 10 million smoking-related deaths each year, 70% of them in the developing world.
- Smoking currently causes just under 20% of all deaths in developed countries.

Nicotine's companions

Carbon monoxide

If cigarette smoke contained only nicotine, it would still be an addictive drug and would still, with its effects on the cardiovascular system, probably be a bad idea. But there are over 4000 different chemical compounds in the smoke from burning tobacco leaves, and whilst it is the drug nicotine that addicts people to smoking cigarettes, it is largely these other compounds that cause lasting and often fatal damage to the body cells. For example, **carbon monoxide** is one component of cigarette smoke. Carbon monoxide is a poisonous gas for which haemoglobin has a greater affinity than it has for oxygen, as shown in figure 4.5.

After smoking a cigarette, up to 10% of the haemoglobin in the blood of a smoker will be carrying carbon monoxide rather than oxygen. This reduction in the oxygenation of the blood can lead to a shortage of oxygen. The effect is most marked in pregnant women. The haemoglobin of a pregnant woman is carrying oxygen for her developing fetus as well as for her respiring tissues.

Figure 4.5 Carbon monoxide combines more readily with haemoglobin than oxygen does. The gas prevents the haemoglobin from transporting oxygen to the tissues.

Fetal haemoglobin has a high affinity for oxygen, and it picks up oxygen from the maternal haemoglobin in the placenta and carries it round the fetal circulation, supplying all the developing tissues. If the maternal blood does not contain sufficient oxygen as a result of smoking, the fetus suffers from long-term oxygen deprivation and this can lead to growth problems, reduced development of the brain, and ultimately to premature birth, low birth weight and even stillbirth (the baby is born dead) or death soon after birth.

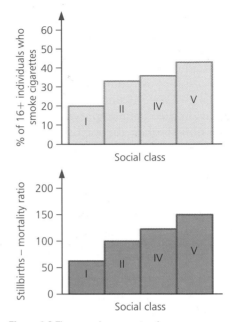

Figure 4.6 These graphs suggest a close relationship between incidence of smoking and incidence of stillbirths.

Smoking and the cardiovascular system

Smoking increases the risk of cardiovascular disease. The effect is particularly noticable in younger people, but is present throughout all the age ranges. It is estimated that 24% of deaths due to coronary heart disease in men and 11% in women are due to cigarette smoking.

Number of cigarettes smoked per day	Annual death rate from CHD per 100 000	Relative risk
0	572	
1–14	802	1.4
15–24	892	1.6
25+	1025	1.8

Table 4.1 The increased risk of coronary heart disease (CHD) caused by smoking

Incidence of atherosclerosis, coronary heart disease and strokes are all raised in smokers. As we saw in chapter 3, strokes involve an interference with the blood supply to the brain, particularly the cerebral hemispheres. This may be due to atherosclerosis in the blood vessels leading to the brain, to clot formation or to the walls of a blood vessel thinning and bursting – an aneurism. We still do not understand fully the reasons why smoking increases the incidence of strokes, as there are so many different chemical compounds in tobacco smoke which could be causing the damage.

Two compounds which we know play a part in the raised risk of cardiovascular disease due to smoking are nicotine and carbon monoxide. Nicotine causes peripheral vasoconstriction and raises the heart rate, which results in raised blood pressure, a known risk factor for cardiovascular disease. Carbon monoxide binds to some of the haemoglobin, so the blood carries less oxygen. As a result the heart needs to beat faster to maintain an adequate oxygen supply. This again puts stress on the cardiovascular system. The raised blood presssure and increased heartbeat which result from the nicotine and carbon monoxide in cigarette smoke mean that the endothelial linings of the arteries are more likely to be damaged. This makes the vessels more vulnerable to the development of atherosclerosis, and also to the formation of a thrombosis. If these events happen in the coronary vessels supplying the heart, then coronary heart disease will result. If they happen in the vessels supplying the brain, then a stroke is the most likely outcome. Thus nicotine and carbon monoxide – and probably other compounds as well – give smokers a raised risk of cardiovascular disease. All patients who have heart disease or a stroke which they survive are strongly advised to stop smoking. If they stopped earlier, or never started, then the problems might never have arisen.

Tar

Another component of cigarette smoke is **tar**. This is a sticky black substance which is not absorbed into the bloodstream. It simply accumulates in the lungs, discolouring the tissue. The lungs of a young child are bright pink. In most adults in the developed world, that pinkness becomes a little diminished as a result of air pollution – including other people's tobacco smoke. The lungs of a serious smoker are not pink but grey. This is partly due to the effect of tar on the ciliated epithelial cells lining the respiratory system (see page 70). In a non-smoker, these cilia are constantly active, moving mucus (along with trapped dirt, dust and bacteria from the inhaled air) up the respiratory tract away from the lungs. This mucus is swept either into the throat to be swallowed and digested, or to the nose to be blown out. In a smoker, these cilia are anaesthetised by each cigarette and stop working for a time, allowing dirt down into the lungs. In a heavy smoker the cilia are permanently out of action during the day when smoking is taking place.

Tar accumulates in the lungs and interferes with gas exchange, covering some of the alveolar surface and preventing gases from diffusing through to the blood. Tar and other chemicals from cigarette smoke make smokers more likely to develop chronic bronchitis, described on page 71. Impaired cilial function prevents the extra mucus produced being cleared, so it accumulates and causes coughing. The accumulation of tar and other compounds in the delicate lung tissue, particularly when associated with chronic bronchitis, can lead to a breakdown in alveolar structure, resulting in the large air spaces and inefficient lung functioning of emphysema.

Lung cancer

Tar is also a major **carcinogen** (cancer-causing substance), one of 60 such substances associated with tobacco smoke. **Lung cancer**, perhaps the best known disease associated with smoking cigarettes, results partly from this accumulation of tar. The carcinogenic chemicals found in tobacco smoke also lead to an increased risk of cancers of the tongue and oesophagus in smokers.

Lung cancer is particularly dangerous because it has plenty of space in the lungs to grow unnoticed without causing any symptoms. It is a treatable disease if it is caught early, but in many cases smokers ignore coughs and breathlessness, or deny the condition to themselves, until the cancer has spread to other parts of the body.

There are several different types of lung cancer. One type occurs regardless of whether or not an individual smokes, but the great majority of lung cancers are found only in the lungs of smokers. Of course not everyone who smokes will develop lung cancer, and a few non-smokers will suffer from the disease, but the epidemiological evidence for the link is extremely strong – up to 90% of all lung cancers are thought to be due to smoking. The link was first noticed by Sir Richard Doll early in the twentieth century, but it has taken many years for the smoking public to accept the link, and even longer for the cigarette manufacturers. Indeed, in spite of carrying out extensive research themselves, many manufacturers have publicly denied both the addictive nature of nicotine and the health risks associated with cigarette smoke for years. In the late twentieth century a number of court cases took place. The aim was to force cigarette companies to accept responsibility for the terminal illnesses of smokers who took up smoking at a time when it is claimed the cigarette companies had evidence of both the health and addiction risks of smoking, and yet continued to advertise their products as 'cool' and 'healthy', with no mention of risks. At the time of writing, enormous sums of money had been paid in compensation by American cigarette manufacturers, and similar cases continued in the UK.

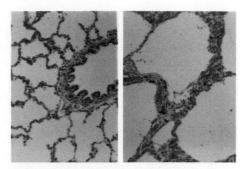

Figure 4.7 Chronic bronchitis and emphysema are well known risks of smoking, caused by the build-up of tar and other damaging chemicals from cigarette smoke. This photograph shows normal lung tissue on the left, and emphysemic alveoli on the right – the spaces are much larger.

Figure 4.8 This health education poster from a few years ago provides a graphic illustration of the carcinogenic tar which accumulates in the lungs of every smoker.

(a) Deaths from lung cancer and smoking

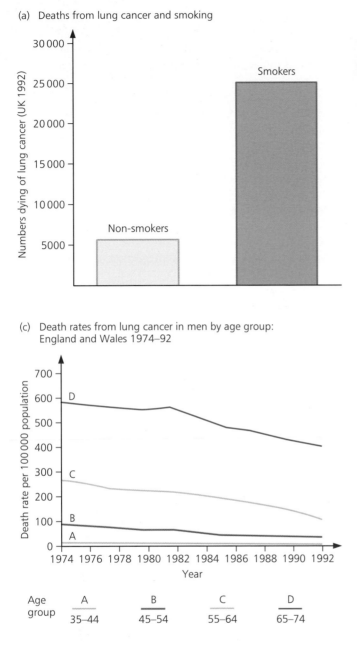

(c) Death rates from lung cancer in men by age group: England and Wales 1974–92

Age group	A	B	C	D
	35–44	45–54	55–64	65–74

(b) Cigarette consumption and risk of lung cancer death

Number of cigarettes smoked per day	Annual death rate per 100 000	Relative risk
0	14	–
1–14	105	8
15–24	208	15
25+	355	25

(d) Percentage of men smoking (manual + non-manual workers) in Great Britain 1974–94

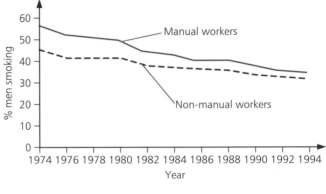

(e)

Scientists say they have found the component of cigarette smoke that causes lung cancer. 'We have found a specific component of cigarette smoke, benzo pyrene, to be strongly implicated in lung cancer development,' said Gerd Pfeifer, a researcher at City of Hope Medical Centre near Los Angeles. When the benzo pyrene compound was added to a culture of human lungs, a gene called p53 that normally suppresses tumours was damaged. The cells began to divide abnormally. The scientists found the DNA in the cells was damaged at the same specific sites where mutations are found in lung cancer cells.

Figure 4.9 Epidemiologists use data such as these to identify causal effects for diseases. (a) shows how many of the people dying of lung cancer are smokers – 81% compared with 19% of non-smokers. (b) shows the effect of the number of cigarettes smoked on the risk of dying from lung cancer. As the risk increases when more cigarettes are smoked, this suggests that something in the cigarettes is responsible for the cancers. (c) and (d) show the death rates of different age groups of men from lung cancer and the percentage of the male population who smoke. Analysis of data such as these leads to research intended to confirm or disprove apparent links. (e) Summarises the result of work done on cigarette smoke in response to the findings of epidemiologists.

Passive smoking

In recent years it has been shown that smoking is not simply a personal health risk chosen by an individual. When anyone smokes a cigarette, the majority of the smoke goes not into their lungs, but into the air around them for others to breathe in. This is called **passive smoking**. In the last ten years evidence has accumulated that passive smoking can cause 'smoker's diseases' such as lung cancer in non-smokers. The evidence has led to no-smoking policies in some offices, shops, restaurants and bars. The majority of the population are non-smokers who feel increasingly aggrieved at having to put up with unpleasant-smelling and potentially damaging smoke from other people. However, bans on smoking in public places have raised some interesting issues of human rights and the arguments look set to continue for some time.

Smoking and children

Figure 4.10 Much of the evidence for the dangers of passive smoking have come from studies on young children.

In recent years there has been increasing evidence that babies and young children who are exposed to passive smoking have an increased risk of health problems.

As discussed on pages 90–1, maternal smoking can lead to a fetus failing to develop properly, and to the birth of premature, low birth-mass or dead babies. After birth, babies and small children are at risk from **environmental tobacco smoke** (ETS).

Sudden infant death syndrome (SIDS or cot death) is a tragic occurrence when an apparently healthy baby dies in its sleep for no obvious reason. For example, in the UK, although the numbers of cot deaths have been falling steadily, as many as two babies each day die in this way. One contributory factor is the position in which the baby is put to sleep, particularly in very small babies who cannot move themselves about.

Overheating may be involved, and there are sometimes undiagnosed infections. But one of the major factors in cot deaths appears to be if the parents, particularly the mother, smoke. A baby whose mother smokes is twice as likely to die from a cot death as a baby with non-smoking parents. It is estimated that if parents with small babies did not smoke, the life of at least one of the babies that die each day from SIDS would be saved. It is interesting that a UK campaign to change the recommended sleeping position of small infants from their fronts to their backs was very successful, halving the death rate from cot deaths. However, that behaviour cost very little effort from parents. Advice about giving up smoking, which would similarly save the lives of many babies but which involves a far greater sacrifice by the parents, is largely ignored.

The children of smokers are more likely to suffer from respiratory infections such as pneumonia and bronchitis. American data suggest that parental smoking – again mainly that of the mother, who is frequently with the child more often than the father – contributes to 150 000–300 000 cases of lower respiratory tract infections in children under eighteen months old. Up to 15 000 of these cases are serious enough to need hospitalisation. In addition, environmental tobacco smoke increases both the numbers of children suffering from asthma, and the severity and number of attacks they have. Perhaps the most damaging effect of all is that the children of parents who smoke are substantially more likely to smoke themselves than the children of non-smokers.

The economics of cigarette smoking

With all the present evidence of the damage smoking causes to health, it is perhaps surprising that cigarettes are still widely available. The cost to health services in caring for people who suffer and die from smoking-related diseases is immense. Even larger is the personal suffering of people who lose their quality of life and indeed, in many cases, lose their lives, and the suffering of their families. So why are cigarettes still manufactured, advertised and sold?

Tobacco products are very cheap to make, so the companies that manufacture them make very large profits and are extremely powerful as a result. Because tobacco products are addictive, customers are almost guaranteed. However, these highly profitable tobacco companies have persuaded governments to subsidise tobacco growing. Members of the European Union put more money into promoting tobacco production *each day* (US$3.8 million) than the European Commission spends on tobacco control in a year. Tobacco is the most subsidised crop in the European Union. If the Union simply paid all tobacco farmers an amount equal to their net income, on condition that they do not grow any more tobacco, subsidy expenditures would be reduced by 44%.

Policies like these are in direct opposition to the policies of governments to control cigarette smoking. However, cigarettes also bring in a large tax revenue both at the point of sale and from the manufacturers. The economic issues linked to cigarette smoking are massive, complex and often incomprehensible.

Why smoke?

All the scientific and medical evidence shows that cigarette smoking is bad for health. Yet people still smoke in their millions, and young people in particular continue to take up the habit. Why?

The reason why smokers continue to smoke is quite simple. Nicotine is a strongly addictive drug with unpleasant withdrawal symptoms. Many of the people currently ill and dying of smoking-related diseases started smoking and became addicted before the health risks were widely known. But when people start smoking today, particularly in the developed world, they have plenty of information available to them. So why do young people start smoking? Research indicates that most young people start smoking for one of the following reasons:

- it is the social norm within their family or peer group
- advertising
- curiosity to 'see what it is like'
- peer group pressure.

Once the smoking habit is established, the reasons largely change and young people report that smoking gives them pleasure, helps them cope and that they smoke because they can't give up. Once addicted, it is not easy to stop smoking. In one study of a group of American 16–18-year-old smokers, 44% believed that in five years' time they would no longer be smokers. Five years later the researchers did a follow-up study, and almost 75% of the young people who had been sure that they were not long-term smokers were still smoking, and smoking more. In 1992 almost two-thirds of American adolescent smokers reported that they wanted to stop smoking, and 70% said that they would not start smoking if they could choose again.

Most smokers begin their habit as adolescents, so if young people can be persuaded to leave tobacco alone, the habit might die. However, converting the knowledge available to people about the health risks of smoking into sensible lifestyle choices is not an easy task.

Needing a cigarette

In the 1990s Hilary Graham carried out some research into the smoking habits of women of different social groups. She obtained clear evidence showing that in some circumstances people need to smoke not just because of physical addiction but also because smoking helps them to cope with their difficult and chaotic lives. When they sit down to have a cigarette they mark out a few minutes of time for themselves, when they cannot be disturbed by the demands of others. Mothers in the most difficult circumstances, such as women on very low incomes who are single mothers or who have a large number of young dependent children, or a child with specific learning or behavioural difficulties, were most likely to smoke – over 60% of these mothers smoke, compared with 28% of the general female population.

Many women were smoking in spite of awareness of the long-term damage to health. In these circumstances it is not health education but social change that is needed to reduce smoking.

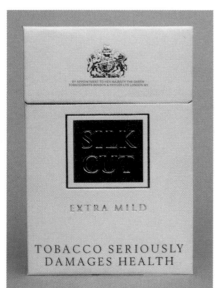

Figure 4.11 The tobbaco companies have worked hard to associate smoking with the glamour and excitment of sport. In the late1990s there was a move by the British Government to end the sponsorship of sporting events by tobacco companies, and this led to much controversy. However, as the cigarette packet shows, no one who can read can claim that they are unaware of the health risks associated with smoking and nicotine addiction.

LEGAL DRUGS: ALCOHOL

The effects of alcohol

Ethanol, C_2H_5OH, or 'alcohol' is a commonly used social drug in many parts of the world. It is poisonous, but the human body can detoxify relatively large amounts of it before permanent damage or death results. Alcohol is primarily a depressant drug along with a weaker but longer-lasting agitating or irritant effect on the central nervous system. Alcohol is physically addictive.

Following an alcoholic drink, the alcohol is absorbed into the bloodstream from all parts of the gastrointestinal tract, with most absorption taking place in the stomach and small intestine. The peak **blood alcohol level** (BAL) occurs 60–90 minutes after taking in alcohol on an empty stomach. The presence of food in the stomach slows the absorption of alcohol into the blood, although it does not reduce the total amount of alcohol that is absorbed. The standard way of describing the amount of alcohol in the blood is as **grams of alcohol per 100 cm³ of blood**, **g 100 cm⁻³** or **g %**. Once the alcohol is in the blood, it passes into nearly every tissue of the body, because cell membranes are permeable to alcohol and there is always a concentration gradient from blood to cells. Because alcohol passes easily into the brain, brain alcohol levels are very similar to blood alcohol levels.

The intoxicating effects of alcohol are caused by its direct action on the brain and nervous system. The sedative effect of the drug causes slowed thought processes and reflexes, and releases certain areas of the cortex of the brain from inhibition. With high doses of the drug, these sedative effects can lead to coma and death. However, the irritant effect of alcohol lasts up to six times longer than the sedative effect. This is partly why people feel jumpy, irritable and unsettled after a hard night's drinking. The 'hair of the dog' – in other words another drink – can help ease these symptoms because the new intake of alcohol has a more immediate and powerful sedative effect to override the irritant effect left over from the previous day. It is easy to see how this becomes a vicious circle, leading to repeated alcohol intake with virtually no return to the fully sober state.

Research suggests that alcohol affects the cell membranes of nerve cells and their axons and dendrites. Thus it affects the functioning of both the central and peripheral nervous systems, reducing their ability to transmit nerve impulses, which in turn leads to the typical behaviour following drinking.

If too much alcohol is absorbed by the body, the drinker may die of alcohol overdose. On average, 50% of drinkers whose blood alcohol level rises over 0.40 g % will die of acute alcohol poisoning. The drinker passes through phases of staggering and slurred speech, loss of emotional control, stupor, severe respiratory depression, coma and death. The later stages often occur after the drinker has passed out, and he or she will be found dead in bed in the morning. Excess drink can also cause death by triggering the vomiting centres. Vomiting may occur whilst the drinker is in a stupor or a coma, and unless someone sits with them to keep their airways free, they have a high risk of choking or drowning in their own vomit.

How much drink makes you drunk?

The amount of alcohol taken in is obviously one main factor that determines how drunk a person becomes, though it is not the only factor. Different alcoholic drinks contain different amounts of alcohol, as shown in table 4.2.

The concentration of alcohol in the blood following the intake of a certain amount of alcohol is affected by body mass, the volume of blood, how much food has been eaten before drinking and how long ago the alcohol was taken.

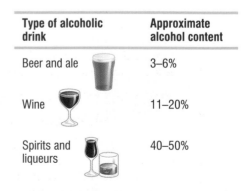

Type of alcoholic drink	Approximate alcohol content
Beer and ale	3–6%
Wine	11–20%
Spirits and liqueurs	40–50%

Table 4.2 The approximate alcohol content of different types of drinks

Even allowing for differences in body mass and blood volume, women have a slightly higher blood alcohol level than men for the equivalent intake of alcoholic drink, as shown in table 4.3. This is probably due to metabolism of alcohol in the stomach, which takes place mainly in men.

Units of alcohol	Beverage intake	Female (45 kg)	Male (45 kg)	Female (70 kg)	Male (70 kg)	Female (90 kg)	Male (90 kg)
1	1 measure spirits (100° proof) 1 glass wine ½ pint beer	0.045	0.037	0.03	0.025	0.022	0.019
2	2 measures spirits 2 glasses wine 1 pint beer	0.09	0.075	0.06	0.05	0.045	0.037
4	4 measures spirits 4 glasses wine 2 pints beer	0.18	0.15	0.12	0.10	0.09	0.07
6	6 measures spirits 6 glasses wine 3 pints beer	0.27	0.22	0.18	0.15	0.13	0.11
8	8 measures spirits 8 glasses wine 4 pints beer	0.36	0.30	0.24	0.20	0.18	0.15
10	10 measures spirits 10 glasses wine 5 pints beer	0.45	0.37	0.30	0.25	0.22	0.18

Table 4.3 The relationship between alcohol intake, body mass and blood alcohol levels (expressed in g %), measured one hour after alcohol intake on an empty stomach

Another factor in how drunk a person becomes is tolerance for alcohol. Heavy drinkers tend to have a higher tolerance to alcohol, which means they can experience higher blood alcohol levels before appearing intoxicated. Alcoholics may have twice the legal limit of alcohol in their blood and still give no appearance of intoxication. On the other hand, someone experiencing alcoholic drinks for the first few times will need very little of the drug to feel intoxicated.

Interestingly, the level of intoxication following drinking is also affected by other, much less readily quantifiable factors. The state of mind of the drinker at the time and the environment in which the alcohol is consumed both have a substantial effect. A drinker may be depressed, or ecstatically happy, or worried, or drinking to forget an unhappy experience, or feeling guilty because a partner disapproves of drinking, or in a cheery social group. Any of these circumstances will affect the brain and thus the brain chemistry differently. As a result the sensations of drunkenness, or lack of them, will vary. At a happy celebration or party we are likely to feel intoxicated more readily than at a funeral. Thus whilst the number of drinks taken in by any individual can easily be measured, as can the blood alcohol levels, predicting the intoxication that results is far more complex and less easy to quantify.

Effects of alcohol related to BAL

The effects of different alcohol levels in the blood vary greatly from individual to individual. Some people are much more sensitive to alcohol than others. Also continued use, as with any drug, tends to mean that higher blood alcohol levels are needed before the effects of the drug are felt. However, some generalised effects of different blood alcohol levels are given in table 4.4.

Blood alcohol level/g %	Physical symptoms
0.02–0.03	Slight euphoria and loss of shyness. Depressant effects not obvious.
0.04–0.06	Feeling of well-being, false sense of increased confidence, relaxation, lowering of inhibitions, sense of warmth and euphoria. Minor impairment of reasoning, memory, insight, concentration and discrimination skills, lowering of caution.
0.07–0.09	Slight impairment of balance, speech, vision, reaction time and hearing. Sense of euphoria. Judgement and self-control substantially reduced and caution, reason and memory impaired.
0.100–0.125	Significant impairment of motor coordination and loss of good judgement. Speech may become slurred; balance, reaction time and hearing significantly impaired. Still a sensation of euphoria. It is illegal to drive a car at this level.
0.13–0.15	Gross motor impairment and lack of physical control. Blurred vision and loss of vision. Euphoria is reduced and feelings of anxiety, restlessness and misery (dysphoria) begin to appear.
0.16–0.20	Dysphoria predominates the emotions; nausea may appear. Motor control poor; muscle reflexes slow so reaction time very slow even to startling events. Beyond this level symptoms of alcohol poisoning occur.
0.21–0.25	Need help to walk, total mental confusion. Dysphoria. Rate of breathing is depressed, lowering oxygen levels. Heart rate decreased, blood pressure may fall. The vomiting control centre of the brain may be activated, causing vomiting.
0.30–0.40	Loss of consciousness. Continued possibility of vomiting with raised risk of choking on vomit whilst unconscious.
0.40 and above	Onset of coma, possibility of death due to respiratory arrest as the respiratory centres of the brain stop functioning.

Table 4.4 The effects of increasing blood alcohol levels

Recent evidence suggests that some alcohol is metabolised in the stomach and never reaches the bloodstream. It appears that men metabolise alcohol in the stomach much more than women. Alcohol affects the performance of the stomach, relaxing both the cardiac and pyloric sphincters. This allows acid and digestive enzymes up into the lower oesophagus, causing the pain known as 'heartburn' or **reflux oesophagitis**. In regular drinkers this can lead to ulceration of the oesophagus. Alcohol also has a diuretic effect on the kidneys, causing an increase in fluid loss through urination. The effect comes about because alcohol suppresses the secretion of ADH (antidiuretic hormone). This is a hormone produced by the hypothalamus which causes more water to be retained in the body, and less water to be excreted in the urine, in response to there being too little water in the blood. As most alcoholic drinks also contain a considerable amount of water, frequent urination often follows a drinking bout.

Apart from any alcohol that is metabolised in the stomach, the alcohol is absorbed from the gut and passes to the liver via the hepatic portal vein. Although alcohol is a poison, a healthy liver can break down alcohol at the rate of about one drink per hour. The breakdown is brought about by the liver enzyme **alcohol dehydrogenase** in the hepatocytes (liver cells). The ethanol is first converted into ethanal, which is then oxidised to ethanoic acid. This can then be converted into acetylcoenzyme A and used in cellular respiration, or used to produce fat. Alcoholic drinks have a very high energy content, and it is through this process of breakdown that the energy is made available to the body.

Thus alcohol is a drug that has very marked and immediate effects on the body. On first usage it can be lethal if an overdose is taken, and this is a particular danger for young people. If a young person drinks sufficient to reach the earlier stages of intoxication, the lack of judgement and sense of bravado that result can lead him or her to drink much larger amounts of alcohol over a relatively short time. The high alcohol intake combined with a relatively small blood volume can lead to serious problems of alcohol overdose. The young person may collapse and be rushed to hospital, where the blood can be detoxified on a dialysis machine. If not found after collapsing, the young person may well die.

Medicinal brandy?

Figure 4.12 The traditional image of brandy as a life-saving medicine to treat shock and hypothermia is misguided – alcohol actually lowers the body temperature.

The medicinal use of alcohol has a long history. For many years it was the only available anaesthetic, and so before surgery such as amputations or tooth extractions were carried out, patients would be given plenty of alcohol to drink, to the point that they were only semi-conscious of what was happening to them. Alcohol was also used to clean both wounds and surgical instruments.

Alcohol has also historically been given to people after a shock, or after exposure to the elements. A common image of alcohol has been the St Bernard dog rushing to the aid of people trapped in avalanches with a barrel of brandy strapped to its collar. Unfortunately it is inappropriate to give alcohol in these circumstances. Alcohol has been regarded as 'warming', because after a few drinks we often do feel warm. This is due to the dilation of the peripheral blood vessels which makes us look pink and lose heat through our skin, in the same way as we do when we are genuinely hot. In spite of feeling warm, we are actually losing body heat as a result of vasodilation. Thus for a person in shock or suffering hypothermia, alcohol is not a good idea. It causes further stress to the system by diverting blood away from the body core and further lowering the body temperature.

The most recent proposals for the medicinal use of alcohol come in the battle to beat heart disease. Alcohol abuse, in the form of regular heavy drinking and alcoholism, has an adverse effect on the heart and circulatory system. It can lead to high blood pressure and an irregular heartbeat. High alcohol levels over ten years or more lead to an enlarged, weakened heart and heart failure, where the ventricles cannot pump the blood around the body and fluid accumulates in the tissues (see page 73). This condition is usually found only in old people, but it can occur in 30-year-olds who have been heavy drinkers since their teens. However, there is evidence that drinking moderate amounts of wine can give some protection against the onset of heart disease. In countries such as France where much of the population eats a relatively high-fat diet but also drinks a moderate and regular amount of wine, occurrences of heart disease and resulting deaths are lower than might be expected. Much research is currently in progress to see if it really is the alcohol that reduces the incidence of heart disease, and whether one type of alcoholic drink confers more protection than another.

Long-term alcohol abuse – alcoholism

Alcohol is a drug that has a immediate effect whenever it is used. Many people all over the world use the drug in social situations, drinking wine with meals, drinking at parties to release inhibitions a little and make it easier to talk and dance, drinking to celebrate the birth of a baby, or to mark reaching adulthood, marriage and death. There are equally many individuals, societies and religious groups which ban the use of alcohol, and they have enjoyable social lives and celebrate major life events quite successfully without it, so alcohol is certainly not necessary for society to function well. In fact, it can be argued that alcohol plays a substantial role in damaging the fabric of society.

Whilst many people drink merely socially, and would suffer no ill effects if they never drank again, many people are addicted to the drug. Some alcoholics need a constant level of alcohol in their system to keep them functioning 'normally' so they may drink first thing in the morning to restore their alcohol levels and continue to drink at intervals throughout the day. This type of alcoholic will be able to maintain a semblance of normal life for some time, in spite of a constant level of intoxication. The drinking is often kept a secret from friends, family and colleagues until their behaviour and health become increasingly affected and so much alcohol is taken that it becomes difficult to hide the evidence. These people are often in complete denial that they have a problem. In another type of alcoholism, the alcoholic does not drink constantly, but has compulsive binges, taking in large amounts of alcohol over a period of several days. This may be followed by a period of remorse about their behaviour and resolutions not to repeat the pattern, until the next craving hits and the drinking starts again. In both patterns of alcoholism the alcoholic risks severe damage to many body systems, but particularly the brain and the liver.

Alcohol has an immediate effect on the functioning of the brain, as already described. In contrast, continued excessive alcohol use over a period of years causes long-term damage to the brain. The evidence for this is clear from the post-mortem examinations of the brains of alcoholics compared with those of non-alcoholics. The brains of alcoholics contain fewer nerve cells, fewer synapses (connections between cells), less white and grey matter and larger ventricles. This damage correlates closely with loss of intellectual functions. The damage in some alcoholics is so extensive, with soft, pulpy and deteriorated brains, that almost all the normal brain structures have been lost. The cause of the brain damage seems to be the toxic action of the alcohol on the nerve cells, along with an indirect effect brought about by liver damage.

People who drink very large amounts of alcohol, or who drink heavily for a long time, substantially increase their risk of potentially fatal liver diseases such as **cirrhosis** of the liver and cancer of the liver. The liver tissue is damaged by excess alcohol. In cirrhosis of the liver, hepatocytes (liver cells) are killed and replaced with fibrous scar tissue which cannot carry out the normal metabolic functions of the liver. The damaged liver cannot detoxify many of the poisons taken in as a normal part of the diet, and so toxic compounds such as ammonia are released into the bloodstream. These compounds then cause damage to the nerve cells of the brain and the peripheral nervous system. A cirrhotic liver is smaller than normal with hardened, bumpy areas of scarring and dead tissue. The liver tissue is irreversibly damaged and when liver function drops below a critical level, the patient with cirrhosis of the liver will die. Sadly death is often brought about by continued drinking of alcohol, as the addiction to alcohol is stronger than the fear of death from a diseased liver.

Cancers of the mouth and throat are more common than usual in heavy drinkers. The brain and peripheral nervous system are also extremely sensitive to the levels of minerals and vitamins such as magnesium, potassium,

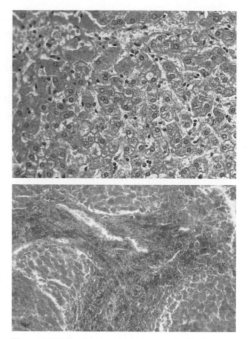

Figure 4.13 The damage alcohol causes to the liver can be seen very clearly here in the contrast between a healthy liver (top) and one taken from an individual who died of alcoholism.

phosphorus and thiamine. Alcoholics often do not eat properly as the energy-rich alcoholic drinks suppress their appetite. In addition, alcohol affects the digestive tract, causing inflammation and irritation of the stomach and small intestine. This reduces the ability of the small intestine to absorb minerals and vitamins, and when these nutrient levels fall the nervous tissue slowly deteriorates. Symptoms of peripheral nervous tissue damage include numbness in parts of the fingers, toes and buttocks.

Many alcoholics show few symptoms in the early stages of their addiction. Then gradually there will be conflict and even violence at home, they have difficulty in concentrating and holding down a job and they may stockpile drinks. Alcoholics may suffer blackouts after binge drinking, leaving them with periods of time of which they have no memory, yet during which time they were awake and taking part in society in some way. It is very difficult for a physically dependent alcoholic to give up drinking. The physical symptoms of withdrawal are traumatic and, for severe alcoholics, may even be life threatening if not carefully supervised by medical staff. After withdrawal from the drug an alcoholic will remain an alcoholic for life, just one drink away from a return to the cycle of abuse. Alcoholics who are not abusing the drug need counselling and support to remain alcohol-free and get on with the rest of their lives.

Alcohol withdrawal symptoms

When a physically dependent alcoholic stops drinking, the withdrawal symptoms range from mild to life threatening. Withdrawal symptoms from alcohol addiction are often far more severe and dangerous than those experienced on withdrawal from many other drugs. Symptoms begin within the first 24 alcohol-free hours, reach a peak of intensity after two or three days and disappear within one or two weeks. As alcohol levels begin to drop the symptoms include:

- shakiness
- restlessness and unease
- nausea
- anxiety
- increased heart rate (tachycardia)
- raised blood pressure.

At this point the craving for alcohol will become strong. Within 24 hours of stopping drinking, the second stage of withdrawal symptoms begin:

- hyperventilation (rapid breathing)
- drop in blood pressure
- fever
- delirium, involving disorientation, delusions (irrational beliefs) and hallucinations which are usually visual but may involve the senses of hearing or smell; these hallucinations are usually unpleasant and often frightening
- convulsions and seizures.

Without treatment the delirium, fever and convulsions may continue for several days, getting increasingly severe and causing disturbances of the cardiovascular system. This is the condition often referred to as 'DTs' (delirium tremens). Without medical intervention, a patient with DTs can harm other people or themselves, or die from a heart attack or stroke. The withdrawal symptoms can be controlled with other drugs under medical supervision until the risk of developing DTs has passed.

Fetal alcohol syndrome

If a pregnant woman drinks, the alcohol in her blood crosses the placenta readily and passes into the blood of her developing fetus. The fetal liver does not function properly until after birth, as detoxification of the fetal blood is largely carried out by maternal systems by exchange across the placenta. As a result, the fetus cannot get rid of the alcohol effectively, and levels in its blood may be twice those in the maternal blood. If a pregnant women drinks enough to make her feel pleasantly relaxed, her fetus may be comatose. The babies born to women who have drunk regularly throughout their pregnancies, and particularly those who drink heavily on a regular basis, are at risk of developing **fetal alcohol syndrome** (FAS). FAS babies are born prematurely with a low birth mass and are slow to mature. They have facial abnormalities which include small eye openings, short upturned noses and thin upper lips. If the main exposure to alcohol comes in the first six months of pregnancy then the victims may suffer deformities of the major organ systems, particularly heart defects. If alcohol exposure continues or begins in the last three months of pregnancy, brain malformation is a greater risk. All FAS babies have smaller heads and brains than non-affected babies. As a result they often suffer dental, visual and auditory problems as they grow up. Many suffer from curvature of the spine, fits and have poor motor coordination. They tend to have low IQs, poor attention spans and can often be hyperactive. They find socially acceptable behaviour difficult. A study published in the *Lancet* in 1993 suggested that whilst some of the physical problems associated with FAS disappear or diminish with time, so that FAS adults cannot be recognised readily in the same way as an FAS baby, the intellectual and psychological impairment continues.

It is estimated that between 50 000 and 70 000 American babies are born each year affected by FAS, and the level is highest in communities where chronic alcohol abuse is common, like many of the American Indian tribes. In many countries, as it has become more acceptable for women to drink, the level of alcohol-damaged fetuses has grown. The advice of the medical profession is that, whilst the very occasional drink during pregnancy is unlikely to harm the developing fetus, the best policy is for pregnant women to avoid alcohol altogether until after the birth, and to keep the intake down to a minimum until breast feeding is completed.

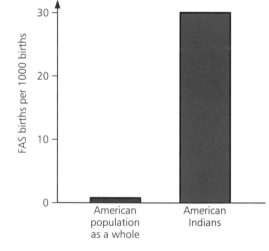

Figure 4.14 The facial abnormalities that indicate FAS are common in American Indian babies, where alcohol abuse is a problem. This Irish mother stopped drinking as soon as she knew she was pregnant, but it was too late.

Alcohol and society

Although smoking is a habit of many individuals, nicotine addiction affects the whole of society through the hundreds of thousands of smokers who are incapacitated or killed by their habit, and through the effect of smoke on the health of children and non-smoking adults over a long period of time.

Alcohol also has extremely damaging effects for society, both in the short term and in the long term. In the long term society pays for the treatment of alcoholics who are withdrawing from the drug, and to treat the various diseases caused by heavy drinking. The state has to support those people whose addiction to alcohol prevents them working, along with their families. However, alcohol also affects people's behaviour, and this plays a large part in some immediate problems in society.

Drinking and driving

Drinking and driving is one such problem. The legal limit for driving a car in Britain is a blood alcohol level of less than 0.08 g % (80 mg per 100 cm^3 of blood), although there are moves to reduce this level. This limit will be reached after a couple of pints of beer or several glasses of wine with a meal for an average-sized man, and less for an average-sized woman. Around 800 people die each year in Britain in road traffic accidents involving drivers or motorcycle riders who are over the legal limit for driving. Almost 20% of all drivers and riders killed in traffic accidents are over the legal limit, and of accidents that happen between 10 p.m. and 4 a.m., 50% of the drivers killed are over the limit. Canadian data from 1989 showed that 38.9% of all drivers killed on Canadian roads had been drinking prior to their deaths. Moreover, it is not only the drunken drivers themselves who are affected – these figures do not show the large numbers of sober drivers, passengers and pedestrians who are killed or injured by drunken drivers. Society has to bear the cost of medical bills and state support for disabled individuals and for families left without a parent.

A single drink will impair your driving ability (see tables 4.3 and 4.4, pages 97 and 98). Twice the legal level of alcohol in the blood makes people at least 30 times more likely to have an accident than if they had not had a drink. Alcohol impairs the ability to control and coordinate movements, making reactions much slower in unexpected situations, and impairs the ability to judge speeds and distances. Perhaps the most dangerous effect of the drug is that it also affects people's judgement of their own driving ability, so that when under the influence of alcohol they believe themselves to be driving far better than they actually are.

Young and inexperienced drivers and people who drink only infrequently are seriously affected at blood alcohol levels below the legal limit. One Canadian study showed that older, experienced drivers with a blood alcohol level of 150 mg per 100 cm^3 of blood were about 100 times more likely to be involved in a fatal accident than if they had no alcohol in their blood. But if a 16–19-year-old (you can drive in Canada at 16) has the same blood alcohol level, the chance of being involved in a fatal accident is 400 times greater than without alcohol.

In most countries in the developed world there are legal sanctions against driving with a blood alcohol level over a set limit. In Britain the police can stop any drivers whom they suspect have been drinking and ask them to take a breathalyser test. This involves breathing into a device that analyses the alcohol content of the breath and shows whether the level corresponds to a blood alcohol level above or below the legal limit. A failed breath test means disqualification from driving for a year and a heavy fine, with the option of imprisonment. Causing death by drunken driving can carry up to five years in prison and an unlimited fine, although there are many groups in Britain who feel this sentence is not imposed frequently enough. If everyone stopped drinking and driving, the financial and personal savings to society would be enormous. However, because of the entrenched position of alcohol as a legal social drug, a total ban on drinking and driving looks to be a long way in the future, and society will continue to pay the price.

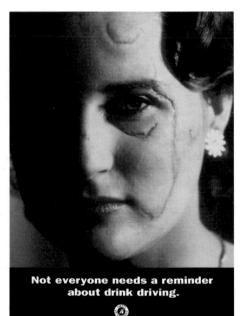

Not everyone needs a reminder about drink driving.

ENJOY A DRINK. LEAVE THE CAR AT HOME.

Figure 4.15 The police in Britain run regular campaigns to raise public awareness of the dangers of drinking and driving. There is usually at least one new initiative each year, often launched in the build-up to Christmas when there is an increased likelihood of people drinking at parties and then driving home.

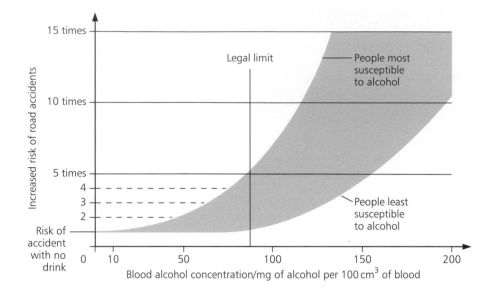

Figure 4.16 Drinking alcohol and then driving a car increases the risk of a road accident, and the more you drink, the more likely is an accident. Many people would argue that driving a car, a potentially lethal piece of machinery, after drinking alcohol is a deliberate act of negligence, and any damage caused to others is no 'accident'.

Drinking and crime

Drinking is also closely linked to crime, particularly in young people. Vandalism, mugging and other 'casual crimes' are high in this age group, and are often linked to drinking. The alcohol lowers inhibitions and perceptions of right and wrong, and also induces a sense of bravado. Alcohol abuse is very closely linked with violence – street and bar fights, football violence and gang warfare are often fuelled by a large intake of alcohol releasing inhibitions and decreasing sensitivity to the feelings of others.

One of the saddest problems caused by drinking is the effect it can have on personal relationships and family life. The violence linked with drinking is most obvious in drunken football hooligans or gangs of youths brawling in the streets. But far more violence resulting from alcohol abuse takes place in the privacy of people's homes. The majority of men who use physical violence against their wives or partners do so after drinking. There is also often an element of alcohol abuse involved in physical or sexual violence against children.

Social problem	% linked to alcohol use/misuse
Suicide attempts	65
Child abuse	20–40
Domestic violence	40
Separation and divorce	39% of men in this situation drink more than the recommended levels
Sexual offences	30
Burglary	33
Street crime	55
Pub and club crime	85
Murders/stabbings	65/75
Employers who feel alcohol misuse is a problem in their organisation	70
Accidents at work	25

Table 4.5 Alcohol abuse plays a major role in many social problems.

Drinking and relationships

Even when there is no violence or sexual abuse involved, alcohol plays a part in the breakdown of many relationships and marriages. People who drink a lot are likely to have unpredictable moods, depending on when they last had a drink and how much alcohol they took in. This makes stable relationships very difficult to sustain. Alcohol also has an effect on sexual performance, so males who drink heavily will often be impotent, and this too can affect a relationship. A drink problem may lead someone to lose their job, adding poverty to the list of problems their family has to cope with. Although alcohol abuse is sometimes linked with poverty – for example, there are very high drinking levels in the poor areas of Scotland – in fact it knows no social boundaries and causes problems for the richest to the poorest families.

Alcohol and societies

When alcohol is suddenly introduced into a society for the first time, the effects can be devastating, causing loss of a social structure that may have been in place for centuries. This has happened in the Australian aboriginals and the Native Americans as well as numerous tribes in Africa. Groups with no previous exposure to the drug have low levels of alcohol dehydrogenase in their livers, so alcohol has a very strong effect and is very addictive. All the damaging effects of alcohol seen in our society are re-enacted even more powerfully in these societies, particularly if they depend on a strong work ethic and close-knit family groups. Under the influence of alcohol, the men may no longer want to work, the women may produce a high percentage of babies damaged by fetal alcohol syndrome and family life will disintegrate into violence and unpredictable behaviour, putting the future of the whole society at risk.

ILLEGAL DRUGS

All the drugs we have discussed so far are legally used in the UK, America and many countries across the world, in spite of the great problems associated with some of them for both individuals and societies. However, there are other intoxicating substances which are **illegal** – their use is banned by law. This does not always prevent them being sold and used. It should be mentioned that, although the problems associated with the abuse of illegal drugs should in no way be dismissed, the number of people who use most of them is very small compared with the numbers using nicotine and alcohol. The number of deaths from illegal drugs also pales into insignificance beside those connected with nicotine or alcohol abuse.

Fashions in illegal drugs tend to come and go. Some, like marijuana, have relatively mild effects. This drug was particularly popular in Britain from the 1960s onwards. It is smoked in a small hand-rolled cigarette known as a spliff, and there are occasional discussions about making it legal for individual use in private. In some countries it is used much more openly and without censure.

Figure 4.17 There are European countries where it is legal to use marijuana in public in certain accepted places.

Ecstasy

Ecstasy (E) was the fashionable drug in the 1990s. Its chemical name is 3,4-methylenedioxymethamphetamine (MDMA) and it is a synthetic drug which has both hallucinogenic and stimulant properties. Its use boomed with the spread of large music and dance parties known as 'raves'. Because alcohol is a depressant, and because increasing levels of intoxication cause poor coordination and reduce the ability to dance well, drinking at raves is not common. However, ecstasy produces feelings of well-being and general warmth towards other human beings. It also gives increased energy and stamina, allowing users to dance for longer and with more enthusiasm without becoming exhausted. Ecstasy brings about its effects by increasing the heart rate and blood pressure, and it can cause nausea, blurred vision, faintness, chills and sweating. One of the main problems which has caused most of the deaths associated with the drug is its effect on water metabolism. Ecstasy increases sweating, but it diminishes the sensitivity of the body to a lack of water. Eventually sweating stops due to lack of water, and the body begins to overheat. In spite of this the ecstasy user is unaware of the need to drink as there is no feeling of thirst. Collapse and death can result from dehydration and overheating. The converse of this is the tragic situation which has overtaken one or two British users, the best known of whom is Leah Betts. Leah was celebrating her eighteenth birthday with friends and during the party took an ecstasy tablet. Her parents were involved in drug education, so Leah knew only too well the dangers of overheating and dehydration linked with ecstasy use. In attempting to prevent these problems, she drank so much water that she went into a coma and died from excess water in her body. Ecstasy was only indirectly to blame, but without the drug Leah would still be alive.

Ecstasy use can lead to psychological problems such as confusion, depression, sleep problems, craving, severe anxiety, paranoia and psychosis (loss of touch with reality). Research published in 1996 suggests that its use can cause degeneration of some of the nerve branches and nerve endings in the brain, and that it can also stimulate the abnormal regrowth of some of these cells, so that they fail to reconnect properly and may connect to a different area. This can lead to permanent changes in mental skills, emotions, learning and memory. Ecstasy is considered by many users to be a safe recreational drug involving no smoking, no injections and simply producing loving feelings and energy. The number of deaths each year from ecstasy is undeniably small, but it looks as if it may cause more long-term damage than anyone might have predicted.

Figure 4.18 Daniel North is one of the young victims of ecstasy use – and the youngsters who die may be just the tip of the iceberg if, as it is suspected, the drug causes long-term damage to the nervous system.

Heroin

Heroin is a member of a family of drugs known as the **opioids**. These include natural **opiates**, which are drugs extracted from the opium poppy, and opiate-related synthetic drugs. The opiates are found in a gummy substance extracted from the seed pods of the Asian poppy, *Papaver somniferum*. The drug opium is produced directly from this gum, and the substances codeine and morphine can be separated out from opium. Heroin is produced synthetically from morphine or codeine. The use of opiates, both medically and as recreational drugs, has a long history, particularly in China. Since the sixteenth century a solution of opium in alcohol known as **laudanum** has been taken as a remedy for 'nerves' or to stop severe coughing or diarrhoea. By the early nineteenth century, morphine had been extracted in a pure enough form to be soluble in water. After the hypodermic syringe was invented in the middle of the nineteenth century, injection of morphine for pain relief became common. Unfortunately, people rapidly became addicted to morphine, and so in 1898 heroin (diacetylmorphine or diamorphine) was introduced. It was thought to be a new wonder drug that would give powerful pain relief without causing addiction. The sad reality was that although heroin is indeed a more powerful painkiller than morphine, it is also much more likely to produce drug dependence. The drug introduced to provide addiction-free pain relief now has a long and bitter history of abuse, addiction and damage both to individuals and to society.

Opium, the original drug derived from the Asian poppy, is usually found as dark brown chunks or as a powder, and it is generally eaten or smoked. Heroin is usually a white or brownish powder which is dissolved in water and injected either under the skin or directly into a muscle or vein. However, the drug can also be 'snorted' into the nose, smoked, eaten or inserted as a suppository into the rectum.

Heroin molecules interact with receptors in the brain which are sensitive to **endorphins**. These are naturally occurring transmitters in the brain which have a molecular structure very similar to the opiates. The endorphins are associated with sensations of pleasure, being released during exercise and sexual intercourse to give a feeling of well-being. They are also part of the body's own pain relief system, produced in large quantities when it is necessary to continue in spite of pain. All of the opiate drugs, including heroin, attach to the endorphin receptor sites in the brain, flooding them and thus releasing very strong feelings of pleasure. This is also how they work as painkillers.

The short-term effects of heroin appear soon after a single dose is taken, and may take several hours or even days to wear off. The drug initially stimulates the higher centres of the brain, after which it depresses the activity of the central nervous system. This means that immediately after heroin is injected into a vein the user feels a strong surge of pleasure, known as a 'rush'. As the central nervous system is depressed, this gives way to a state of calm gratification. Most users do not experience hunger, pain or sexual feelings while under the influence of the drug. Relatively low doses of heroin may cause restlessness, nausea and even vomiting. Higher doses leave the body feeling warm, the extremities heavy and the mouth dry, after which the user passes in and out of consciousness, sometimes awake, sometimes in a drowsy sleep. This state is called 'on the nod' and at this time heroin users are usually relatively unaware of the world around them. With increasing doses, the breathing becomes gradually slower, until with very large doses the user cannot be roused. The pupils become contracted to pinpoints and no longer respond to light, the skin becomes moist, bluish and cold and respiration is severely depressed – indeed it may stop altogether, resulting in death.

Heroin overdose is of particular risk to people who buy heroin from dealers on the street. This heroin is not the pure drug, but an unreliable mixture that may include chalk, sugar, quinine and other cheaper drugs. Relatively pure heroin is one of the most dangerous compositions, because people overdose accidentally. Whenever a batch of particularly pure heroin goes into circulation, drug users are found dead in toilets, in their bedsits and on the streets, where they have injected their usual dose and found – too late – that the drug concentration is far higher than usual, high enough to stop them breathing.

The long-term effects of heroin appear after repeated use over a long period. Many of the risks are side-effects of the lifestyle resulting from heroin abuse rather than from the drug itself. An addict in need of a fix may not bother to sterilise the needle, or to prepare the skin first. For example, an infection of the heart lining and valves called **endocarditis** can result from infections due to unsterile injection techniques. Intravenous drug users who share needles run a high risk of getting HIV and AIDS (see pages 3–5). Unsterile injection techniques also increase the risk of abscesses, cellulitis (inflammation of the connective tissue), liver diseases such as hepatitis and even brain damage. Because heroin addicts tend to spend most of their money on the drug, and also because heroin suppresses the appetite, users tend to have very unhealthy lifestyles with poor nutrition. This leaves them vulnerable to lung diseases such as pneumonia.

With regular use, tolerance develops to the effects of heroin and so users take higher doses to achieve the same intensity of effect. They become both physically and psychologically addicted to the drug. Withdrawal symptoms include uneasiness, yawning, tears, diarrhoea, goose pimples, runny nose, shivering, abdominal cramps and a craving for the drug. These symptoms peak between 48 and 72 hours after the last dose of the drug, although it can take up to six months for the body to return fully to normal. Although withdrawal from heroin is unpleasant, it is less life-threatening than withdrawal from alcohol.

Figure 4.19 Persuading heroin addicts to use a needle exchange, where they are provided with new clean syringes when they return used ones, or to use prescribed methadone so the strength of the drug is always known, can help maintain the health of addicts who cannot cope without the drug.

Heroin is an illegal drug in most areas of the world, and the penalties for trafficking in the drug or supplying it are severe – in some countries the punishment is death. Heroin is often seen as the most dangerous and frightening drug, and many people fear that the use of any illegal drug leads automatically to intravenous injection of heroin. The facts are in some ways reassuring, in other ways far more worrying. Death from heroin addiction is still relatively rare in Britain, compared with deaths from other drugs such as nicotine and alcohol, which should perhaps give rise to more concern than is currently the case.

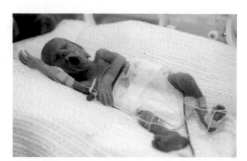

Figure 4.20 Women who take heroin during pregnancy have a greatly increased risk of spontaneous abortions, premature births and stillbirths. Babies born to heroin-dependent mothers are smaller than average and are usually addicted to the drug themselves, suffering withdrawal symptoms during their first few weeks of life.

Heroin in Lanarkshire

The city of Glasgow in Lanarkshire, Scotland, has had a somewhat difficult history. It was once a major industrial centre, but in the past century many factories have disappeared. There has been grinding poverty in the area and for many years people turned to alcohol as the most available drug to help them cope with the hardships of life. There is still a higher proportion of alcoholics in the Lanarkshire population than the average for Britain as a whole, but what has been particularly noticeable over the last 20 years has been the way young people with no apparent future have turned to heroin.

- In 1995 there were 6559 new drug addicts visiting a drug agency in Lanarkshire.
- There are three Scottish male drug addicts for every one female.
- Eighty per cent of the new addicts were under the age of 29.
- Sixteen per cent were under 20.
- Eighty-seven per cent were unemployed.
- Heroin was the main drug abused, often combined with temazepam, a sedative.
- In 1995 police arrested 169 children (aged 10–15) for drug possession, 31 of whom were thought to be dealing.
- Over the course of 1995, 97 people in the area died of drug overdoses or complications of drug use.

If this is happening in one small depressed area of Scotland, then perhaps society as a whole should be looking more seriously at what drives young people to drug addiction, and how they might best be helped.

SUMMARY

- A **drug** is a substance that alters the functioning of the mind, the body or both. Many drugs are used for the treatment of disease. Some drugs are used for pleasure because people enjoy the effect of the drug on the mind. These are called recreational drugs.

- Recreational drugs may be **sedatives** (which slow down the responses of the brain), **stimulants** (which speed up the activity of the brain), **hallucinogens** (which distort the user's view of reality) or **painkillers** (which are used because of the sensation of well-being and power they give).

- Many recreational drugs are **addictive** – the user is unable to function without continued doses of the drug. **Psychological** addiction produces cravings for the drug, and **physical** addiction means the body cannot function properly without the drug. Many drugs are both psychologically and physically addictive. When users stop taking an addictive drug, they suffer **withdrawal symptoms**.

- **Caffeine** is a mild stimulant found in tea and coffee. It is a legal drug which stimulates the brain and increases the heart rate and blood pressure. It may be addictive if taken in large amounts.

- **Nicotine** is the drug in cigarette smoke. It is a legal drug which has a mild stimulant effect on the brain and causes constriction of the peripheral blood vessels and an increase in heart rate. Nicotine is physically and psychologically addictive. Cigarette smoke also contains **carbon monoxide**, which binds to haemoglobin and prevents it carrying oxygen, and **tar**, which accumulates in the lungs and prevents gaseous exchange in the alveoli. Cigarette smoke stops the cilia on the ciliated epithelial cells beating and moving mucus up the airways, and causes lung cancer as a result of the carcinogens it contains.

- **Alcohol** (ethanol, C_2H_5OH) is a depressant drug which also has an irritant effect on the central nervous system. It is absorbed from the gut into the blood, and passes into the rest of the body, including the brain. The **blood alcohol level** (BAL) is the concentration of alcohol in the blood.

- The BAL following drinking depends on the amount of alcohol taken, the body mass, the blood volume, how much food was eaten previously, whether the drinker is male or female (males metabolise alcohol in the stomach to a greater extent than females) and the drinker's tolerance for alcohol. The level of intoxification can also be affected by the surroundings and social circumstances.

- Alcohol relaxes the sphincters of the stomach, and can cause **reflux oesophagitis**. It has a diuretic effect on the kidneys. The alcohol absorbed from the gut passes to the liver, where the enzyme **alcohol dehydrogenase** breaks it down.

- Too much alcohol can cause death from alcohol overdose in a young inexperienced drinker. Taken over a period of time, alcohol is addictive. Continued alcohol abuse leads to brain damage and diseases of the liver such as cirrhosis or cancer of the liver. The withdrawal symptoms from alcohol addiction are severe. There are also social problems linked with drinking alcohol, such as increased numbers of road accidents, domestic violence and child abuse and the break-up of relationships. When alcohol is introduced into a society for the first time, it may lead to the breakdown of that society.

- **Ecstasy** (MDMA) is an illegal drug which is hallucinogenic and a stimulant. It produces feelings of wellbeing and warmth to others as well as increased energy and stamina. Ecstasy increases the heart rate and blood pressure and can cause nausea, blurred vision, faintness, chills and sweating. It can cause dehydration as it stops the body recognising its need for water. Collapse and death from overheating can result. Ecstasy can also cause psychological problems.

- **Heroin** is another illegal drug, produced synthetically from morphine, which is extracted from the opium poppy. **Opioids** (drugs based on opium) can be used as painkillers, but are psychologically and physically addictive. Heroin interacts with endorphin receptors in the brain to produce sensations of pleasure. Following injection, heroin stimulates the higher centres of the brain, but then depresses the central nervous system. Accidental heroin overdose can cause death by depressing the respiratory system. Long-term heroin abuse can lead to injecting with unsterilised needles, HIV and other infections, abscesses, hepatitis and brain damage.

QUESTIONS

1 a What are the main types of drugs used in our society? List examples of each type.
  b Of the drugs you have listed, which are legal and which are illegal?

2 Choose either alcohol or tobacco and explain:
  a the effect of the drug on the physiology of the body
  b the health risks associated with the drug
  c the social problems caused by the drug and the reasons why it remains legal.

3 a Summarise the main types of illegal drugs used in this country. For each type explain the effect it has on the user both psychologically and physically.
  b Most people are aware of the potential health risks of smoking, drinking or using illegal drugs, yet young people in particular continue to start taking these potentially lethal substances. What strategies do you feel would be effective in either helping to prevent people starting to use these substances, or to enable them give them up?

5

Reproductive health and genetic diseases

Humans appear to be the only mammals in which copulation is not necessarily linked with reproduction. The human sexual drive or **libido** is not seasonal. Whilst tiredness, ill health and many other factors may influence the frequency of copulation between a couple, in theory intercourse may occur at any time throughout the year. People may have sex because it is a satisfying and rewarding part of their relationship, they may have sex because they want to conceive a baby, or both. Many human beings have **monogamous** sexual relationships – that is, they have a stable partnership and only have sexual intercourse with their partner. Others are more promiscuous, having sex with a wide variety of partners. Even those who are monogamous within a relationship may have several different relationships or marriages during their life, and so have sex with several different people. The choice of monogamous or polygamous sexual relations depends both on the society and the individuals concerned.

Because of the complex nature of human reproductive behaviour, there are several aspects to reproductive health. The **sexually transmitted diseases** (STDs) are passed from one person to another through sexual intercourse, and these affect not only the sex life but also the overall body health. Then there are **fertility problems**, aspects of reproductive health which only become apparent when a couple want to have a child. Some of these problems may be the result of sexually transmitted diseases past or present, but often fertility problems have nothing to do with STDs. Finally, once conception has been achieved, there may be problems for the offspring in the form of **genetic diseases**. All these strands of reproductive health raise social and moral issues which need careful consideration.

Figure 5.1 Human beings have many different ways of marking commitment to each other. In this wedding ceremony of the Unification Church, 35 000 couples were married worldwide at once.

SEXUALLY TRANSMITTED DISEASES

Sexually transmitted diseases have been part of the human experience for many hundreds if not thousands of years. It is widely believed that some of the diseases described in the Old Testament of the Bible are the sexually transmitted diseases known today as syphilis and gonorrhoea. Sexually transmitted diseases are passed from one individual to another through acts of sexual intimacy, and so the infections generally begin in the penis, vagina, cervix or uterus, or the anus, rectum, mouth or throat. The microorganisms that cause sexually transmitted diseases cannot survive outside the body, so infection from toilet seats, door handles or towels is highly unlikely.

Anyone who is sexually active can be infected by a sexually transmitted disease. Even someone who only has one sexual partner can be infected if that partner is already infected, or becomes infected from elsewhere. Thus a sexually transmitted disease does not mean the sufferer is promiscuous, although having lots of different sexual partners obviously increases the likelihood of contracting one.

Syphilis and gonorrhoea are both very unpleasant if left untreated, and until the development of antibiotics the treatments were often almost as bad as the diseases. However, both diseases can now be cured, although the gonorrhoea bacteria have become resistant to a large number of antibiotics. Because many sexually transmitted diseases are very infectious, it is most important that all the sexual partners of an infected individual are treated at the same time. Tracing and treating these partners is an important if difficult part of the therapy.

The main sexually transmitted diseases include:

- syphilis
- gonorrhoea
- chlamydia, also called non-specific urethritis (NSUs)
- candida albicans (thrush)
- genital herpes
- human papilloma virus which causes genital warts and has been linked to cervical cancer
- AIDS, caused by the human immunodeficiency virus (HIV), the most recently recognised and high profile sexually transmitted disease at the end of the twentieth century. AIDS is discussed in more detail on pages 3–5.

Prevention of most sexually transmitted diseases is not easy. Knowledge of a partner's health status before having sex with them, having very few sexual partners and remaining faithful within relationships all help. Although most sexually transmitted diseases can now be treated effectively and relatively easily, if they are left untreated most can lead to infertility through damage to the Fallopian tubes, the vas deferens and the epididymis, and also to serious health problems. Using barrier methods of contraception – condoms or female condoms in particular – offers some protection against the spread of many sexually transmitted diseases. However, human nature and sexual urges mean that in many cases these precautions are not taken. Sexually transmitted diseases and their dark legacies of health and fertility problems will doubtless be with us for many generations yet.

CONTRACEPTION

Methods of contraception

Many people do not wish to risk pregnancy whenever they have sex, and for centuries various methods of **contraception** (ways of preventing conception) have been used. These have included vinegar-soaked sponges placed in the vagina before intercourse, mixtures of camel dung and various herbs similarly placed, and reusable condoms made from animal intestines.

At the present time methods of contraception fall into four main categories. **Natural methods** are based on an understanding of the menstrual cycle and accurate predictions of the time of ovulation. Their major advantage is that they are accepted even by religious groups which condemn other methods of controlling family size. They can be considered as birth control rather than contraception, because they use the natural cycles of the body to space out the children born. The idea is simply to avoid sexual intercourse at the fertile time to ensure that the ovum and the sperm do not meet. On the other hand, contraception prevents the conception or implantation of the embryo whilst sexual activity continues whenever the couple desire it.

Physical or **barrier methods** of contraception involve physical barriers which prevent the meeting of the ovum and sperm. **Chemical methods** involve chemicals which either kill sperm or prevent ovulation. **Sterilisation** is the ultimate form of contraception. Conception is rendered almost impossible by cutting or tying the tubes along which the ovum or sperm travel. This has the additional benefit of removing the human element of contraception – remembering to use it properly – which is the major cause of failure in the other methods. These methods of contraception are summarised in table 5.1.

In fact contraception is largely used by people in the developed world. In the developing world, a combination of factors which include a desire to have a large family for fear of children dying and therefore lack of support in old age, lack of medical supervision, expense and religious condemnation mean that contraception does not as yet play a major role.

Method of contraception	How it works	Advantages/disadvantages
Rhythm (natural) **method**	Depends on monitoring the menstrual cycle and pinpointing ovulation by the rise in temperature associated with it or by changes in mucus. Intercourse is then avoided for several days before and after the expected date of ovulation to prevent ovum and sperm meeting.	*Advantages:* No side-effects and permitted by, for example, the Catholic church. Carried out carefully and using precise recording techniques it can be very effective. *Disadvantages:* Depends on full co-operation of both partners. Not always easy to pinpoint time of ovulation so pregnancy can result.
Condom (barrier method)	A thin latex sheath is placed over the penis during intercourse to collect the semen and so prevent ovum and sperm meeting.	*Advantages:* No side-effects, no medical advice needed, offers some protection against sexually transmitted diseases such as syphilis and AIDS. *Disadvantages:* Can interrupt intercourse. Sheath may tear or get damaged during intercourse allowing semen to get through. Gives better protection when combined with spermicide.
Diaphragm or **cap** (barrier method)	A thin rubber diaphragm is inserted into the vagina before intercourse to cover the cervix and prevent the entry of sperm.	*Advantages:* No side-effects, offers some protection against cervical cancer. *Disadvantages:* Must be fitted by a doctor initially. May be incorrectly positioned or damaged and allow sperm past. Gives better protection when combined with spermicide.
Female condom (barrier method)	Fitted inside vagina to cover the cervix and vagina and anchored externally.	*Advantages:* No side-effects, no medical advice needed, offers some protection against sexually transmitted diseases. *Disadvantages:* May be damaged and allow sperm through. Gives better protection when combined with spermicide.
Intrauterine device (IUD)	This does not prevent conception – the ovum and the sperm may meet – but it interferes with and prevents implantation. An IUD is a device made of plastic and a metal, frequently copper, which is inserted into the uterus by a doctor and remains there all the time.	*Advantages:* Once inserted, no further steps need to be taken. Relatively effective at preventing implantation. *Disadvantages:* Can cause pain and heavy periods. Can cause uterine infections which may lead to infertility. If pregnancy does occur it has a high chance of being in the Fallopian tubes (ectopic pregnancy).
Spermicides (chemical method)	Chemicals which kill sperm when they come into contact with them. Often used as creams, foams, gels or pessaries with barrier methods of contraception such as condoms or the diaphragm.	*Advantages:* Readily available. *Disadvantages:* Used alone they are relatively ineffective at preventing pregnancy.
Contraceptive pill (chemical method)	'The pill' consists of synthetic chemicals which mimic the effects of the sex hormones. The combined pill combines both oestrogens and progestogens, and this prevents pregnancy by inhibiting ovulation as well as altering the environment of the vagina and the consistency of the mucus. The progesterone-only pill does not inhibit ovulation and needs to be taken at very precise time intervals to be effective.	*Advantages:* The combined pill in particular is very effective at preventing pregnancy. The pill is taken at regular daily intervals and so does not interfere with intercourse. It may offer some protection against certain tumours. *Disadvantages:* The pill may increase the risk of certain tumours. It can cause raised blood pressure and an increased tendency for the blood to clot.
Sterilisation	In men the vas deferens is cut (**vasectomy**) preventing sperm from getting into the semen. In women the Fallopian tubes are cut or tied to prevent the ovum reaching the uterus or the sperm reaching the ovum.	*Advantages:* Almost 100% guaranteed to prevent pregnancy. Permanent control of fertility. *Disadvantages:* For women in particular it involves a general anaesthetic. Not easily reversible.

Table 5.1 A summary of the main available methods of contraception

How does the contraceptive pill work?

The reproductive cycle of the human female is controlled by hormones produced in the pituitary gland – **follicle stimulating hormone** or **FSH** and **luteinising hormone** or **LH** – and by the ovaries. The ovaries produce **oestrogen** and **progesterone** in response to these pituitary hormones. FSH stimulates the development of follicles and thus of ripe ova in the ovary, and at the same time LH stimulates the production of oestrogen by the ovary. The rising oestrogen then suppresses the production of FSH and stimulates the **endometrium** (lining of the womb) to become thicker and more vascular ready to support a pregnancy. The hormones also bring about changes in the pH and thickness of the vaginal mucus, making it more suitable for the survival of sperm. After a peak of LH and oestrogen, ovulation occurs around the fourteenth day of the cycle, and the levels of all the hormones except progesterone then drop. Progesterone maintains the endometrium for pregnancy, but if the ovum is not fertilised, the level of progesterone also drops after about ten days and the lining disintegrates to be lost as the menstrual period. Figure 5.2 shows the cycle.

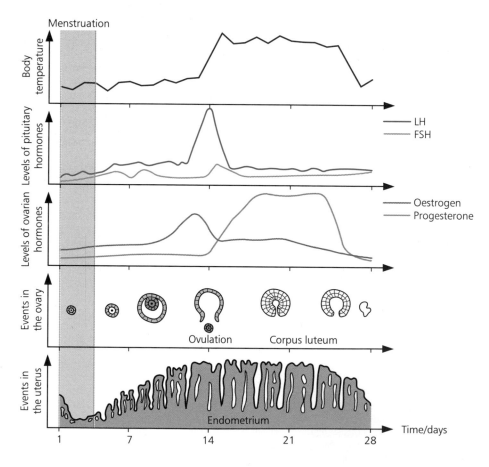

Figure 5.2 The menstrual cycle is an integrated sequence of events, the end result of which is a mature ovum ready for fertilisation and a uterus prepared to receive it every month.

There are two main types of contraceptive pill. The **mixed pill** contains synthetic oestrogens and progesterones in very small amounts which are nevertheless sufficient to inhibit the production of the pituitary hormones FSH and LH. As a result, no follicles ripen, so no ova are produced in the cycle. The endometrium does not build up and the changes in vaginal mucus do not take place. Thus the mixed pill has several different contraceptive actions. It is taken for the first 21 days of the cycle, then stopped for 7 days to give a light menstrual bleed. This is not biologically necessary but it was found that women felt it psychologically disturbing to have no periods at all! Although the low dose of oestrogen gives a slightly raised risk of thrombosis and possibly some cancers, it also offers protection against other cancers, and the health risks of pregnancy are greater than the risks from taking the pill.

The other type of pill available contains no oestrogen – it is known as the **progesterone only pill**. This does not prevent ovulation, but it does prevent the build-up of the endometrium and the changes in the mucus. It is not quite as effective as the combined pill, and because it only affects parts of the cycle it has to be taken at the same time every day to make sure it is effective. If either type of pill is forgotten or lost due to vomiting and diarrhoea, then the natural hormones may surge and normal fertility resume – this is the most common cause of pregnancies when women are taking the pill.

Contraception and iron control

For many women all over the world, anaemia due to lack of iron is a major health problem. Often it is not lack of iron in the diet that is the cause of the problem, but rather loss of iron through heavy menstrual bleeding and pregnancy. How does contraception fit into iron control? At the most basic level, contraception prevents pregnancies. Women who have too many pregnancies one after the other are more likely to suffer from anaemia than women who do not undertake repeated childbearing. Thus effective contraception reduces the likelihood of severe anaemia in women.

However, one method of contraception is linked to an increased risk of anaemia. The IUD can cause women to have heavier periods than normal, increasing their iron loss. Thus women who use an IUD as their method of contraception are more likely to suffer anaemia than those who use another method. On the other hand, women who are taking the contraceptive pill do not have true periods – the build-up of the endometrium is suppressed and so the volume of their menstrual blood loss is significantly reduced. Thus the pill reduces the incidence of anaemia in women who use it as a contraceptive method.

Social issues of contraception

The social consequences of effective contraception are very far-reaching. As a country develops and becomes industrialised, and particularly as the women become educated, the rate of population growth tends to fall. Contraception of various types is used increasingly and the average family size drops. Eventually, as in the UK at the moment where the average family size is around 1.7 children, the population is no longer replacing itself. The long-term prediction is that the population size will fall and a decreasing number of young people will be supporting an increasing number of old people as medical advances promote longer lives.

In the developing world the situation is very different. People in general have larger families, and the use of contraception is not widespread. This is for a variety of reasons. In some areas of the world where there is an imposed religion, particularly Roman Catholicism or Islam, active contraception is condemned. However, in many places a large family is a positive choice. If the childhood mortality rate is high, people want plenty of children to ensure that some of them survive to adulthood. If there is no state support for old age or infirmity, a large family is one way of ensuring that you will be cared for as you get older. In many societies, the number of children in a family is a status symbol, and those with the largest families are those who will be most successful. Added into this equation is natural birth control. In societies where mothers have only subsistence levels of nutrition, and where babies are breast fed for several years, ovulation and menstruation may not begin again until two or three years after the birth of a baby. The hormone **prolactin** is produced in response to the frequent suckling of infants, and this suppresses the production of FSH and thus of oestrogen, preventing the ripening of an ovum. When the mother has only low levels of nutrition, ovulation can be suppressed for a long time, presumably as an adaptation to avoid an excessive, damaging number of pregnancies. Thus breast feeding separates the children, often giving bigger family spacings than those seen in developed countries where couples make their choice using a variety of contraceptive techniques. The suppression of ovulation by breast feeding is not a reliable method of contraception for women in developed countries with good levels of nutrition. Here, the socially acceptable time interval between infant feeds tends to be longer and few babies are fully breast fed even for the first six months. Once extra food is introduced and breast feeding drops off, ovulation will start again very quickly.

Abortion: the choice

One of the important issues of birth control, which is also central to some of the implications of genetic diseases, is that of **abortion**. Most abortions are spontaneous and natural, when for some reason an embryo or fetus is not carried to term but dies and is lost. Natural abortion or **miscarriage** is very common indeed in the first three months of pregnancy. Most women will experience at least one early miscarriage during their child-bearing years. Some of these are so early that the woman does not even realise that she is pregnant, simply that her period is a bit late. In many cases the embryo or fetus has some sort of genetic problem, but sometimes there is no apparent reason for the loss.

However, there are circumstances where an apparently healthy pregnancy will be ended deliberately in a medical abortion. These are usually carried out if there is a risk to either the physical or mental health of the mother, or if the baby is handicapped in some way. Depending on both the culture of the country involved and the attitude of the individual doctor, the interpretation of these criteria varies greatly. In some European countries where there is relatively little use of contraception, abortion is used as a method of limiting family size, and almost every woman will have had at least one or two abortions. In other countries abortion is illegal and women have to go to extraordinary lengths if they need to terminate a pregnancy. Southern Ireland is an example, where even young girls who become pregnant by rape or abuse have been denied abortion and have had to travel abroad for help.

Most abortions are carried out in the first three months of pregnancy, when the embryo is still very small and a long way from being capable of independent life. The lining of the uterus, including the embryo, is removed either by vacuum extraction or by scraping away the uterine lining (a D and C, dilatation and curettage). However, in many countries abortion is legal until 20 weeks or even later. This is a traumatic process as the woman has to give birth, and it is usually only used when serious genetic handicaps are identified by amniocentesis testing later in the pregnancy.

The ethics of abortion cause great divides. On one side are those who believe that women have a right to decide if and when they wish to have a baby, and that every child born has the right to be a wanted child. Whilst everyone would prefer it if abortions were not necessary, these people feel that if a woman is pregnant and does not wish to be, or if the fetus has a genetic disorder or some other developmental problem, then a termination of that pregnancy is the right course to take. Other people feel equally vehemently that it is never right to take a human life, even that of an embryo a few weeks old. They believe that the rights of the unborn should be equal to or take priority over those of the parents and any other siblings who might already be in the family, and that abortion is always wrong.

These are issues of great sensitivity about which people feel very strongly. The views on both sides need careful consideration, and each individual must reach his or her own conclusion.

INFERTILITY

The conception of a baby always involves decisions. A couple may make a conscious decision to try and conceive a baby, or they may simply decide to have sexual intercourse and conception is the unplanned result. But as a result of rapidly developing reproductive technology, the decisions involved in human reproduction are becoming more complex all the time. In the developed world reproduction is taught in schools and colleges and discussed by parents and their children. The assumption is always made that producing babies occurs naturally and easily – indeed, at times almost too easily. For the majority of couples this proves to be the case – they will achieve a pregnancy within a few months of deciding to start a family.

But at least one couple in ten, and in some countries now almost one in six, do not conceive after a year or more of trying. Alleviating the distress of those who want children but cannot have them has been the driving force behind much research into infertility treatments. Coupled with investigations into and manipulation of human genetic information, a brave new world of reproductive technology has been opened up, enabling many people to have children who in the past would have remained childless. Many of the developments have already been beneficial, but equally there is the potential for great damage. Society as a whole as well as individuals will need to make many difficult decisions in the future as a result of these new technologies.

Figure 5.3 The moment of conception when a sperm enters an ovum and a new life begins. But for some couples the journey to this moment is long and tortuous, complicated by the problems of reproductive systems which for one reason or another do not function in the normal way.

What causes infertility?

There are many reasons why a couple cannot produce children. In about 30% of cases there is a problem in the reproductive system of the female partner, and in another 30% the malfunctioning is in the male reproductive system. For the remaining couples both partners may be less fertile than average (**sub-fertile**), or both may be infertile, or there may be no apparent reason why pregnancy does not occur.

Infertility in women

Difficulties in conception in a woman can be the result of a great variety of problems. If the ovaries do not contain ova then pregnancy is obviously

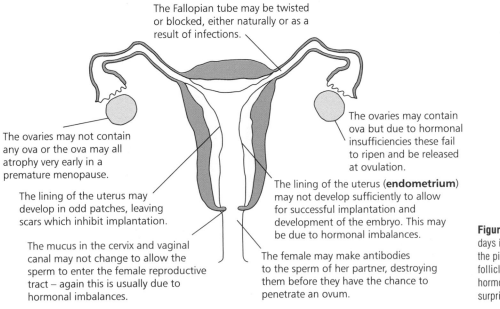

The Fallopian tube may be twisted or blocked, either naturally or as a result of infections.

The ovaries may not contain any ova or the ova may all atrophy very early in a premature menopause.

The lining of the uterus may develop in odd patches, leaving scars which inhibit implantation.

The mucus in the cervix and vaginal canal may not change to allow the sperm to enter the female reproductive tract – again this is usually due to hormonal imbalances.

The ovaries may contain ova but due to hormonal insufficiencies these fail to ripen and be released at ovulation.

The lining of the uterus (**endometrium**) may not develop sufficiently to allow for successful implantation and development of the embryo. This may be due to hormonal imbalances.

The female may make antibodies to the sperm of her partner, destroying them before they have the chance to penetrate an ovum.

Figure 5.4 The production of a fertile ovum every 28 days is a complex sequence of events coordinated by the pituitary hormones luteinising hormone (LH) and follicle stimulating hormone (FSH) and the female hormones oestrogen and progesterone. It is not surprising that sometimes the system fails.

impossible. This is very rare, however. Far more commonly the ovaries contain ova but they are not released in the normal monthly cycle – **ovulation** does not occur. The Fallopian tubes carrying the ova from the ovaries to the uterus may be blocked, and the uterus itself may not accept a pregnancy due to an imbalance in the normal reproductive hormones. Some of the main causes are summarised in figure 5.4.

Infertility in men

Infertility in the male has been recognised only relatively recently. Before that it was assumed that any inability to have children was the woman's problem. We now know that malfunctions of the male reproductive system are just as likely as those of the female, and the main problems occur with the process of sperm production known as **spermatogenesis**. Obviously if no sperm are produced, then fertilisation is impossible. More common than the complete absence of sperm is the presence of a high proportion of abnormal sperm. In the semen of a normal individual, about 15% of the sperm are abnormal, as illustrated in figure 5.5. If this proportion is substantially increased then the chances of successful conception fall.

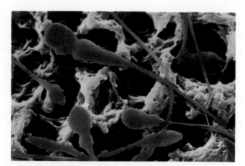

Figure 5.5 All men produce some abnormal sperm. But if there are too many sperm with double heads, broken necks or miniature heads, their chances of remaining suspended in the semen, reaching the ovum and achieving fertilisation are substantially reduced.

Spermatogenesis takes about 70 days, and can be affected by a variety of factors such as the general health of the man, his alcohol intake and smoking. Spermatogenesis is under the control of hormones, particularly follicle stimulating hormone (FSH) and so hormonal imbalance can affect sperm production. The testes need to be about 1 °C below body temperature for normal sperm production to occur, so if the testes are undescended (held in the body cavity) or if the temperature is increased in any other way, sperm production drops. Even the wearing of tight underpants and trousers has been indicated as a possible cause of sub-fertility in men because of the effect on testicular temperature. In some cases the sperm cannot be released due to a blockage in the vas deferens, the tube carrying them from the testes towards the urethra, often as a result of earlier sexually transmitted diseases.

Overcoming infertility

For many years the techniques available to help infertile couples were very limited. Artificial insemination by a donor (AID), where sperm donated by an anonymous donor was inserted into the uterus, could help those couples where the malfunction was in the male sperm production. But AID could not help couples whose problem lay in the female reproductive system. In recent years many new methods of treatment have become available. Some of these are outlined below.

Using drugs to stimulate ovulation

In recent years it has become possible to overcome some of the causes of infertility, particularly in women. As our knowledge of the hormonal control of fertility has increased, so has our ability to manipulate it artificially. The inability to ovulate has been treated for some time now with what are commonly known as **fertility drugs**. These may be synthetic hormones such as clomiphene which stimulate the pituitary gland to produce more gonadotrophins (hormones that act on the ovary to bring about ovulation), or they may be the gonadotrophins themselves, extracted from the urine of post-menopausal women. In the early days of this treatment the risk of multiple pregnancies was high, and women conceived as many as eight embryos at once. Although a few women did give birth to quads, quins and sextuplets, with most of the babies surviving, many more had their hopes dashed as they miscarried the unnaturally high number of embryos. However badly a couple want children, four or five babies at the same time is an enormous physical, emotional and financial strain. Nowadays the treatment has been greatly refined and the drug preparations are far more sophisticated. As a result, although there is still a higher risk of twins and triplets resulting from treatment with fertility drugs than from an unassisted pregnancy, many couples are treated successfully and large multiple births are generally a thing of the past.

In vitro *fertilisation – a major breakthrough*

The biggest breakthrough in the treatment of human infertility problems, and the technology which has opened a Pandora's box of possibilities for the future, is known in the popular press as the 'test tube baby' technique. More properly described as ***in vitro* fertilisation** (IVF), it involves the fertilisation of an ovum outside the mother's body and then the replacement of the embryo into the uterus to implant and develop as normal.

The first step in the process is to induce **superovulation**, giving fertility drugs to ensure that not just one but several ova ripen in the ovarian follicles. Just prior to natural ovulation these ova are harvested surgically and they are then mixed with sperm from the male partner in a Petri dish. Examination under a high powered microscope shows which ova have been fertilised, and those that appear undamaged are incubated until several cell divisions have occurred. The woman is meanwhile given further hormones to ensure that her uterus is ready to accept a pregnancy, and then several embryos are placed into their mother's body, as shown in figure 5.6. Different medical centres replace varying numbers of embryos. Some replace only one, but should that not implant the procedure needs to be repeated. Most centres replace two or three embryos, so that the failure of one or two to implant can still have a successful outcome. The risk of twins or triplets is thus increased when the technique works.

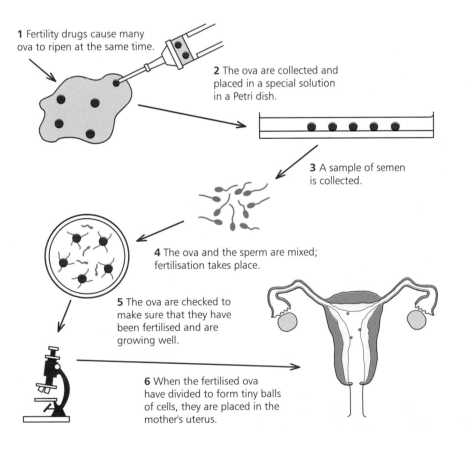

1 Fertility drugs cause many ova to ripen at the same time.

2 The ova are collected and placed in a special solution in a Petri dish.

3 A sample of semen is collected.

4 The ova and the sperm are mixed; fertilisation takes place.

5 The ova are checked to make sure that they have been fertilised and are growing well.

6 When the fertilised ova have divided to form tiny balls of cells, they are placed in the mother's uterus.

Figure 5.6 *In vitro* fertilisation

The technique of *in vitro* fertilisation was first developed by Patrick Steptoe and Robert Edwards in the 1980s. It is still very expensive, with a relatively low success rate, and is not widely available. Other easier and cheaper techniques have developed from it, such as **gamete intra-fallopian transfer** (GIFT). Here the ova and sperm are collected and replaced immediately in the body again, but on the uterus side of the tubal blockage. Several eggs are placed in the Fallopian tube in an attempt to ensure fertilisation, but no control can then be exercised over the number of embryos that eventually implant. Also, to enable couples to donate ova only once (it is a time-consuming, expensive and uncomfortable process), work has been done on the freezing of both ova and embryos. (Sperm have been successfully stored in liquid nitrogen for many years.) It is now possible for a couple to donate ova and sperm, have some of the fertilised ova implanted immediately and have the remainder frozen to be implanted later when they want another child.

A moral dilemma

Techniques such as IVF, GIFT and the freezing of embryos leads to possible conflict between those developments which are of benefit to the individuals concerned and those which benefit society as a whole. IVF has resulted in a great many 'spare' embryos. What is to be done with them? In most cases the parents give permission for them to be used for experimentation, to further our knowledge of reproduction and development. But in Britain and many other countries a limit on the age of these embryos has been set. At 14 days of development the developing embryo is no longer likely to split and form identical twins, and the very beginnings of the nervous system are forming. Beyond this point no further experiments on *in vitro* human embryos are allowed. The problem is that now the technology is there, someone, somewhere might continue these experiments to a later stage.

Donating genes, borrowing bodies

Some reproductive technologies involve using other people to help a couple produce a baby. For many years now artificial insemination by donor sperm (AID) has been available. The biggest problem with this is that the offspring do not know who their biological father is, and so have the very remote chance of meeting, falling in love with and marrying a half brother or sister. However, this can happen with natural fathers too, so the situation is really very little different. More recently, it has become possible to harvest the eggs from one woman, fertilise them outside the body with sperm and implant them into a different woman who does not have any ova of her own. The issues involved in this are very similar to those involved in the donation of sperm except that the process is much more complicated and needs much more dedication from the donor. She has to be brought to superovulation by a course of injected fertility drugs, and then have the ova removed in a rather uncomfortable process. Apart from the risk of accidental sibling marriage, there is also the problem that donating gametes is a confidential process, and so although parents would be advised to tell their offspring about their origins, it would be difficult for the offspring to trace their biological parent. As most people donate gametes because they want to help an infertile couple, not because they want children themselves, any moves to make it easier for offspring to trace their parents are likely to reduce the already short supply of donors.

Another recent development has been the use of surrogate mothers. This has always been possible, but IVF has extended the possibilities. A **surrogate mother** carries a baby through pregnancy for someone else, and gives up the baby at birth. This is usually done for a woman who has no uterus, either from

Ethical issues of IVF

IVF has enabled many couples to overcome the heartbreak of being unable to have children. However, there are many implications and possible misuses of the technique. For example:

- If embryos are frozen for future use, what happens if the parents divorce? To whom do the embryos belong?

- If parents and their first child are killed there could be great difficulties over the estate. Do the frozen embryos inherit, and if so should they be implanted in a surrogate mother and allowed to develop in order to collect their inheritance?

- In some countries such as America and Italy, IVF is now being used to allow women who are past the menopause, in their 50s and 60s, to have babies. The treatment has substantially higher success rates than IVF in younger, infertile women. IVF specialists in Britain feel that this is not an appropriate use of the technology because of the social issues it raises. What are these social issues? Men can father children into their 70s and even 80s – why shouldn't women too prolong their reproductive life? The main concerns seem to be for the health of the mother and the mental wellbeing of the child, which is more likely than most to lose its parents whilst still relatively young.

birth or as a result of surgery. It is still relatively rare and often very controversial, particularly when women are paid for the use of their uterus.

Strong feelings tend to be expressed in the media about a paid surrogate, or a surrogate who changes her mind and cannot give up the baby. A grandmother acting as surrogate for her childless daughter and son-in-law (see figure 5.7) seems to be more generally approved of, even though it involves the often frowned-on technique of restoring the fertility of a post-menopausal woman using drugs. In society in general, discussion about such issues is rarely detached and based on science. It is more often stirred up by emotive and at times inaccurate reporting of both the situation and the science.

GENETIC DISEASES

Some human health problems are neither infections nor caused by lifestyle or environmental factors. They are the result of the DNA we inherit from our parents, or the result of mutations to that DNA, changes that occur before or at the moment of conception. These are **genetic diseases**. A single defective gene or a whole chromosome mutation can lead to a reduced level of a particular enzyme. This is turn can disrupt the entire biochemistry of the cell and cause major problems for the whole organism.

Figure 5.7 The ultimate gift? A mother acts as surrogate to her own grandchild when her daughter cannot carry a baby to term.

Figure 5.8 The process of meiosis, which produces ova and sperm in the ovaries and testes

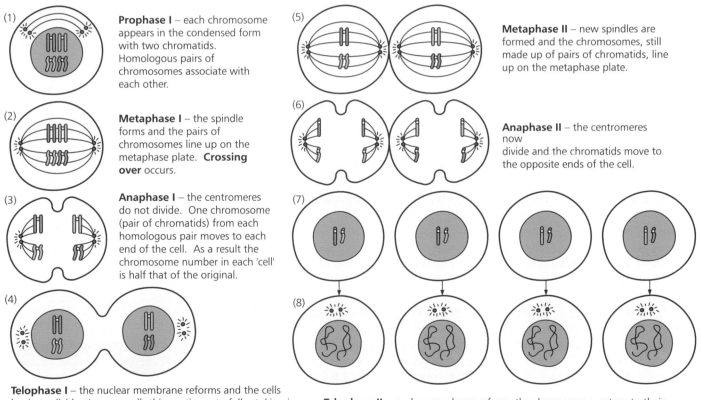

(1) **Prophase I** – each chromosome appears in the condensed form with two chromatids. Homologous pairs of chromosomes associate with each other.

(2) **Metaphase I** – the spindle forms and the pairs of chromosomes line up on the metaphase plate. **Crossing over** occurs.

(3) **Anaphase I** – the centromeres do not divide. One chromosome (pair of chromatids) from each homologous pair moves to each end of the cell. As a result the chromosome number in each 'cell' is half that of the original.

(4) **Telophase I** – the nuclear membrane reforms and the cells begin to divide. In some cells this continues to full cytokinesis and there may be a period of brief or prolonged interphase. During this interphase there is *no further replication* of the DNA.

(5) **Metaphase II** – new spindles are formed and the chromosomes, still made up of pairs of chromatids, line up on the metaphase plate.

(6) **Anaphase II** – the centromeres now divide and the chromatids move to the opposite ends of the cell.

(7)

(8) **Telophase II** – nuclear envelopes reform, the chromosomes return to their interphase state and cytokinesis occurs, giving four daughter cells each with half the chromosome number of the original diploid cell.

Aneuploidy

A change from the normal diploid chromosome number of 46 is the most common type of whole-chromosome genetic defect in humans. **Aneuploidy**, the absence of one or more chromosomes or the presence of one or more extra chromosomes, often results in a highly abnormal embryo which is spontaneously aborted at a very early stage. However, this does not always happen and some individuals with abnormal chromosome numbers survive to adulthood.

When cells in the ovaries and the testes undergo meiotic divisions to produce ova and sperm, the chromosome number of the original cells is halved. Each gamete formed should contain 23 chromosomes, including one sex chromosome, to pass on into the next generation. However, an error called **nondisjunction** can occur – during the reduction division of meiosis, individual members of an homologous pair of chromosomes fail to separate during anaphase. This means one of the gametes has two copies of that chromosome and the other has no copies of it. If one of the abnormal gametes joins with a normal one in fertilisation, an individual will result who is either **monosomic** for a particular chromosome (with only one member of the homologous pair present) or **trisomic** (with three rather than two chromosomes of a particular type). Most examples of aneuploidy are lethal and affected embryos abort, but some examples can and do survive.

Autosome abnormalities

The **autosomes** are all the chromosomes except the sex chromosomes – the 22 pairs of chromosomes that carry most of the information about you as an individual. Most autosome abnormalities are lethal, and the fetuses fail to develop to full term. Trisomy of chromosome 13 causes harelip, cleft palate and various eye, brain and cardiovascular defects. It only occurs in about one in every 10 000 live births and usually results in death within the first three months of life. Similarly trisomy of chromosome 18, found in one in every 5000 live births, causes malformation of almost every organ system. About 80% of the affected babies born are female – it is possible that males are so badly affected that almost all abort. Again, most of these afflicted babies die in the first few months of life. The most commonly occurring major autosome abnormality, and almost the only one compatible with continued life, is trisomy on autosome 21, known as **Down's syndrome**.

Aneuploidy of all kinds increases with maternal (and paternal) age. All the future ova of an individual woman become frozen in prophase I of meiosis while the woman herself is still an embryo. Meiosis is completed in the ovum only after ovulation and fertilisation by a sperm. Forty years or more of waiting and being exposed to all the chemical and radiation hazards of modern life appears to be too much for some of the ova and nondisjunction increases. This is demonstrated both by the raised level of spontaneous abortion of abnormal embryos in older women, and by the increased numbers of trisomic fetuses aborted after diagnostic tests and Down's syndrome babies born to older women.

Down's syndrome (see figure 5.10) causes mental retardation and abnormal physical development. The skull is small and flattened from front to back. The nose is short and flat, and the mouth cavity is small with an enlarged tongue. Other problems include squints, abnormal ears and teeth, cataracts and quite often an abnormal heart. There is also a substantial lack of muscle tone, which means that Down's syndrome individuals tend to lack facial expression, although most are capable of smiles. Most individuals with Down's syndrome are infertile, although babies have been born to women with Down's

Anaphase II

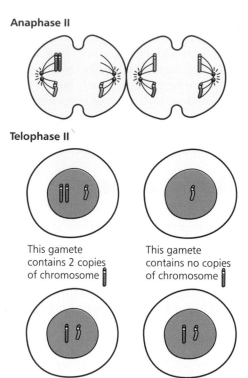

Telophase II

This gamete contains 2 copies of chromosome ▌

This gamete contains no copies of chromosome ▌

Figure 5.9 Nondisjunction during meiosis results in gametes with an extra chromosome or a missing chromosome.

Figure 5.10 Down's syndrome results from trisomy (three copies) of chromosome 21.

syndrome. Half of these babies are normal, half also have Down's syndrome, reflecting that half of the ova formed will contain one chromosome 21 and the other half will contain two. The level of mental retardation varies quite widely – many sufferers can learn to speak, and others can also write and read at a simple level and develop sufficient skills to be relatively independent. However, the majority are much less fortunate and most Down's individuals will need substantial care for the whole of their lives. Although their life expectancy is lower than normal, many Down's individuals outlive their parents, which can be very traumatic if they then have to be moved from loving care in a normal home into an institution. Many Down's syndrome individuals are very affectionate and loving, and this continues into adulthood. This is one of the major compensations felt by parents who are bringing up children disadvantaged in this way by their chromosomes.

Figure 5.11 These techniques make possible an accurate diagnosis of Down's syndrome and other genetic disorders before birth.

Amniocentesis involves removing about 20 cm³ of the amniotic fluid which surrounds the fetus. The fluid is withdrawn using a needle and syringe, at about the sixteenth week of pregnancy. Fetal epithelial cells and even fetal blood cells can be recovered from the fluid after centrifugation. After the cells have been cultured for several weeks, a number of genetic defects as well as the sex of the baby can be determined from examination of their chromosomes.
Disadvantages: Can only be carried out relatively late in the pregnancy, so that should termination of the pregnancy be necessary it is more traumatic. Have to wait several weeks after the test for the results. Carries about a 1% risk of spontaneous abortion following the procedure, regardless of the genetic status of the fetus.

Chorionic villus sampling involves taking a small sample of the embryonic tissue from the developing placenta. This makes a much bigger sample of fetal tissue available for examination. The embryonic cells are then tested for a wide range of genetic abnormalities. This technique can be carried out much earlier in the pregnancy, so that if a termination is necessary it is physically less traumatic for the mother. It yields information more rapidly.
Disadvantages: There is a risk that the embryo may spontaneously abort after the tissue sample is taken. All paternal X chromosomes are inactivated in fetal placental cells, so any problems in the genes on that chromosome cannot be detected by this technique.

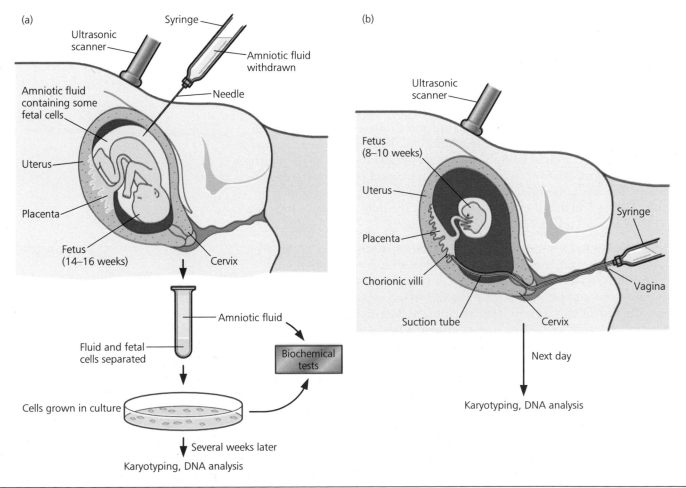

Prenatal testing is widely used to discover if a fetus has Down's syndrome early enough in the pregnancy for the parents to be offered an abortion if they do not wish to continue with the pregnancy. In the UK a blood test is offered to all pregnant women at around 12 weeks of pregnancy. The levels of specific markers seen in the blood and the age of the mother allow an assessment of the risk that the fetus may be Down's syndrome. In addition, at 16 weeks of pregnancy the **alpha-fetoprotein** blood test is carried out. If the levels are low, this suggests an increased likelihood of a chromosome abnormality, particularly Down's syndrome. If the levels are raised, this can indicate that the fetus has spina bifida. Older mothers are offered testing automatically, as the risk of having Down's baby increases with age, although the age at which testing is offered varies from area to area.

The least invasive procedure for finding out about the health of an unborn baby is the use of **ultrasound**. Very high frequency sound waves are bounced off the fetus and the reflected sound is used to build up a visual image. This shows whether the fetus is growing as it should and also checks for limb, heart and gross brain abnormalities. More information can be yielded by **fetoscopy**, where the fetus can be seen directly using a very fine fibreoptic telescope (fetoscope) inserted through the abdominal wall into the uterine cavity. However, to discover for sure the chromosomal make-up of the fetus, a **karyotype** (complete chromosome picture) needs to be made from the chromosomes of the fetal cells. The required fetal tissue can be obtained in one of two ways – chorionic villus sampling or amniocentesis. These are described in figure 5.11.

It may be difficult for parents to come to terms with the fact that the child they are expecting will not be the normal, healthy baby they had hoped for. Many parents who find that their fetus is affected by Down's syndrome decide to terminate the pregnancy, rather than condemn the child to a life of handicap and themselves and any other children they may have to a life of caring for the Down's child. Other parents either do not sanction abortion or choose to carry their child to term in spite of the genetic handicap it carries. For these couples too the testing is valuable. It allows them time to grieve the loss of the normal healthy baby they thought they were carrying and to come to terms with and welcome the child when it is born. The amniocentesis test only gives knowledge of Down's syndrome around half-way through a pregnancy, and so the abortion is late and therefore relatively traumatic if the parents choose to terminate the pregnancy. However, most people feel that the option of knowing should be available. Others feel that the view of society that the only acceptable baby is a perfect baby is a sad reflection of materialistic times.

Making a karyotype

To make a karyotype, cells need to be actively in mitosis, so the cells from the individual being tested are cultured and grown. Chromosomes only take up stain just before mitotic division, when they coil up tightly to form dense rods of chromatin. The mitotic cells are treated with a fluorescent dye which has an affinity for DNA and which fluoresces when exposed to ultraviolet light. The stained chromosomes are then photographed and the individual chromosomes are cut from the picture and arranged roughly in descending order of size. The dye binds more tightly to some areas of DNA than others, producing a banding effect, and because each chromosome has a unique banding pattern it is possible to identify each pair.

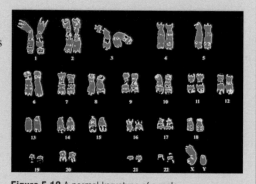

Figure 5.12 A normal karyotype of a male

Sex chromosome abnormalities

Very few embryos with aneuploidy of the autosomes survive even until birth, apart from those with Down's syndrome. In contrast, the absence of a sex chromosome or the presence of several sex chromosomes is less unusual and less life threatening, although in most cases there will be fertility problems. The presence or absence of the Y chromosome determines the route for sexual development in humans. Any embryo with at least one Y chromosome will develop male characteristics, whilst any embryo lacking a Y chromosome will develop female characteristics.

Nondisjunction in either the mother or the father can give a gamete without a sex chromosome. On fertilisation this can lead to an XO offspring, monosomic for the X chromosome. This is known as **Turner's syndrome**. If two gametes meet that both have no sex chromosome, resulting in an O individual, the embryo aborts spontaneously.

The individual with Turner's syndrome has female sex organs and genitalia, but her ovaries lack ova and do not produce hormones. This means that growth is affected, puberty will not occur, secondary sexual characteristics are missing and, of course, the individual is infertile. If the syndrome is detected, hormone treatment with ovarian hormones can overcome most of the obvious physical problems but cannot restore fertility. For some Turner's syndrome individuals there are added complications of 'webbing' of the neck, mental deficiency and an abnormal aorta.

Nondisjunction of the sex chromosomes during meiosis can also result in gametes carrying two sex chromosomes instead of the normal one – XX ova or XY sperm. If one of these fuses with a normal gamete carrying an X or Y chromosome, a variety of individuals are possible. An XXX female is known as a **metafemale**. There is no apparent difference in the development of a metafemale, and the condition often only comes to light if women are involved in research or screening situations. There is some evidence that XXX women may have a slightly higher incidence of mental illness that their XX counterparts. The normal development is possible because in any female cell only one X chromosome remains active, and the other condenses to form a coiled up mass called the **Barr body**. In metafemales two X chromosomes condense and so their cells contain two Barr bodies. Females with three X chromosomes show normal fertility, but their potential gametes are either X or XX, which may cause problems in the next generation.

In a similar way, men who have an extra Y chromosome, with sex chromosomes XYY (arising because the Y chromosome is doubled but does not separate during meiosis), do not seem to suffer any obvious biological consequences. They appear as normal males and have normal fertility rates. This is probably because the information carried on the Y chromosome is believed to be almost entirely associated with being male. There was a popular theory at one time suggesting that the presence of an extra Y chromosome predisposed men to aggression and criminal tendencies, and in America this was even accepted as a defence in trials. However, this idea has now been discredited.

Most of the other possible combinations of sex chromosomes result in a condition known as **Klinefelter's syndrome**. The most common combination seen with Klinefelter's syndrome is XXY, when either an XX ovum joins with a normal Y sperm, or an XY sperm joins with a normal X ovum. Multiple nondisjunction can result in XXYY, XXXY and even larger combinations. Individuals with Klinefelter's syndrome have normal male external sexual characteristics and the condition is often unnoticed until puberty. However, at this point the testes remain small and underdeveloped and do not produce sperm, while at the same time there may be some breast development and other female characteristics such as body shape may appear. Because the testes do not produce sperm, an individual with Klinefelter's syndrome will be infertile, and like an XXX female has a higher than average risk of developing mental health problems.

Barr bodies and the diagnosis of abnormalities of the sex chromosomes

In every somatic (body) cell of a normal female there will be a **Barr body**, a dense condensed blob of chromatin formed from the inactivated second X chromosome. Which X chromosome is inactivated is a random choice, so at an early stage of development the X chromosome from the mother is inactivated in some cells and the X from the father in others. These cell lines then reproduce, so that a woman is a mosaic of cells, some expressing the phenotypes from the maternal X chromosome and others expressing those from the paternal X chromosome.

Cells from a normal male do not contain a Barr body, as males have just one X chromosome inherited from the mother which stays active in every cell. However, when there are abnormalities in the numbers of X chromosomes, this will be reflected in the Barr body status of the cells even when the outer appearance of the individual is normal. Thus a metafemale, XXX, will have two Barr bodies in each cell, whereas an individual with Turner's syndrome, XO, will appear female but have no Barr bodies in the cells. Men with Klinefelter's syndrome, on the other hand, will have at least one Barr body in their cells as the extra X chromosomes are inactivated.

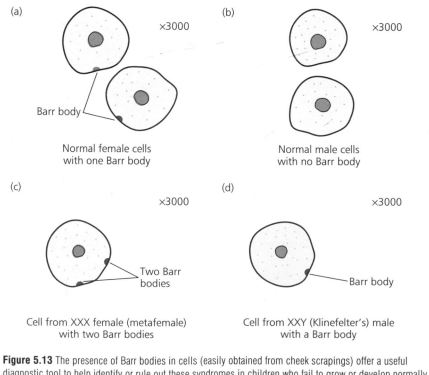

Figure 5.13 The presence of Barr bodies in cells (easily obtained from cheek scrapings) offer a useful diagnostic tool to help identify or rule out these syndromes in children who fail to grow or develop normally or in cases of unexplained infertility.

The frequencies of the various chromosome abnormalities that result from nondisjunction discussed in this section are summarised in table 5.2.

Syndrome	Chromosomes	Average frequency at birth
Metafemale	XXX	1/700
Turner's syndrome	XO	1/5000
Klinefelter's syndrome	XXY, etc.	1/500
Down's syndrome	3 copies of chromosome 21	Ranges from 1/2000 at maternal age 20 to 1/12 as maternal age approaches 50

Table 5.2 Chromosome abnormalities as a result of nondisjunction

Genetic diseases that are not the result of aneuploidy

So far we have looked at genetic diseases in which there is an extra chromosome or a missing chromosome. However, most genetic diseases are caused by individual genes rather than entire chromosomes. In **Duchenne muscular dystrophy**, a mutated recessive gene is carried on one of the X chromosomes of the mother. If this fuses with a normal X chromosome from the father resulting in a girl, all will be well. But if a boy has an affected X chromosome, at around the age of seven or eight deterioration of the muscle tissue begins. The child becomes wheelchair bound and will die in the early teenage years. Girls do not suffer from this disease because affected boys die before they are capable of reproduction, so double recessive females with two affected X chromosomes are not conceived. It is possible that even if they were, the effect would be so catastrophic that the fetus would not develop to term.

This example shows that a mutation of just a single gene can cause far-reaching and even lethal damage to the physiology of the human body. New techniques for analysing DNA sequences and engineering genes have recently opened up the whole area of treatment of genetic diseases. Until very recently these diseases struck sometimes at random, sometimes following a family pattern, but nothing could effectively be done to cure them. Now, in some cases at least, problems can be detected before birth, and the chances of an apparently unaffected individual developing a disease or passing it on to another generation can be worked out. There is even the possibility of cures being developed. But these developments present us as individuals and as societies with some complicated ethical issues. We shall look at two genetic diseases, cystic fibrosis and Huntington's disease.

Cystic fibrosis

Cystic fibrosis is a genetic disease that is usually carried by a recessive gene on chromosome 7. It occurs in about one in every 2500 babies born to white Europeans, but is much less common in other ethnic groups. Because cystic fibrosis is caused by a recessive allele, even if both parents are carriers of the disease they will only have a one in four chance of any particular pregnancy being affected, as shown in figure 5.14.

Cystic fibrosis causes severe respiratory and digestive problems, along with very salty sweat. The exocrine glands, including mucus-secreting and sweat glands, cannot reabsorb chloride and sodium ions, and this results in thick, sticky mucus secretions which obstruct the ducts in the exocrine glands and can cause irreversible damage. Clogged bile ducts can cause cirrhosis of the liver, and pancreatic tubules can rupture, releasing digestive enzymes into the body cavity which cause damage followed by the build-up of fibrous scar tissue. Without sufficient pancreatic enzymes, the digestion and reabsorption of protein and fats is often incomplete, so the individual can suffer from

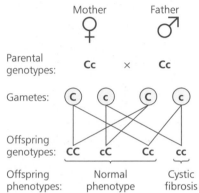

C represents the normal allele
c represents the allele for cystic fibrosis
Cc represents a carrier with a normal phenotype (no symptoms)

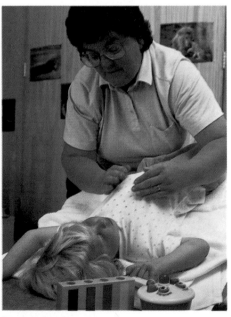

Figure 5.14 Individuals carry the recessive allele for cystic fibrosis without knowing it. If two carriers have a child which inherits both recessive alleles, it will have cystic fibrosis. The child will need several daily sessions of physiotherapy to keep the lungs clear, as well as constant medication.

malnutrition. Thick sticky mucus accumulates in the small airways of the lungs, leading to severe coughing fits and breathlessness, and also leaves the respiratory system very vulnerable to bacterial infections, which can often be fatal. Physiotherapy may be needed at least twice a day to clear the lungs, and the effects on the digestive system can be controlled to some extent by taking replacement enzymes. With better management and drugs, more cystic fibrosis sufferers now lead relatively normal lives and grow up into early adulthood. However, most sufferers are infertile, as the mucus also clogs the tubules in the testes and affects the Fallopian tubes.

The position of the mutated gene on chromosome 7, which causes 70–5% of cystic fibrosis cases, was isolated by scientists in August 1989. Because it is recessive, the allele has to be inherited from both parents for the disease to manifest itself. Anyone with a single allele is simply a carrier, with the potential to pass the gene on to their own offspring. By 1990 the normal allele had been copied and added to cells affected by cystic fibrosis in the laboratory, where it proved effective in correcting the defective biochemical pathway. Throughout the 1990s work continued to find a way of converting this major discovery into a treatment to help cystic fibrosis sufferers, most of whom are young as the life expectancy of sufferers is only 25 to 30 years.

Huntington's disease

Huntington's disease or **Huntington's chorea** is a genetic disease caused by a dominant allele. This means that anyone who inherits the allele will get the disease, and that any children of an affected parent will have a 50% chance of inheriting it too. Until very recently, the victims of Huntington's disease have only found they were affected when symptoms began to show at between 30 and 50 years of age, so many affected people have already had children before they discover their own disease. It is very rare, affecting about one in 20 000 of the white American population, for example.

Huntington's disease involves progressive degeneration of nerve cells in the central nervous system. The individual begins to have involuntary jerking or writhing movements of the arms and legs, and strange facial grimaces. Changes in personality occur, including inappropriate laughter and tears, anger, memory loss and bizarre, almost schizophrenic behaviour. The pattern of symptoms is very variable, but the patient usually sinks into a virtually vegetative state for several years before inevitable death. In 1983 Dr James Gusella working in Boston, Massachusetts decided to compare the DNA of family members affected by Huntington's disease with those who did not have

Figure 5.15 Because the symptoms of Huntington's disease do not appear until early middle age, and because the dominant genetic nature of the disease was only recognised relatively recently, the disease has devastated families for generations, as can be seen in the family tree of this American family.

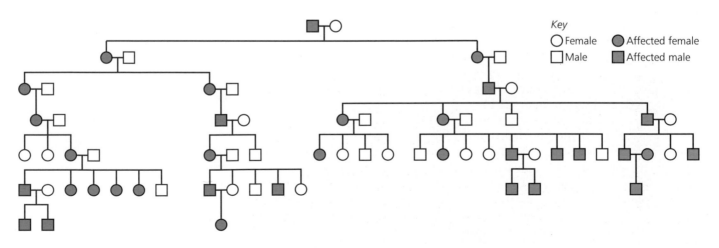

Key
○ Female   ● Affected female
□ Male   ■ Affected male

the disease. He used gene probes to discover a genetic marker present only when the Huntington's disease allele was there in an individual. This discovery was the basis for a genetic test to be developed for use with families when one member develops Huntington's disease. If that family member is your parent, you are faced with many years of uncertainty before you know if you too have inherited the disease. The test opens the door for people to face and plan their own future, and also to plan whether and how to bring children into the world. For example, if one partner has the Huntington's allele, a couple may choose not to have children and thus risk passing on the allele. On the other hand they may have children, but choose to have the fetuses screened, terminating the pregnancy if the Huntington's allele is present.

As workers move closer to identifying the gene itself, the possibilities of genetic cures also move closer. But the new knowledge about Huntington's disease raises many difficult issues.

Multiple sclerosis – genetic disease?

Not all diseases can be described neatly as genetic, or environmental, or infectious. In spite of our greatly improved understanding of diseases, there are still some about which remarkably little is known. **Multiple sclerosis** (**MS**) is one such disease. It has an unknown cause, no known cure and an unpredictable course. It often starts when people are in their 20s and 30s, disrupting their lives but rarely shortening them. Multiple sclerosis causes inflammation of random patches of the central nervous system. The myelin sheath is damaged, causing permanent disruption and slowing of the conduction of nervous impulses. Symptoms include difficulty in walking, slurred speech, reduced vision, bladder dysfunction, spasticity (jerky movements) and tremors (shakes). It is most common in white Caucasians of Northern European ancestry, although it has appeared in all ethnic groups and about twice as many women as men are affected.

Canada has a particularly high proportion of sufferers. About 15% of those with the disease have a close relative who is also affected. Diagnosis involves MRI scans (see page 13) and lumbar punctures in which cerebrospinal fluid is withdrawn from the spinal cord through a needle. The disease may be active, with very noticeable deterioration and great fatigue, or it may remain stable for many years. Treatment varies greatly and is mainly based on alleviating the symptoms as much as possible.

For some time an obscure viral infection was suspected of causing MS. Whilst this idea has not been eliminated, evidence is increasingly pointing to a number of genes interacting in individuals who have the disease. This means that the likelihood of any offspring inheriting all the affected genes is only 3–4%. Although this is higher than for the general population, it is a lot lower than for genetic diseases caused by one gene. Research into this mysterious and debilitating disease goes on.

Gene probes

Gene probes allow scientists to identify particular pieces of DNA in a cell, such as a piece of recombinant DNA in a microorganism such as a bacterium, or specific disease-causing genes in a human cell. Whatever the use, gene probes all use similar technology. To find a particular gene out of the hundreds of thousands present in the DNA of a human cell, a very specific probe is needed. The unique feature of any gene is the sequence of nucleotides of the DNA. This can be recognised by a stretch of RNA with the complementary sequence, in a process known as **DNA–RNA hybridisation**. The DNA is isolated from some cells and heated gently. This breaks open the weak hydrogen bonds holding together the two strands of DNA. Radioactively labelled mRNA for the required gene is added – this is the probe. Any DNA–RNA hybridisation that takes place indicates the presence of the required gene, and can be pinpointed by the radioactive label on the mRNA. Gene probes have been used to identify genetic markers in families with severe genetic problems such as Huntington's disease. They have also been used to identify and isolate genes that code for the production of antibiotics and hormones, which have then been used in genetic engineering to enable microbes to make, for example, human insulin. The use of gene probes in the identification of genetic traits in an individual and in the world of genetic engineering will surely continue to increase in the next decade as our knowledge of the human genome expands.

Genetic testing and screening – issues and ethics

Genetic testing involves the testing of the members of a family into which a child with a genetic disorder has been born, to try to estimate the risk of any further babies being affected and to identify the individuals who are carriers of the faulty gene. **Genetic screening** involves the genetic testing for a particular faulty gene of a large proportion of the population who are reproducing. At first sight the idea of genetic screening sounds excellent. Find out what your faulty genes are (and we all have some!) before you pass them on to any children you might have in the future. But what are the implications of this type of knowledge? And can genetic screening as it stands give us all the information we need? These questions need to be addressed. There is currently a major research drive known as the **Human Genome Project** which aims to produce detailed maps of all the genes on all the human chromosomes. In six countries, 265 laboratories are working towards determining the locations, DNA nucleotide sequences and functions of all the 100 000 or so human genes. It is estimated the cost at completion will be around \$3 billion. As this project moves forward it will be possible to identify the genes responsible for all the single-gene genetic disorders, and doubtless to provide screening tests for them. It should also clarify the situation in **multifactorial** diseases resulting from a number of genes and lifestyle factors too. All this knowledge will raise some tough issues for society to consider.

For example, in a family affected by Huntington's disease, some individuals might find it unbearable to learn that they have inherited a completely untreatable disease which is fatal, leading them to depression, a greatly reduced quality of their remaining healthy life or even suicide. Indeed, in America where genetic testing for Huntington's disease is available, it is not uncommon for family members to refuse testing, preferring to face an uncertain future with some degree of hope rather than one filled with the knowledge of their own horrendous decline and death.

Another problem about this sort of information is who should have access to it. If an individual is screened and it is found either that they have a dominant allele for a specific disease like Huntington's, or that they are carriers of a recessive allele, then the information could remain confidential, available only to the individual concerned. This leaves it to each individual to decide whether to tell partners, parents and friends, whether to have children and indeed, whether to tell their insurance companies. However, some people would argue that society has a right to know. You have a right to know that the person you plan to have children with is not going to knowingly pass on abnormal genes, and financial institutions should not be tricked into lending money or offering cheap life insurance to someone who knows they carry a genetic time bomb. However, on these arguments every one of us could be a bad risk. Most individuals will not carry the allele for Huntington's disease, but in the UK one in 25 will carry the gene for cystic fibrosis. Should this affect our choice of partner? Many more of us will carry genes which mean that, if certain environmental conditions are met – for example, we smoke, or eat too much – we will be far more likely to develop heart disease or cancer than someone else with the same habits but different genes. Perhaps an individual with genes increasing the possibility of heart disease might be refused a driving licence after the age of 25 because of the increased likelihood of dying at the wheel and causing a serious accident. If it is known that a young person is at high risk of serious disease later in life, will he or she be disadvantaged when looking for college places, grants for education, loans, jobs and relationships?

These scenarios can sound a little far-fetched, but it would be better for society to consider in advance the possibilities that knowledge from the Human Genome Project will open up, and set down some guidelines, rather than waiting until the situation is upon us. When we consider that for many insurance and finance companies in the 1980s and 1990s, simply having an HIV test would either deny you life insurance and a mortgage or at least ensure that your premiums were many times higher than anyone else's *even if the test result was negative*, perhaps some of the above possibilities seem less unlikely.

It can certainly be argued that it is unfair to have children affected with a serious genetic disease when the knowledge is there to prevent it. But the knowledge does not solve the problems, it simply raises further dilemmas. Should all couples who plan to start a family – or indeed, who plan to have sex (as there is always a risk of pregnancy unless one of the partners is sterilised) – be screened to see if their genetic weaknesses are compatible? Amongst the Ashkenazi Jews of North America, a genetic disease called **Tay-Sachs disease** is very common, in which an enzyme required for lipid metabolism is not produced. The nervous system degenerates and sufferers die by the age of five. The rabbis themselves have organised screening of each couple who plan to marry. If it is found that they are both carriers of the Tay-Sachs gene, then the marriage is forbidden. The distress for couples who find they are genetically incompatible must be great, yet the saving of human misery if Tay-Sachs disease can be reduced or removed from the population would be enormous. In the North American community the incidence of the disease has already been lowered by about 80%. Similarly, screening of couples for **thalassaemia**, a hereditary blood disease, has been extremely effective in countries where the risk is high for the whole population, such as the

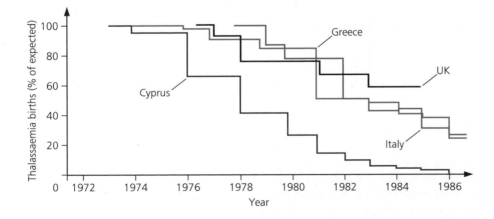

Figure 5.16 Results of thalassaemia control programmes in Cyprus, Greece, Italy and the UK

Mediterranean countries. It is less successful in countries like the UK where the affected group is a minority scattered through the rest of the population, and may be less aware both of the risks and of the screening that is available.

Screening all couples to see if they are carrying a particular gene can be prohibitively expensive, and very much a blunt instrument in some cases. In Tay-Sachs disease the screening is limited to a relatively small community, so is viable. For cystic fibrosis, the whole reproductive population of Europe would have to be screened, and then only 70–5% of the possible cases of cystic fibrosis would be prevented because sometimes it is caused by a gene other than the one isolated on chromosome 7. The economic value of screening programmes can be studied for each disease to see if they are financially worth carrying out. For example, **phenylketonuria (PKU)** is an inherited defect in which the amino acid phenylalanine cannot be metabolised. Levels of phenylalanine build up in the blood and damage the brain. In 1979 it was estimated that it cost £20 000 to screen 15 000 babies, of which one was likely to suffer from PKU, and then to supply the affected baby with a special diet until adulthood, when the brain loses its sensitivity to high levels of phenylalanine. However, the treatment of a PKU baby who is not detected early and is therefore so severely handicapped that it will need institutional care throughout its approximately 45-year or so life cost £126 000, so the cost of the screening of all newborn infants was well justified. For cystic fibrosis screening, however, the cost benefit of whole-population screening would be much smaller (as calculated in 1989). The cost of screening 2000 fetuses to find and abort the one with cystic fibrosis was £80 000. The cost of treating a child suffering from cystic fibrosis throughout its relatively short life was £125 000. Figures like these look only at the medical costs – the human suffering of affected individuals and their families is not, and probably cannot, be quantified. Thus, partly because of economic analyses like these and partly because screening does not guarantee the correct answer as more than one gene may cause the same problem, for cystic fibrosis only families in which the disease has occurred are screened.

Couples who find they are at risk of producing children with genetic defects have several options open to them. They can go ahead and have a family, hoping that in the genetic lottery they are lucky and their children inherit healthy genes, but prepared to support and take care of them if not. They may decide not to have children at all, to prevent passing on a faulty gene even in a carrier. The third option is to go ahead with pregnancies but to have each pregnancy screened and terminated if the fetus is affected. This option can be very traumatic, and is not open to some individuals because of their beliefs about abortion issues, but it is effective at preventing the birth of children with genetic diseases. What it doesn't do is weed out individuals who are carriers, so the gene continues into the next generation. A more sophisticated version of this technique is to use IVF. The ova and sperm of a couple at high risk of producing offspring affected by genetic disease are fertilised outside the body. When the embryos are small balls of cells, a single cell is removed from each (this appears to cause no harm to the development of the embryo), and the genetic make-up is checked. Only those embryos free of the problem genes are placed in the mother's uterus to implant and grow. For example, in the case of sex-linked diseases such as haemophilia and Duchenne muscular dystrophy, only female embryos would be replaced.

Another aspect of this complex picture is that with techniques of genetic manipulation, inserting a healthy gene into the cells of an individual with a genetic disorder is becoming a possibility. Trials are already going ahead in people with cystic fibrosis, providing cells which can manage sodium and chloride ions appropriately and so allow normal, healthy mucus to be produced, and the results are promising. Another disease which is being considered for this sort of treatment is diabetes. If the gene for healthy islets of Langerhans can be inserted into sufferers' pancreas cells so that new insulin-producing islets are formed, the days of insulin injections for diabetics might be numbered. But as with most emergent technology, there are more ethical dilemmas here. At present, genetic manipulation of the germ cells is completely forbidden. The downside of this sensible decision is that whilst in the foreseeable future, affected individuals may be helped in their lifetime to be free from the effects of the genetic disorder they have inherited, they will nevertheless still be at risk of passing it on to their offspring. This means treatment has to be ongoing through the generations, which is an expensive option. It can only be a matter of time before it is suggested that manipulation of the germ cells as well as the somatic cells would treat not just the individuals concerned but all their potential future descendants too. Once it is permitted to manipulate the genes of the germ cells for medical reasons, there are those who fear this would lead to changes being made in the genes for intelligence, or beauty, or height, or aggression. The manipulation of the human breeding stock and the creation of sets of 'designer humans' might then become not science fiction but science fact.

These complex issues can arouse very emotional and not always scientifically informed debate. However, it is very important that we as a society address these problems with care in full and open debate before decisions are made for us behind closed doors without our understanding or consent.

Genetic counselling

For most people, finding out about genetic diseases in the family is very traumatic. Instead of seeing themselves as normal healthy people who will go on and produce a normal healthy baby, they suddenly realise that they carry a gene that could make them (or more probably their children) seriously ill or handicapped. All of the issues just discussed about whether to have children, to abort affected pregnancies, who to tell, etc. are suddenly of immediate and personal relevance. Because many couples first realise they have a problem when they are pregnant or shortly after their baby is born, the trauma is even harder to bear.

Genetic counsellors are trained to help people come to terms with carrying an abnormal gene that can cause genetic disease. They help people understand how the genetic information is passed from one generation to another, and the relevance of dominant and recessive characters. A family pedigree will be worked out, which may be useful in confirming the diagnosis and can also be used to indicate any other individuals who might unknowingly be affected as carriers. This however raises another difficult question – should those other potential carriers, some of whom may be quite distant relations, be told or not? Genetic counsellors help people come to a decision about issues like this. They also assess the statistical risk of a couple producing another child with the same defect. If the problem is caused by a single recessive or dominant gene then the risk can be calculated easily using Mendel's laws, and even if it is polygenic or the result of a whole-chromosome abnormality the risk can be calculated using accumulated medical data.

For most genetic defects, as already mentioned, the only real options are to avoid having children (or any more children) or to undergo prenatal screening and abort affected pregnancies. Again the role of the genetic counsellor is to help couples recognise the options and work their way through to the alternative that is right for them within their own framework of moral,

Figure 5.17 Trained genetic counsellors can help couples to understand their choices when they become aware that they are carrying genes which could result in their children suffering genetic diseases.

family, religious and social beliefs and traditions. There are as yet no easy solutions to this problem. All that can be hoped for is that a couple reach as comfortable an acceptance of the facts as they can. Whether the advances promised by techniques such as genetic engineering and gene manipulation will bring real help and relief to families affected by genetic diseases is still to be seen. The problems such techniques themselves bring might be just as difficult for individuals and society to resolve.

SUMMARY

- **Sexually transmitted diseases** ('social diseases') are passed from one person to another during sexual acts. The microorganisms that cause them cannot survive outside the human body. Treatment of an STD involves tracing all the sexual partners of an infected person and treating them at the same time.

- **AIDS (acquired immune deficiency syndrome)** is caused by **HIV (human immunodeficiency virus)** which is spread by sexual contact and by infected blood or needles. People may be infected with HIV but not show symptoms of AIDS – they are referred to as **HIV positive**. In AIDS, HIV affects the immune system and so the body is vulnerable to all sorts of infections. AIDS is an incurable fatal disease.

- **Contraception** is the prevention of conception occurring in spite of having sexual intercourse.

- **Natural methods** involve abstaining from intercourse during the woman's fertile period.

- **Barrier methods** include the **condom**, **female condom** or **diaphragm** (cap). A physical barrier is placed between the penis and cervix to prevent the sperm reaching the ovum.

- The **IUD (intrauterine device)** is a device placed inside the uterus which prevents an fertilised ovum from implanting.

- **Spermicides** are chemicals which kill sperm. They are used with barrier methods.

- The **contraceptive pill** interacts with the female hormonal cycle to prevent ovulation.

- **Sterilisation** is an operation which makes the person permanently unable to have children. In men the vas deferens is cut, and in women the Fallopian tubes are cut or tied.

- **Abortion** may be spontaneous, when a fetus dies and is lost in a miscarriage, or it may be medically induced. Medical abortions are carried out when the health of the mother or the fetus is at risk, but it is an issue of great sensitivity.

- **Infertility** is the inability of a couple to conceive. In women, ovulation may not occur, or the Fallopian tubes may be blocked, or the uterus may not accept a pregnancy due to an imbalance in the hormones. In men, no sperm may be produced, or fewer sperm than usual, or many abnormal sperm.

- Artificial insemination by a donor **(AID)** may be used to treat infertile couples where sperm production is the cause. **Fertility drugs** can help women who do not ovulate, and *in vitro* fertilisation involves fertilising the ovum outside the body and re-inserting the fertilised ovum into the uterus.

- **Genetic** or **inherited diseases** result from the DNA inherited from parents, or from mutations (changes) to that DNA. **Aneuploidy** is the absence of a chromosome or presence of an extra chromosome. **Nondisjunction**, the failure of a homologous pair of chromosomes to separate during meiosis, can result in **monosomy** (only one of a pair of chromosomes) or **trisomy** (three of a type of chromosome instead of two). Examples are **Down's syndrome**, caused by trisomy on chromosome 21; **Turner's syndrome**, females with monosomy on the X sex chromosome (XO); a **metafemale**, trisomy on the X chromosome (XXX); and **Klinefelter's syndrome**, males with various extra sex chromosome combinations such as XXY or XXYY.

- Genetic diseases may be the result of a single gene rather than whole-chromosome mutations. Examples include **Duchenne muscular dystrophy**, a paralysing disease caused by a recessive allele on the X chromosome; **cystic fibrosis**, in which the exocrine glands produce sticky mucus, again caused by a recessive allele; and **Huntington's disease**, degeneration of the nerve cells in middle age, caused by a dominant allele.

- Genetic testing makes it possible to identify individuals who are carriers of a faulty gene, and thus in theory could prevent the birth of affected offspring. The techniques raise difficult social issues with implications in many areas, including insurance and jobs.

QUESTIONS

1 a What are the main types of contraception?
  b How can the use of different types of contraceptive affect the health of women?
  c There are many different contraceptive methods available, yet the world population continues to grow rapidly. Discuss possible reasons for this.

2 'Infertility is a tragedy for any couple who want to have a family. If it is possible to enable an infertile couple to have a child, it should always be done.' Discuss this statement, considering both biological and social issues.

3 a Genetic diseases are the result of problems in the DNA of the cells of an individual. Choose one disease from list **i** and one from list **ii**. For each disease explain the biological basis of the condition and the symptoms.
    i Down's syndrome, Turner's syndrome, Klinefelter's syndrome, metafemale
    ii cystic fibrosis, Tay-Sachs disease, Huntington's disease
  b What are the currently available options for overcoming genetic diseases, and why do they pose problems for society?

6

Ageing and death

Humans have a longer average life span than almost any other mammal, but in common with all other mammals, after a period of maturity we show signs of ageing and eventually die. It is possible to monitor the decline in function of the body by such measures as reduction in running speed, smaller lung capacity and weaker grip, and it is also possible to describe the cellular changes that can be observed as the body ages. What has not been possible so far is to identify a mechanism for ageing. Research into this is driven partly by scientific interest and by the search for advances in the treatment of diseases associated with ageing. However, there is also a desire on the part of many people to understand what causes ageing in the hope that it might be possible to stop the clock, or at least delay it!

THEORIES OF AGEING

Each individual begins life as a single cell, then enters the world as a tiny newborn baby, after which the physical appearance changes rapidly as we grow and mature. After young adulthood, the appearance changes less rapidly, but the changes that do occur are increasingly associated with ageing. Different cultures look on ageing differently. In some cultures age is venerated and thus the signs of ageing are welcomed because they bring added status. Unfortunately, in much of the developed world, the culture values youth and youthful looks, and so changing distribution of body hair (baldness), change in hair colour (going grey) and the appearance of facial wrinkles are often dreaded. It is interesting that within one society the same symptoms can send different messages simply depending on the sex of the individual concerned. In the UK certain signs of maturity such as greying hair and a few wrinkles are regarded as positive and distinguished in men, giving them a level of respect among their peers and in the work place. The same early symptoms of ageing in a woman are often regarded as negative, showing that she is losing her sexual and reproductive appeal.

Ageing does not start at one particular time or continue at a constant rate once it has started. Cellular and tissue changes accumulate over time and become increasingly evident with age. But the rate at which these changes occur varies greatly from individual to individual, depending on genetics, lifestyle and the environment in which an individual has lived. Ageing can be defined as *a progressive, generalised impairment of function resulting from a loss of adaptive responses to stress and resulting in a growing risk of age-related disease*. As we go through life more and more genetic errors are made as cells replicate, there are degenerative changes in cells and the immune system becomes less effective so diseases have a greater effect.

Why do we age? Some people have put forward theories that there is an adaptive advantage to ageing and indeed to death, on the basis that if individuals did not age and die the population would get too large and there would be insufficient resources for the younger, reproductive members of the species. The problem with this argument is that natural selection acts on the individual, not the population. Looking at other animals as well as humans, it would seem to be of little individual advantage to suffer from the disabilities of old age, and even less of an advantage to be dead! It may be that ageing is

Figure 6.1 Whilst we may not understand the mechanism for ageing, we can certainly recognise the signs as it takes place.

genetically programmed, but because the damaging 'age' genes do not become apparent until after reproduction has taken place, there is no effective way of removing them from the population. Another idea suggests that some genes may have multiple effects, with favourable effects dominating during early life and the reproductive years which leads to them being passed on, but with harmful ageing effects which only become apparent later in life. Another idea about ageing is that it is inevitable, rather along the same lines that a car or washing machine has built-in obsolescence. In the **disposable soma theory**, resources are not wasted in producing a body capable of eternal life when it is likely to die in some sort of accident anyway. Sufficient resources are used to produce a body which will reproduce and take care of the offspring to adulthood but which is then disposable. All other resources are put into reproductive effort, using a lower level of resources for the body than would be needed for eternal youth.

OBSERVING AGEING

Cells and ageing

There are certain changes in cells that seem typical of ageing. Ageing cells can be observed in tissue culture, where they are isolated from all the normal biochemical changes in the body which may affect their behaviour. Alternatively, cells from individuals at different stages of their lives may be compared, though it is difficult to tell which differences are due to lifestyle changes (e.g. taking less exercise) and which are genuinely due to ageing. However, combined evidence from both types of study suggests there are certain changes common to all ageing cells.

The turnover of proteins in normal cells and body fluids provides a good marker of ageing. Proteins are broken down into their constituent amino acids ready for recycling. When this process occurs inefficiently, granules of a yellow fatty substance called **lipofuscin** begin to accumulate in the cells. Protein recycling becomes increasingly inefficient as cells age and so the level of lipofuscin granules offers a measure of cell age. Lipofuscin has the effect of slowing cell metabolism, so as it builds up the cell metabolism becomes slower and less efficient in a vicious circle of ageing.

The number of **lysosomes** (vesicles full of digestive enzymes) in a cell also increases as it ages. Some aged cells die before the organism dies, and in some tissues these cells are not all replaced, leading to a net degeneration of the tissue and to organs working less effectively in older people. New theories suggest that cells are genetically programmed to die unless they are continuously stimulated by chemical signals from other cells. It may well be a failure of these communication systems which leads to cell death as the lysosomes burst.

Most of our organ systems operate with a large amount of overcapacity when we are young. For example, we can manage with only half a kidney functioning instead of the normal two. Much of this **reserve capacity** is lost as we get older. We can continue to operate quite normally for a long time, but are less well equipped to cope with sudden physiological stresses placed on our bodies. This is why diseases or injuries can have more serious consequences in older people. As can be seen in figure 6.3, some organs lose a lot of cells and become significantly less efficient as we get older, while other tissues are affected very little. These average figures will vary greatly from individual to individual as well, depending on both genetic and environmental factors.

Another cellular effect of ageing seems to be a reduction in the effectiveness of the immune system when faced with an unknown pathogen. As people get older they usually maintain their immunity to pathogens which they have met

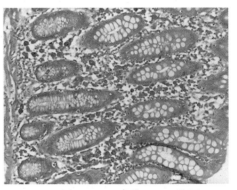

Figure 6.2 The build-up of lipofuscin in cells (shown as brown granules in this picture) seems closely associated with ageing and loss of function.

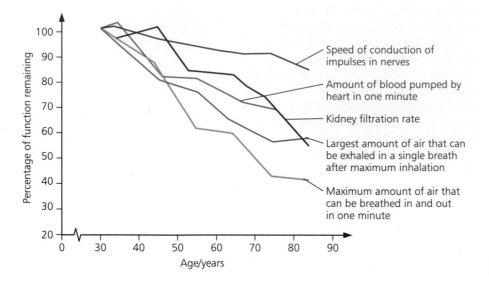

Figure 6.3 The decline of a range of body functions with age.

during their lifetime. Problems arise when they meet new pathogens for the first time. This failure of the immune system is particularly marked with respect to infections of the respiratory system. This vulnerability may be due in part to the effect of a lifetime of breathing in pollutants, particularly tobacco smoke, or it may be partly due to the shallow breathing which is common in older people. As a result of this, parts of the lungs are not inflated properly, providing bacteria with a suitable habitat in which to multiply.

Signs of ageing

A number of changes typically occur during the ageing process in human beings.

- Skin becomes less elastic and wrinkles, hair loses colour and becomes grey and (in males particulary) may fall out.
- The lean body mass reduces – in other words muscle and bone are lost – and there is also a steady reduction in the water content of the body. These changes are the result of a decline in function of a variety of organs.
- After the menopause, women are unable to conceive a baby naturally.
- Problems of the muscles and skeletal system become more common. For example, joints tend to move less freely, bones break more easily and muscles are often weaker.
- The senses tend to deteriorate, leading to poorer sight and hearing. Less obviously, the senses of balance, taste and smell may also be reduced.
- There is increased susceptibility to infectious diseases which seems likely to be the result of the reduced efficiency of the immune system.
- Homeostasis becomes less reliable. For example, the mechanism to maintain a constant body temperature when the surroundings are cold becomes less efficient.
- There is often mental deterioration, with older people finding it difficult to remember recent events.
- Arthritis, cancer and diseases of the cardiovascular system (like heart attacks and strokes) become much more common with age.

The majority of these changes are inevitable, but at what age and to what degree they occur are variable, and in some cases can be delayed with the right lifestyle choices. For example, an increase in the protein collagen in the skin cells, causing some loss of elasticity and wrinkling, is unavoidable with old age, but if we choose to smoke these changes will be speeded up. The blood supply to the skin is reduced with each cigarette and this accelerates the process of ageing. Similarly, if we maintain a high level of weight-bearing exercise and a diet rich in calcium and vitamin D, many of the skeletomuscular changes associated with ageing will be substantially reduced or even avoided.

The menopause

One of the landmarks of ageing for women is the **menopause**. This is the period of time, usually over several years, when biological changes happen which reduce and finally end the ability of a woman to have a child. The age at which the menopause occurs varies, but it is usually between 45 and 55 years of age. The ovaries contain only a limited number of ova, which are all present at the time of birth. Throughout the reproductive life many of these ova die, and some are released as part of a menstrual cycle. As the number of follicles becomes low, the ovaries become less sensitive to the pituitary hormones, so less oestrogen and progesterone are made. In turn, the levels of pituitary hormones drop, until a point is reached when hormone levels are no longer high enough to trigger ovulation. The endometrium may still build up enough to cause menstrual bleeding, but this then becomes less regular as the hormonal balance of the cycle is lost. For some women this means periods every couple of weeks for some time, but for the majority the menstrual bleeding becomes increasingly spaced out until it stops completely. Yet other women experience a sudden, complete halt in their periods. Because of the erratic nature of the physical change, the menopause is considered to be over one year after the last menstrual period.

The menopause has a number of other associated symptoms as well as the loss of fertility. Because the sex hormones also affect the vaginal mucus and the libido, some women find that their vagina becomes dry and thus love-making can be painful. The libido may also drop, though for many women the removal of any risk of pregnancy overcomes any hormonal decrease in desire. The fluctuating levels of sex hormones can also trigger mood swings and symptoms such as 'hot flushes' when massive vasodilation occurs, night sweats, sleeping problems, headaches, sore breasts, palpitations, irritability and depression. Very often those women who have most difficulties already in their lives are the ones most likely to suffer severe symptoms.

Most women find the menopause little more than an inconvenience, but about 30% experience symptoms severe enough to make them feel ill. The current medical practice is to offer **hormone replacement therapy** (**HRT**). This involves a regular dose of low levels of oestrogen and progesterone (not unlike the contraceptive pill) which help maintain an artificial balance until the menopause is over. HRT causes the woman to have periods for as long as she takes it, but she is not fertile. The use of HRT is still quite contentious, with some people arguing that it should be given to the majority of menopausal and post-menopausal women, and others that the long-term effects are unknown and that it should be used only when absolutely necessary.

HRT and health

HRT offers protection against heart disease by maintaining the levels of protective oestrogen, and seems to protect against some cancers too. However, there are concerns that it may increase the risk of breast cancer and endometrial cancer. Different groups present the evidence in different ways, but the jury is still out on the overall long-term health effects.

The skeletal system

Loss of muscle fibres

Elderly people often suffer from lack of muscle strength, loss of flexibility, stiffness and pain in the joints and fragile bones which break easily and mend only slowly. The loss of muscle strength is very irritating, because it can make it difficult or impossible to perform simple everyday tasks such as opening a screw-topped jar or carrying a heavy bag. It appears that there is a measurable loss of muscle fibres which is noticeable from the age of 45 onwards. The loss seems to be associated with a loss of motor neurones which stimulate the muscle fibres. If the fibres are not activated and used they eventually die and are removed. However, this loss of muscle seems to be linked to a tendency to become less active in the later stages of life rather than an inevitable decline linked with ageing. If an individual maintains a high level of exercise and fitness as part of their lifestyle, the loss of muscle fibres will be substantially reduced or avoided. Moreover, if an elderly individual begins a programme of gentle exercise, some of the muscle loss can be reversed. Studies have shown elderly people who need a high level of assistance in their daily lives becoming much more independent again after an exercise programme has built up muscle, enabling them to carry out far more tasks than previously and also improving their feelings of confidence and well-being.

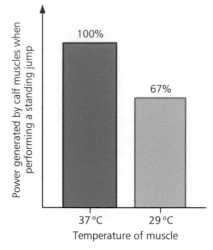

Figure 6.4 This graph shows the effect of temperature on the output of human calf muscles. Older people are often cold, through lack of heating, poor circulation and poor homeostatic mechanisms. If old people keep warm, their muscles will function better and they will be able to do more.

Hypothermia

The main factors that cause **hypothermia** are a low environmental temperature and poor thermoregulation. As these two conditions are most commonly met by elderly people, accidental hypothermia is most common in this age group. In hypothermia the core body temperature drops below the normal 37 °C, causing many physiological problems and even death. Five hundred deaths each year are attributed directly to hypothermia in the UK, although this is probably an underestimate. During the three main winter months in the UK there are up to 9000 hospital admissions of elderly people suffering hypothermia.

The symptoms include cold skin, blue lips, drowsiness, sluggish movement, slow thought and speech, stiff limbs, slow heart rate and low blood pressure. These symptoms develop as the individual gets colder. If the core body temperature drops to 35–30 °C then 33% of those affected will die. If the body temperature goes below 30 °C, the mortality rises to 70%. If you find someone suffering from hypothermia the most important thing is to get medical help, and to start warming the person up *gradually*. Because of the low blood pressure it is very important to warm up only very slowly, or the blood pressure can drop to dangerous levels and the heart can lose its rhythm, causing death.

Why are old people so prone to hypothermia? First they are often poor, or at least concerned about money, so do not keep their homes very warm. A national survey in England showed 75% of elderly people had living room temperatures below 18.3 °C. Second, this cold environment is frequently combined with lack of exercise, not enough warm clothing and poor thermoregulation. In elderly people the autonomic responses may be reduced or lost, so they do not produce heat by shivering when they get cold and vasoconstriction in the skin is much less efficient.

Once hypothermia begins, the slowing of thought and drowsiness make it very unlikely that the affected person will realise what is happening and take action. A campaign to increase awareness of the dangers of hypothermia had the slogan 'Cold kills the old', but it needn't if elderly people can be provided with the means to keep warm and if they can be encouraged to take a little more exercise and eat and drink regular warm food and beverages.

Arthritis

Measurable changes also take place in the bones and joints as we age. Cartilage and connective tissues such as tendons suffer changes as a result of cell ageing that can affect the functioning of the joints. It is difficult to distinguish which joint problems are simply the result of wear and tear, and which are the result of age-related cellular changes. The ability to maintain the joint tissues in good working order is certainly reduced with age, but like so many things is dependent on many variables. Within the major ball and socket joints the cartilage may become worn away, or thin as it is replaced less effectively. This may lead to **arthritis**. As the cartilage degenerates, the bones no longer slide smoothly over each other and bony knobs may develop on the articulating surfaces as shown in figure 6.5. This is **osteoarthritis**, a condition which causes great pain and disability in the ageing population. In **rheumatoid arthritis**, bone cells begin to appear in the cartilage which also makes the joints considerably less mobile and very painful. In a study of 14 000 people over the age of 60 in the USA, about 49% showed some degree of arthritis. Because osteoarthritis is very much a disease associated with 'wear and tear', it is not perhaps surprising that it increases in old age. However, we do not yet have a clear explanation of why some people suffer from arthritis in many joints, whilst others who have been very active throughout their lives, and thus given their bodies a great deal of wear and tear, have no apparent arthritis at all.

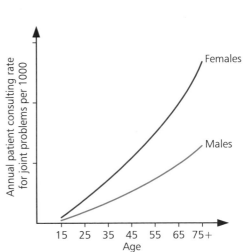

Figure 6.5 The effect of osteoarthritis on the joints is shown diagrammatically on the left, and the graph above of symptoms reported to doctors during one month in the UK shows how much more frequently joint problems such as these are suffered in old age.

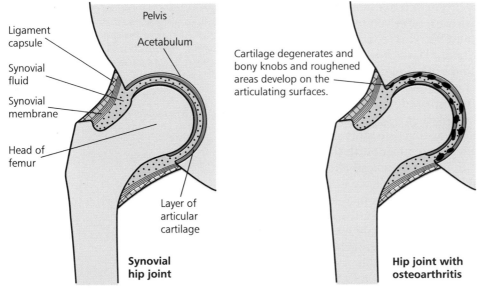

In arthritis, bony deposits may form in the **costal cartilage** which joins the ribs to the sternum. The joints become more rigid and the movement of the rib cage becomes restricted during breathing, reducing the amount of air that can be breathed in and out. The fibrous cartilage of the intervertebral discs loses fluid, making it less efficient as a shock absorber. This can cause both postural problems and a reduced ability to carry any weight.

Osteoporosis

The bones themselves are also prone to problems which are the result of ageing. In young, healthy individuals bone is a relatively fluid material, with old bone being removed and new bone being laid down constantly in response to the needs of the body. The skeleton remains in equilibrium, unless changed physical demands result in an overall increase or loss of bone mass. However, as people get older bone is destroyed faster than it is replaced. This happens in all individuals, although the age at which it begins and the speed at which it progresses is very variable. If the loss of calcium salts from the bones becomes too marked, the individual will suffer from **osteoporosis**.

Osteoporosis is a disease that appears from middle age onwards, and causes a major problem in the mobility and well-being of older people, particularly older women. Women are particularly at risk from osteoporosis once they have passed through the menopause. Older women can actually excrete more calcium in their urine than they take in in their diets. There seems to be some imbalance in the hormones involved in normal bone formation which results from the marked drop in the female hormone oestrogen after the menopause. Another major factor in the development of osteoporosis in both men and women seems to be age-related changes in the cells lining the gut and their ability to absorb calcium from the diet. The cells lining the gut are continuously replaced. In young people this replacement occurs every 30 days, but in older people the replacement takes about 40 days. This reflects a general slowing in the metabolic processes of these gut lining cells. They secrete less mucus and fewer enzymes with age, and also absorb less well. Vitamin D is important in the diet for promoting the absorption of calcium across the wall of the gut, as well as in promoting the uptake of calcium by the bone itself. Vitamin D is itself also absorbed in the gut, so the ageing of the gut lining cells affects its uptake too. To have a metabolic effect, the vitamin D once absorbed must be converted to an active form in the cells of the liver and the kidneys. These organs too show degeneration with age. Kidney function begins to deteriorate from the age of about 30 due to the progressive loss of nephrons. Liver volume too is lost, up to 30% disappearing between the ages of 25 and 90. This reduced function in the kidneys and liver reduces the amount of vitamin D which is converted to the active form, and therefore reduces the amount of calcium absorbed by the cells of the gut. Less calcium is therefore deposited in the bone, slowing down the growth of new bone to replace that which is destroyed.

Once substantial bone thinning has taken place it is very difficult to repair the damage. However, if evidence is found early that osteoporosis is developing, women in particular can be offered treatment with the female hormone oestrogen. This has been shown to have a beneficial effect on calcium balance, and also slows the rate at which bone density is lost. The oestrogen needs to be given with progesterone to avoid an increased risk of developing uterine cancer. This effect in preventing osteoporosis is one of the benefits for women who are given hormone replacement therapy after their natural menopause. There are other things which can be done to help reduce the likelihood of osteoporosis becoming a problem. If people have a high bone density whilst young, they are less likely to reach a point where their bones are so fragile that they break very easily. The best way to develop high bone density is to eat a diet rich in calcium and vitamin D, and also to undertake plenty of weight-bearing, bone-building exercise such as walking and jogging. If this type of diet and exercise is then continued into later life, the risks of serious osteoporosis developing are substantially reduced. However, there is also a genetic factor. The tendency to develop osteoporosis runs in families, and is probably concerned with inherited tendencies in vitamin D and calcium metabolism.

Prevention of age-related skeletal problems

It certainly appears that an active lifestyle along with a healthy diet reduces the likelihood of major musculoskeletal problems in later life. Prevention of obesity is another way in which we can help ourselves, as the strain on muscles

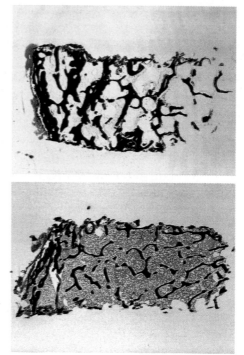

Figure 6.6 In these sections of bones, a silver stain has been used that shows the calcified (healthy) areas of bone in black. A normal bone is shown in the top photograph. The bottom photograph shows osteoporosis – there is less calcified bone, making the bones fragile. They are also very prone to breaking, and difficult to heal.

and joints in the very overweight is substantially more than on those of a person with more moderate weight. A survey by the Office of Population Censuses and Surveys in the UK in 1988 showed that disorders of the muscles and bones were responsible for about 40% of all physical disability. Anything we can do to reduce the likelihood of joining those disabled by the effects of ageing and lifestyle on their skeleton must be seen as a positive move.

Fitness, heart disease and ageing

Look back to figure 6.3. It shows the effect of ageing on both the cardiovascular system and the respiratory system. The output of the heart per minute falls steadily from the age of about 40 until 70, and then levels out. This is due at least in part to a weakening of the heart muscle along with the other body muscles, so that less blood is pumped with each ventricular contraction, but it may be associated with other lifestyle changes as well. The maximum exhaled volume and the amount of air that can be breathed in and out over a minute both drop sharply over the same timescale. The combined effect of these changes is to substantially reduce the amount of oxygen supplied to the body cells, and also to diminish the ability to remove the carbon dioxide produced by them. This is turn means that the individual will feel less fit, become breathless more easily and find physical exertion more difficult. Partly as a result of these changes many older people become

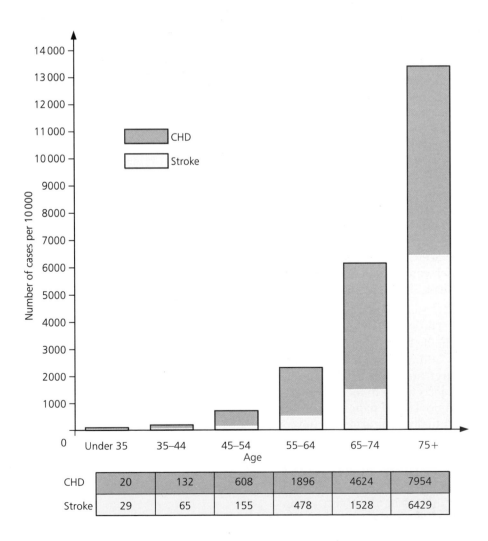

	Under 35	35–44	45–54	55–64	65–74	75+
CHD	20	132	608	1896	4624	7954
Stroke	29	65	155	478	1528	6429

Figure 6.7 The increasing incidence of coronary heart disease (CHD) and strokes with age are shown in these data from Scotland, 1994.

decreasingly active as they go through life, producing a vicious circle of decreasing fitness. The biological basis for these cardiovascular and respiratory changes involves the general loss of muscle tissue, a reduction in elasticity of the tissue of the lungs and a loss of flexibility in the joints between the ribs and the sternum. In addition, the elastic recoil of the arteries is gradually lost and the blood vessels throughout the body become narrower and less flexible, with a greater resistance to the flow of blood around the body. This in turn often leads to raised blood pressure and an increased load on the heart. The levels of lipofuscin in the heart muscle cells also increase dramatically in some individuals, though not in everyone – the range is very wide. An additional problem in an ageing cardiovascular system is that increasing amounts of fatty deposits may be laid down on the walls of the arteries over the years, and also the endothelium of the blood vessels is increasingly likely to become roughened. Both of these factors increase the likelihood of the artery becoming blocked either by the fatty deposit itself or, more likely, by clots forming around the site of the fat or the roughened wall. This leads to the increase in heart attacks and strokes evident with increasing age, as illustrated in figure 6.7.

It can be difficult to tell how much the changes in the cardiovascular system and respiratory system associated with age are due to the ageing process and how much they are due to changes in lifestyle. Certainly in developed countries, where people tend to live longer and therefore the problems of old age are easier to study, there is a tendency for adults in their middle years to begin to adopt a more sedentary, less energetic lifestyle. As they are often financially better off at this stage of their lives they are also likely to eat and drink more and, if smokers, to smoke more. These changes will themselves lead to many of the effects described in the ageing cardiovascular system and respiratory system. In older people who maintain physically active lives, eat and drink in moderation and do not smoke, the changes in these major body systems are much less marked. There is some inevitable loss of elasticity and function, but they are still capable of remarkable physical endurance. Also, if elderly people who have considerable loss of both cardiovascular and respiratory function begin to build up a programme of gentle physical exercise, the deterioration can be halted and reversed, leading to measurable improvements in cardiac output and respiratory volumes. This in turn leads to a greater feeling of well-being and the ability to do things which had been given up because of 'lack of breath'.

The nervous system and ageing

Eyesight and hearing

Age-related changes take place throughout the nervous system. Some of the more obvious changes are in the sense organs. The eyesight deteriorates with age for a variety of reasons. First, the lens gradually loses its ability to change focal length. Throughout life the lens grows by adding protein fibres known as crystallins. By the age of 50–60 the lens is so large and thick that it cannot change shape. This usually results in distant objects being in focus, but near objects appearing blurred. People tend to hold books and papers further and further away to bring them into focus until eventually their arms are not long enough and they have to resort to wearing glasses, for close work at least. Second, lipofuscin begins building up in the rods and cones from the age of about 10 years old. By 24 years old up to 8% of the volume of the rods and cones is lipofuscin, and this rises to over 20% by the time we reach 80 years old. As a result of this gradual accumulation of lipofuscin, the ability of the rods and cones to respond to light is reduced. This in turn slows the

Ageing and the basal metabolic rate

The **basal metabolic rate** (BMR) reflects the energy requirements of our bodies for survival and maintenance, but undertaking no additional activity. As we get older the metabolism of our cells slows down. Cells divide less frequently, tissues are renewed less often and there is no further growth. Thus as people age their BMR falls. This is part of the reason why older people feel cold so easily – they are generating less body heat as a result of basal body metabolism than younger people. In addition to this, many older people become less active, so the energy demands of the whole body drop as well as those of individual cells. Thus men of 75 and over require an average energy intake of only 8800 kJ daily and women of the same age only 8000 kJ. This compares with 12 600 kJ and 9200 kJ daily for moderately active 30-year-old men and women.

The appetite often diminishes with age, probably because the body is demanding less energy. Those people who continue to eat the same amount as they get older will tend to put on considerable amounts of fat, as their energy intake increasingly outweighs their output. Of course, if people remain very active as they get older their energy needs remain far higher than if they become increasingly sedentary.

manufacture and recycling of the visual pigments of the eye, contributing to the gradual loss of visual power which is almost inevitable with increasing age.

Hearing too is affected by age. The hearing loss common in older people is associated with degeneration of the sensory cells of the inner ear, or of the nerves involved in sound sensitivity, or both. There is often a family tendency to hearing loss in old age, suggesting some genetic basis for the problem. However, it seems likely that for many people there is a strong environmental factor to the hearing loss. It has been known for some time that exposure to very loud sounds such as pop music or pneumatic drills can damage the hearing. It is now becoming increasingly apparent that constant background noise from traffic, music and other sources can cause high-tone hearing loss due to the gradual destruction of sensory cells. It is obviously difficult to avoid exposure to this background noise, but people who live in quiet, isolated places are least likely to suffer from environmentally induced hearing loss in old age.

Alzheimer's disease

Some changes that can occur in the nervous system as part of the ageing process are even more devastating than deafness and blindness, both to the individuals concerned and to their partners and families. **Alzheimer's disease** can affect people in their earlier years, but is most common in old age. Research indicates that it is a multifactorial condition with age as one of the major factors. In Alzheimer's disease the brain cells shrivel and disintegrate, leaving sticky clumps of damaged cells and tangled fibres as the only remains of a once healthy, functioning central nervous tissue. As this disintegration of the brain tissue progresses, normal brain function is gradually lost. Although the disease progresses differently in each individual, there is a common overall pattern to the deterioration.

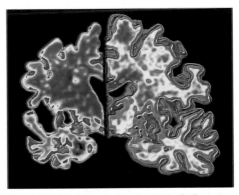

Figure 6.8 The slow reduction of active brain tissue to sticky clumps of damaged cells is mirrored in the loss of memory and control and the changes in behaviour as an individual progresses through the stages of Alzheimer's disease. The affected brain (left) is shrunken compared with the normal brain (right) due to degeneration and death of the nerve cells.

The initial deterioration of the cells of the brain obviously precedes the behavioural symptoms, but is not usually detected unless the brain is investigated for other reasons, such as a suspected brain tumour. So for the vast majority of sufferers, the onset is completely unexpected. The first symptoms are relatively minor, and easily ignored as the sort of memory lapses and mistakes we all make from time to time, particularly as we get older and our memories have more information to store and sift. The memory lapses develop into more serious problems, such as disorientation over time, and an increasing tiredness and lethargy can become obvious. Sufferers may feel persecuted, thinking that people are stealing from them or falsely accusing them of blunders. They may hoard things and hide them for years. As the disease progresses individuals often begin to wander, leaving their homes at all hours of the day and night. They also lose control of their bladder and bowels, yet may remain aware enough to be enormously embarrassed about this initially and try to pass the blame onto others. It is a great relief in some ways when the awareness, although not the continence problem itself, is lost in the disintegrating brain. The memory of how to perform simple everyday tasks such as laying the table or cleaning the teeth disappears. Control of the emotions becomes much reduced, returning to the tantrums and unreasonable demands of toddler years, along with a similar need for comfort, reassurance and the presence of only very familiar faces.

Gradually the power of speech is lost, and eventually Alzheimer's victims can no longer care for themselves, control their bodily functions, feed themselves or speak. By this stage they have lost most of their ability to recognise their loved ones, so that before speech is completely lost husbands, wives and children may hear their partner or parent asking who they are.

Eventually Alzheimer's disease leads to death. The distress this disease can cause within a family is immeasurable, because whilst the family has to cope with all the problems of managing an individual suffering from Alzheimer's and the sadness of losing the person they knew and loved, they still have an emaciated human shell of the same name and appearance and so can neither grieve properly nor enjoy the existence of that person. The only blessing is that for the person affected by Alzheimer's, the progression of the disease ensures that their awareness of the situation and their own tragedy is continually and slowly eroded as their brain tissue dies.

DYING AND DEATH

At the end of the ageing process, if we are fortunate enough to live long enough to experience ageing, comes death. The subject of death is treated very differently in different societies. In the developed world it is something of a taboo subject. Death in the young is a great tragedy, and something we are no longer used to. Death in the elderly is generally ignored as much as possible and in the majority of cases takes place in hospitals or hospices, away from the home environment and so removed from the experience of most younger people (see table 6.1).

Year	Deaths in hospital/%	Deaths in hospice, nursing home, etc./%	Deaths in own home/%	Deaths in someone else's home/%	Total number of deaths (100%)
1960	50.0	3.0	42.0	5.0	526 268
1991	65.7	7.6	22.5	4.2	573 096

Table 6.1 Places of death in 1960 and 1991, UK

In many other areas of the world, death is frequently seen at first hand. A combination of lack of medical treatment, poverty and malnutrition along with few health and safety regulations in workplaces mean that death is common. There are still many countries where parents can expect at least half the children they bear to die in the early years of life. Women still die in large numbers during childbirth, and many children lose at least one of their parents during their childhood. Old age means living into the 50s rather than the 70s, 80s and even 90s we can expect in the developed world. This means that people are much more familiar with death, and that the care of the dying is much more a part of everyday life. The losses of death are felt just as keenly, but effective strategies for coping with grief have to be in place to make it possible to carry on with life in a meaningful way.

What is death?

The moment of death is when the cellular processes of the living body cease to take place. This is most easily seen when the breathing stops and the heart stops beating. Once the blood stops circulating, it is only a matter of about 2–3 minutes before the cells of the brain stop functioning due to lack of oxygen and glucose. In these circumstances, once the brain is dead, so is the entire individual. However, it is possible for the brain to be effectively dead while the heart carries on beating and respiration continues. In this case the individual cannot respond to the environment, but is in some way alive, although artificial feeding is needed to maintain life. There have been a number of legal cases where, after a patient has been fed artificially in a brain dead state for years, the family have applied to have feeding stopped so that the patient may die in all senses. There is a great deal of discussion about the ethics of this type of decision and the circumstances in which it should be made. In some cases, the functions of the heart and lungs are maintained artificially until the damage to the brain can be assessed. If the patient is shown by repeated tests to be brain dead then the artificial ventilation will be turned off.

For many old people death creeps up very gently as their body systems become increasingly less able to cope with the demands of everyday life. However, many others both old and young have to face up to the knowledge of their own impending death from a terminal illness. This is very difficult for people to come to terms with. The process of acceptance generally has five phases. The first response is denial – 'It can't be me'. This is usually followed by anger at the situation and those involved – 'Why me?' is the most frequently expressed emotion. Many people then go through a stage of bargaining with fate, trying to gain a bit more life, followed by depression as the symptoms of illness increase and physical deterioration becomes more obvious. People often feel very afraid of death and the process of dying at this point. Finally comes an acceptance of the inevitable as the end approaches. Although most death certificates show a specific cause of death, which may be cancer, stroke, heart failure, etc., many people really die of old age after a lengthy and gradual process of physical decline. Death in hospital may be a peaceful event, with the dying person surrounded by the family that they love. But sadly there are many people for whom death in an institution is a very lonely affair, with no one except professional care-givers around. These people may well die alone.

The hospice movement

The modern hospice movement was founded in 1967 by Cicely Saunders. She founded St Christopher's Hospice in London to cope with the problem of incurable people, particularly cancer patients, dying in hospitals. She felt that the purpose of hospitals was to cure patients. As a result, doctors and nurses were not comfortable with incurable patients and so dying patients were given painkillers but largely ignored as they were a reminder of failure. Hospices set out specifically to help and support dying patients. They specialise in **palliative care**, offering treatment to ease pain and maintain dignity but not using unnecessary and ineffective treatment in an effort to cure the disease. They openly discuss death and its implications, offering counselling to both patients and their families. If possible, the hospice helps people to die peacefully in their own homes, with hospice beds available to provide respite for both patient and carers. The family of the patient is often closely involved, and volunteers from the community also help people in the hospice to get as much quality out of their lives as possible. The hospice movement in the UK and Ireland has grown rapidly in the 30 years since it began, with around 3000 beds now available.

Figure 6.9 Hospices like Rachel House try to address all the needs of dying patients – physical, emotional and spiritual – and to help make the death of a loved family member as positive an experience as possible for all those involved.

Attitudes to ageing

Ageing presents us with some major issues both as individuals and as a society. Many of the health-related issues of ageing have been dealt with in the preceding paragraphs. There is also the question of how we deal psychologically with the process of ageing. Some people find the onset of the signs of ageing, such as greying hair, wrinkling skin and baldness in men, deeply distressing and difficult to deal with. This is particularly so in many countries in the developed world, where society decrees that youth and youthful looks are important, particularly for women. Enormous sums of money are spent annually on creams and lotions, hair colorants and hair restorers, exercise routines and plastic surgery as men and women alike try to hold back the tide of time and make themselves look younger than their chronological age. In other cultures, age is revered for the accumulated years of wisdom it brings, and this must make living with the ageing process much easier for the individual. However, there are many older people in our society who are quite comfortable with their looks and who maintain both physically and intellectually active lives into great old age.

In addition to individual issues, our increasing knowledge of the processes of ageing, and our increasing ability to prolong the lives of many people by successful medical intervention, raise many questions for us as a society. As people get older, in general their need for support within the community increases. The life expectation in the population of the UK is increasing, and is predicted to continue increasing well into the next century, as figure 6.10 shows.

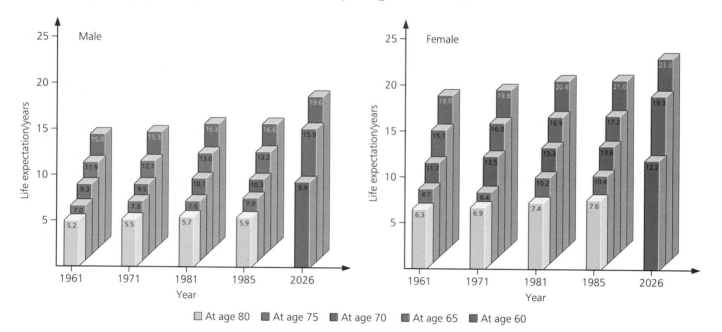

Figure 6.10 Predicted patterns of life expectation at different ages in the UK.

Changes in family and social structures in the late twentieth century, such as children living and working in different parts of the country from their parents and increasing numbers of marriages ending in divorce, make it more and more unlikely that ageing individuals will be cared for by their own families. The burden of care for the elderly falls onto society as a whole. At its most intensive (and expensive), support for the elderly involves residential nursing care. Other elderly people need residential care once they can no longer manage to cook, shop, wash and clean – in other words, take care of themselves and their homes. Yet others need the support of carers within their own homes. All this support for the elderly population costs a considerable amount of money. As figure 6.11 shows, in the UK, demographic trends suggest that the elderly population is set to increase substantially over the next 30 years, whilst the birth rate is falling. A growing ageing population will demand more support from a shrinking young working population.

These data also show that the group predicted to show the greatest percentage increase is the 80+ age group, and they are most likely to need help and support from the community. Thus the main issue for society raised

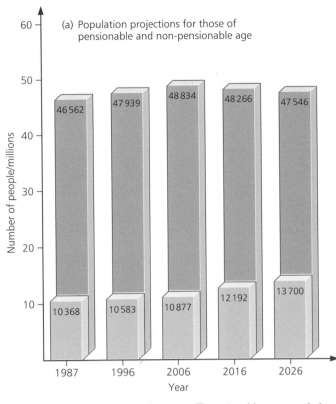

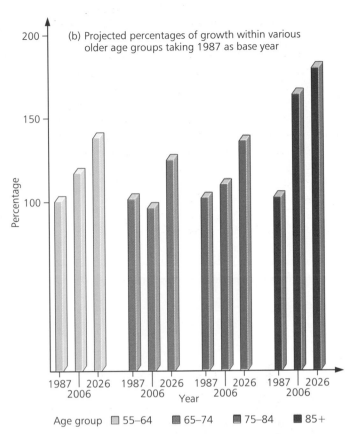

Figure 6.11 Demographic predictions of population trends in the UK. The pensionable age groups will form a larger percentage of the population as a whole, and the numbers in each older age group will rise substantially, particularly those over 85.

by these trends, which result from years of improved nutrition and health care, is who pays? At present in the UK, a base level of long-term care is provided for anyone who needs it, regardless of their ability to pay. However, the support is means tested and so many elderly people have to contribute to their own care, sometimes costing up to £20 000 a year. To fund this, people have to use their savings and sell their houses which they had planned to pass on to their children, whilst others with no savings get the same care for nothing. In addition, there are many private old people's homes and nursing homes. Many of these are excellent, but in others the conditions of care leave much to be desired as there are few regulations governing the setting up of such institutions. To try and alleviate some of the dissatisfaction of the current system, the UK government began in the 1990s to look at schemes whereby the cost of care in old age could be shared between the state and the individual. This would involve insurance companies setting up policies which individuals could pay into to cover the cost of care in old age and so protect against loss of savings. There would also need to be a commitment by the government that those who could not afford insurance would be guaranteed accommodation, and that health care would be free to all. Whether or not this sort of plan will come to fruition, and if not, what will take its place, is still very much open to discussion. However, it is certain that as society in the developed world moves further and further away from the model in the developing world, where care of elderly relatives falls directly to the younger generation, and parents expect to live with their children when they get old, the problem of how to finance the care of an ageing population is not going to go away.

The whole of the human life span involves a battle between health and disease. As ageing gradually takes place, the odds are stacked higher in favour of disease. And finally, in every human lifetime comes the point of death, when

Figure 6.12 The process of ageing can be tracked through the lifetime of an individual, as these pictures of HM Queen Elizabeth QM show. Biological deterioration occurs in the bodies of royalty and commoners alike.

SUMMARY

- Ageing is a progressive generalised impairment of function resulting from a loss of adaptive responses to stress and resulting in a growing risk of age-related diseases. There are degenerative changes in cells and the immune system becomes less effective with age.

- Ageing cells accumulate granules of a fatty substance called **lipofuscin**. This slows down cell metabolism. Whole-body changes include wrinkling of the skin, reduction in muscle and bone mass, problems with muscles and joints, deterioration of sight and hearing, increased susceptibility to cold and mental deterioration.

- During the **menopause**, the ovaries stop releasing ripe ova and the levels of hormones that control the menstrual cycle gradually fall, so the woman becomes infertile. Menstruation stops and other body changes are experienced.

- Elderly people cannot maintain their body temperature as well as they did when they were younger. This combined with a lack of proper heating and exercise can lead to **hypothermia**.

- There is a loss of muscle fibres from middle age onwards, which can be reduced by maintaining exercise and fitness. Cartilage becomes worn in the joints, which can lead to **osteoarthritis**, or bone cells appearing in the cartilage, making movement painful (**rheumatoid arthritis**). **Osteoporosis** is loss of bone density due to a loss of calcium salts from the bone. Hormone replacement therapy for women helps the calcium balance, and eating a diet rich in calcium and vitamin D and regular weight-bearing exercise help prevent the disease.

- The heart output falls with age, and the function of the respiratory system also falls, resulting in a reduction in the oxygen supplied to the cells and decrease in overall fitness. Regular gentle exercise improves this condition. The blood vessels become less flexible and fatty deposits may be laid down in the blood vessels, leading to increased risk of heart attacks and strokes.

- In the eye, the lens loses its ability to change shape, leading to visual difficulties. Lipofuscin builds up in the rods and cones, and vision is gradually impaired. In the ear, the sensory cells of the inner ear or the nerves or both may degenerate, leading to loss of hearing.

- **Alzheimer's disease** is a disintegration of the brain cells, leading to behavioural changes, disorientation, loss of memory, loss of control of bodily functions and eventually death.

- At **death**, the cellular processes of the body cease. The heart stops beating and breathing stops. The brain dies minutes after the blood stops circulating. It is possible for the brain to be dead while the heart and respiration continue.

QUESTIONS

1 Describe the effects of ageing on
  a the body cells
  b the heart and lungs
  c the muscles and skeleton
  d the reproductive system
  e the nervous system.

2 a Why are the elderly more prone to disease than the young?
  b What are the social implications for the developed world of an increasing life expectancy for the older population along with a falling birth rate?

Exam questions

1 a Describe the ways in which the human immunodeficiency virus (HIV) is transmitted. **(6 marks)**

b Discuss the effects of social, economic and biological factors on the control of HIV transmission. **(12 marks)**

(UCLES March 1997)

2 a What type of organism causes athlete's foot? **(1 mark)**

b How does this pathogen
  i obtain food **(1 mark)**
  ii reproduce? **(2 marks)**

c Suggest how the spread of athlete's foot can be limited by:
  i using disinfectants to wash the floors of public changing rooms **(1 mark)**
  ii thorough drying of the feet. **(1 mark)**

d Give *one* example of a chemical which may be used to treat athlete's foot. **(1 mark)**

(NEAB June 1996)

3 Mild food poisoning can be caused by a number of different types of bacteria. One such group of bacteria belongs to the genus *Campylobacter*. Humans usually become infected by *Campylobacter* by eating contaminated meat (especially chicken) or by drinking contaminated milk. The incidence of food poisoning caused by *Campylobacter* in England and Wales over a three-year period is shown in the graph.

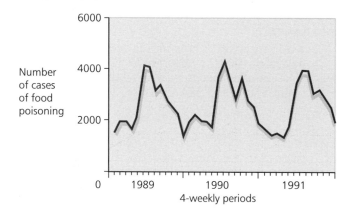

a What is meant by the term *genus*? **(2 marks)**

b Use the information given and your own knowledge to explain the seasonal variation in the incidence of food poisoning by *Campylobacter*. **(4 marks)**

(AEB June 1996)

4 If a woman does not breast-feed her baby, normal ovulatory cycles begin again eight to twelve weeks after the birth. However, if breast-feeding occurs, the cycles can be delayed for as long as four years, due to the inhibition of the hormones FSH and LH.

a Explain how lack of FSH and LH produces an infertile period. **(2 marks)**

b In hunter-gatherer societies, women breast-feed for as long as four years. Suggest and explain *two* reasons why this is important for such societies. **(4 marks)**

(NEAB June 1996)

5 a The pedigree shows the inheritance of ellipsocytosis, a condition which causes oval erythrocytes in humans. Only those with the dominant allele (**E**) are affected. The Rhesus phenotype caused by the presence of the dominant allele (**R**) is also shown.

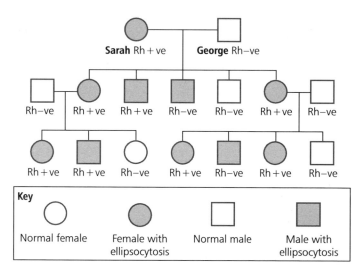

  i Assuming that the gene for ellipsocytosis and the gene for the Rhesus factor are found on the same chromosome, draw a fully labelled genetic diagram of the cross between Sarah and George. **(6 marks)**

  ii What evidence is there in the data provided that the genes for ellipsocytosis and the Rhesus factor are linked on the same chromosome? **(2 marks)**

  iii Is there any evidence in the data that either of the genes is sex-linked? Explain your answer. **(2 marks)**

  iv One form of ellipsocytosis can produce harmful effects. A man and his father suffer from this form of the disease, but the man's mother was normal. The man has married a normal woman. Assuming that the harmful allele can be detected in a fetus, what advice might be given to the couple who are worried about having an affected baby? **(2 marks)**

b The diagram shows the karyotype of an individual affected by Klinefelter's syndrome.

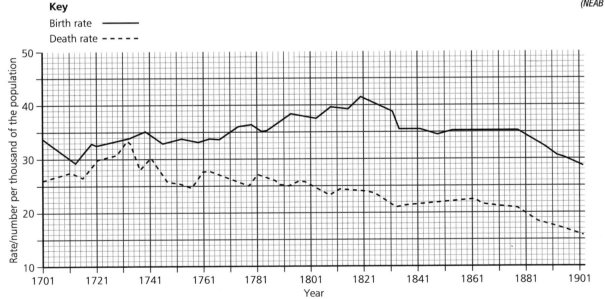

1 2 3 4 5

6 7 8 9 10 11 12

13 14 15 16 17 18

19 20 21 22 X X Y

i Giving your reasons indicate the gender of this individual. **(1 mark)**

ii What is this *type* of chromosomal mutation called? Suggest how it could arise during gametogenesis. **(3 marks)**

iii Some males have an XYY genotype. Such males are usually fertile. If such a man married and had children by a normal female, what possible genotypes could arise in their offspring? Your answer should include a labelled genetic diagram to explain this. **(4 marks)**

c Explain how the *gene* mutation which causes sickle cell anaemia could give rise to changes in the gene pool. **(4 marks)**

(AEB June 1995)

6 a Describe briefly the effects of nicotine and carbon monoxide on the cardiovascular system. **(6 marks)**

b Discuss the social and medical difficulties encountered in controlling heart disease. **(12 marks)**

(UCLES March 1996)

7 a Describe briefly how cholera and malaria are transmitted. **(6 marks)**

b Discuss the social, economic and biological problems involved in controlling the spread of *either* cholera *or* malaria. **(12 marks)**

(UCLES March 1996)

8 The graph below shows the changes in birth rate and death rate in England and Wales during the eighteenth and nineteenth centuries.

a i During which year did the population grow least? **(1 mark)**

ii Calculate the population growth rate in 1861. Show your working. **(2 marks)**

b Two reasons for the change in death rate between 1741 and 1901 were the introduction of vaccination and the effective disposal of sewage. Explain how each of these two factors was effective in reducing the death rate. **(4 marks)**

(NEAB June 1996)

Key

Birth rate ———

Death rate - - - - -

9 **a** Give *three* ways in which antibiotics may prevent the growth of microorganisms. **(3 marks)**

b The graph shows the number of cases of a sexually transmitted disease caused by bacteria resistant to penicillin between the years 1976 and 1982.

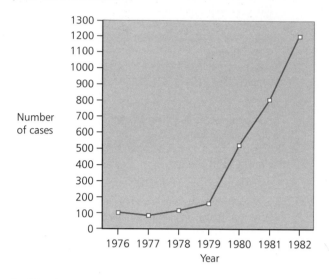

Explain why the incidence of this disease between 1976 and 1982 underwent the pattern of change shown in the graph. **(3 marks)**

(NEAB June 1996)

10 **a** Give *two* symptoms of Down's syndrome. **(2 marks)**

b The diagram shows the chromosomes of a male with Down's syndrome.

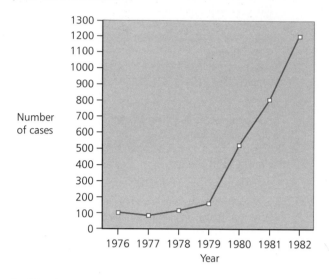

i What chromosome abnormality is responsible for Down's syndrome in this male? **(1 mark)**

ii Explain how this abnormality occurs. **(3 marks)**

c The unborn babies of women over 35 years old may be routinely screened for Down's syndrome. Suggest a suitable technique for this purpose. Give a reason for your choice. **(2 marks)**

(NEAB June 1996)

11 **a** The table below shows how some human infectious diseases are spread. Copy the table and fill in the blank spaces. **(3 marks)**

Disease agent	Method of transmission	Example
Bacterium	Drinking water	
		Influenza
H.I.V.		AIDS
	Contact with animals	

b Schistosomiasis (Bilharzia) is a disease produced by a parasite whose life cycle is shown below.

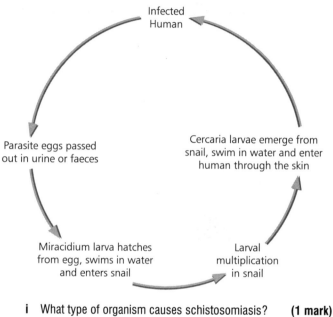

i What type of organism causes schistosomiasis? **(1 mark)**

ii Describe *one* effect that the organism has on the human host. **(1 mark)**

iii The eggs hatch when exposed to a hypotonic solution (one of less negative solute potential).
Why is this a useful adaptation to the parasite's way of life? **(2 marks)**

iv Describe *one* method for the *prevention* of schistosomiasis. **(1 mark)**

c Fig. 1 shows the world distribution of schistosomiasis and Fig. 2 shows the distribution of malaria.

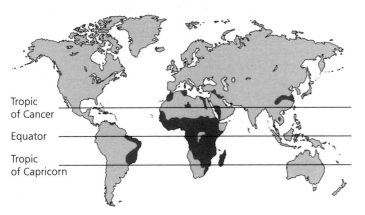

Fig. 1

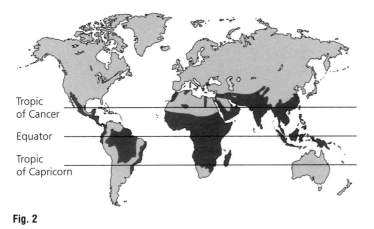

Fig. 2

Comment on the different distributions of the two diseases and give a possible explanation. **(2 marks)**

(O&C June 1997)

12 a Explain how viruses cause disease. **(2 marks)**

b Explain why diseases caused by viruses are difficult to treat using drugs. **(2 marks)**

c The diagram shows the structures of the molecule deoxyguanosine used in DNA synthesis and an anti-viral drug, acyclovir. This drug is used to treat infections caused by the Herpes virus. Acyclovir is activated by an enzyme present only in cells infected by the Herpes virus.

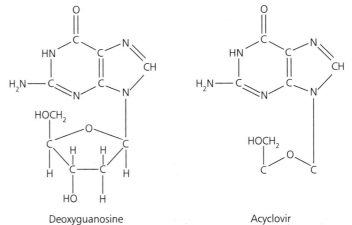

Deoxyguanosine   Acyclovir

i Suggest how the drug acyclovir may help to inhibit viral reproduction. **(2 marks)**

ii Explain why this drug would not be effective in the treatment of other viral infections. **(1 mark)**

(NEAB June 1996)

13 The nutritional information below is typical of that given on packets of fruit and flake cereal.

INGREDIENTS
Wheatflakes (wheat, sugar, salt, malt); raisins; cornflakes (maize, sugar, salt, malt); dates; honey-dipped banana; dried apple

---

NUTRITION
Average value

	Per 100 g	Per 40 g serving
Energy	1358 kJ	571 kJ
	325 kcal	135 kcal
Protein	5.9 g	2.4 g
Carbohydrate	72.1 g	28.8 g
of which sugars	30.4 g	12.2 g
Fat	2.8 g	1.1 g
of which saturates	1.6 g	0.6 g
Fibre	6.2 g	2.5 g
Sodium	0.4 g	0.2 g

---

a Explain why it is useful for consumers to be given information about the product's fibre and sodium content. **(4 marks)**

b Do you consider this product to be a balanced, healthy food? Give reasons for your answer. **(4 marks)**

c What additional information could the manufacturer have provided that would have been useful to health-conscious consumers? **(2 marks)**

d Sugars are listed separately from total carbohydrates.
  i Calculate the percentage of carbohydrate in the form of sugar in a 100 g portion of this cereal. Show your working. **(1 mark)**
  ii Give *two* reasons why sugars such as sucrose are alleged to be bad for your health. **(2 marks)**

e Some women eat relatively low amounts of dairy foods because they are considered to be too high in calories and saturated fat. Give a scientific explanation of the possible long-term harmful effects on such women of not eating dairy foods. **(2 marks)**

(O&C June 1996)

14 Thalassaemia is an inherited condition controlled by a single gene with two alleles, the allele for thalassaemia being recessive. It is a disorder which affects the functioning of red blood cells causing anaemia. This condition was common in Cyprus twenty-five years ago, but since then the incidence has decreased significantly. This decrease resulted from a programme of genetic screening and counselling.

a Genetic screening involves testing individuals in the population for the presence of the thalassaemia allele. Which genotype would it be important to identify by this process? Explain your answer. **(2 marks)**

b Explain how genetic counselling might have led to a reduction of the incidence of the disease. **(3 marks)**

c Suggest why it is unlikely that the allele for thalassaemia will be eliminated from the population. **(2 marks)**

(NEAB June 1996)

15 The drawing shows the structure of an influenza virus.

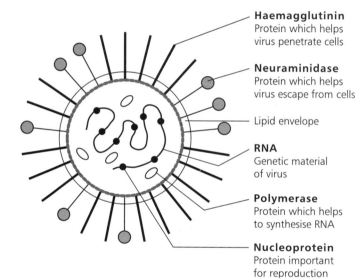

Haemagglutinin
Protein which helps virus penetrate cells

Neuraminidase
Protein which helps virus escape from cells

Lipid envelope

RNA
Genetic material of virus

Polymerase
Protein which helps to synthesise RNA

Nucleoprotein
Protein important for reproduction

a Influenza vaccines may be made from parts of viruses. Give *one* part of the virus that would be suitable for making a vaccine. Give a reason for your answer. **(2 marks)**

b In order to provide protection against influenza, it is necessary to vaccinate people with a different vaccine every year. Suggest an explanation for this. **(2 marks)**

c Explain why it is unlikely that influenza affected early human hunter-gatherer groups. **(1 mark)**

(AEB June 1996)

16 A student designed an investigation to find out how much exercise was necessary to improve the aerobic fitness of a group of seventeen year olds. The student planned the investigation as follows:
- select twenty people who do not take exercise on a regular basis
- organise the group into pairs, matching them for gender, age, body mass and height
- select one member of each pair to carry out the training programme
- train by swimming several lengths of a swimming pool at a fixed speed so that the pulse rate reaches approximately 70% of the age predicted maximum (calculated by subtracting the person's age from 220)
- train for twenty minutes on three occasions every week
- measure the resting pulse rate of the whole group at regular intervals.

a In this investigation,
  i explain why the resting pulse rate is recorded throughout **(2 marks)**
  ii state *one advantage* of measuring resting pulse rate. **(1 mark)**
b Explain why
  i the student selected people who did not take exercise on a regular basis **(1 mark)**
  ii one of each pair did *not* follow the training programme **(1 mark)**
  iii the subjects were matched for gender, body mass, age and height **(1 mark)**
  iv the subjects exercised at approximately 70% of their maximum pulse rate. **(1 mark)**
c Suggest how the student should analyse the data collected from this investigation to find out if there was a significant improvement in aerobic fitness. **(4 marks)**
d Explain why swimming for twenty minutes is better than weight lifting for improving aerobic fitness. **(2 marks)**
e State *one long-term* consequence of exercise on muscle. **(1 mark)**

(UCLES March 1997)

17 The table shows the timing of some of the aspects of puberty in a large sample of girls and boys.

Event	Average age at which event begins/years	Range of ages at which event begins/years	Average age at which event ends/years	Range of ages at which event ends/years
Height spurt in girls	10.5	8.5–14.0	14.0	12.5–15.5
Development of breasts	10.8	8.0–13.0	14.8	12.0–18.0
First menstrual period	13.0	10.5–15.5	not applicable	not applicable
Height spurt in boys	12.5	10.5–16.5	16.0	14.0–17.5
Growth of penis	12.5	10.5–14.5	14.5	12.5–16.5
Growth of testes	11.5	9.5–13.5	15.5	14.0–17.0

a Suggest *two* possible explanations for the variation in the age at which puberty begins in girls. **(2 marks)**
b Use the information in the table to give
  i the earliest age at which a girl in the sample could have completed the aspects of puberty shown **(1 mark)**
  ii the range of ages when *all* boys in the sample were in the process of puberty. **(1 mark)**
c Which hormone is mainly responsible for
  i the development of the breasts **(1 mark)**
  ii growth and development of the testes? **(1 mark)**

(NEAB June 1996)

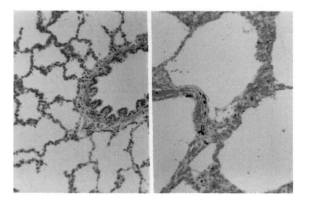

Healthy lung tissue showing a bronchiole and about 25 alveoli

Lung tissue from a person with emphysema

18 The photomicrographs above show healthy lung tissue and lung tissue from a person with emphysema. The photomicrographs are to the same scale.

   a Give *two* differences that can be seen between healthy lung tissue and lung tissue from the person with emphysema. **(2 marks)**

   b Explain why people suffering from severe emphysema may find it difficult to climb stairs or walk up hills. **(3 marks)**

   c i Emphysema is a common industrial disease of people who have worked in mining and quarrying industries. Suggest *one* feature these industries have in common that could increase the risk of emphysema. **(1 mark)**

    ii Suggest *one* way in which the workers in these industries could be protected from exposure to this factor. **(1 mark)**

(NEAB June 1996)

19 Measles is still a leading cause of death in young children in many developing countries. In 1992, at the World Summit for Children, the World Health Organisation (WHO) announced the target of reducing mortality in children under the age of five to less than 70 per 1000 live births by the year 2000. This target was to be achieved by immunising children against childhood diseases (diphtheria, whooping cough, measles, polio and tuberculosis), to reduce the number of cases of measles by 90% and the numbers of deaths by 95% by 1995.

Measles immunisation coverage worldwide reached a peak of 80% of children under one year old in 1990, but by 1995 it had fallen to 78%. The number of cases of measles, however, did decrease. The Americas region of the WHO has committed itself to eliminating measles by the year 2000 and now has a campaign to interrupt the transmission of the disease. In 1996, the incidence of measles was at the lowest ever recorded in the Americas.

   a Explain why measles is an important disease in developing countries. **(3 marks)**

The first measles vaccine to be used routinely was introduced in Britain in 1964. However, in 1993, there were over 9000 cases of measles notified to the health authorities in England and Wales.

   b Explain why measles has not been eliminated in Britain. **(2 marks)**

   c Explain how vaccination interrupts the transmission of measles. **(2 marks)**

The incidence of measles in a country in 1992 was 350 cases per 1000 children below the age of one year old.

   d State the incidence that had to be achieved if this country was to meet the WHO target of a 90% reduction by 1995. **(1 mark)**

   e Explain why it is important for the World Health Organisation to set targets, such as those for reducing childhood mortality. **(2 marks)**

   f Explain why it will be far more difficult to eliminate malaria than it will be to eliminate measles. **(3 marks)**

(UCLES March 1997)

20 Write an essay on the biological problems associated with ageing. Credit will be given not only for the biological content, but also for the organisation and presentation of the essay, and use of grammar, punctuation and spelling. **(25 marks)**

(AEB June 1996)

21a Copy and complete the table below to show reasons for including each of the following substances in the human diet. The first example has been given as an illustration. **(4 marks)**

Constituent of diet	Reasons for inclusion in diet
Fluorine	Hardens tooth enamel
Iron	1.
	2.
Niacin	
Essential amino acids	

   b Intake of saturated fat increases the risk of coronary heart disease. Apart from diet, state *two* other factors that increase such risk. **(2 marks)**

   c What effect does exercise have on the following at rest?
    i the stroke volume
    ii the vascular resistance
    iii blood volume and haemoglobin content. **(3 marks)**

(O&C June 1997)

22 When foreign antigens enter the body, they often initiate an immune response which leads to the production of antibodies and an immunity. Vaccinations have been used for many years as a means of inducing an immune response and immunity without contracting the disease. The vaccines used in the United Kingdom against influenza are based on inactivated viruses which must be injected. In other countries, the vaccines used contain "live", attenuated viruses which can be delivered by a nasal spray.

a **i** What is an antigen? **(1 mark)**
   ii What is an antibody? **(2 marks)**

b Suggest a biological advantage in being able to deliver an influenza vaccine by means of a nasal spray. **(1 mark)**

c Suggest a possible danger in using "live", attenuated viruses in vaccines. **(2 marks)**

(AEB June 1996)

23 a During a hospital check-up it was found that Mr Binge's liver removed alcohol from his bloodstream at the rate of 9.4 cm³ alcohol per hour. One evening Mr Binge consumed the following drinks.

Beverage	Measure consumed	Volume of each measure (cm³)	Alcohol content (%)
Beer	4 cans	440	3.7
White wine	1 glass	180	8.6
Whisky	2 glasses	45	40.0

Assuming that the entire alcohol content of these beverages was absorbed into Mr Binge's bloodstream, calculate how long it would take for all the alcohol to be removed. Show your working. **(2 marks)**

b Suggest *two* different factors that might affect the rate at which alcohol is absorbed from the human gastrointestinal tract. **(2 marks)**

c Explain how excessive, long-term consumption of alcohol might adversely affect the following body systems:
   i gastrointestinal tract **(2 marks)**
   ii nervous system. **(2 marks)**

(O&C June 1996)

24 The photograph shows a section through a mammalian ovary. The magnification of this photograph is 90 times.

a **i** Calculate the *actual* diameter of *A/B* in micrometres. Show your working. **(2 marks)**
   ii In a human ovary, how many chromosomes would one of the cells labelled **X** contain? **(1 mark)**

b Suggest how a similar section of an ovary would be different in:
   i an infant shortly after birth **(1 mark)**
   ii a sixty-five year old woman. **(1 mark)**

c Some methods of contraception affect the ovary; others do not. Explain why:
   i the ovary from a woman using an oestrogen based oral contraceptive would not contain maturing ovarian follicles **(2 marks)**

   ii the ovary from a woman who had been sterilised by cutting and tying her oviducts might contain all the stages of follicle development shown in the photograph. **(2 marks)**

d Some women are infertile because their anterior pituitary glands do not produce enough hormones to trigger the development of any immature ovarian follicles.
Suggest how the use of drugs might improve the chance of conception. **(3 marks)**

(AEB June 1996)

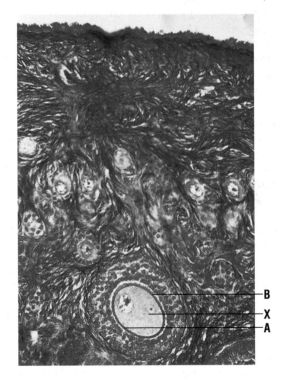

Index

abortion 116
acquired immune deficiency
    syndrome see AIDS
acute diseases 71
acyclovir 41
addiction 88
    to alcohol 96, 100–1
    to barbiturates 86
    to heroin 107–8
    to nicotine 89–90, 92, 95
additives see food additives
ADH see antidiuretic hormone
adjuvants 44–5
adrenaline 77
    allergy treatment 56
    and heart rhythm 75
aetiology of disease 8–10, 14
age, and causes of death 15
age standardised mortality ratios
    17, 18
ageing 137–6, 150
    attitudes to 147–9
    and basal metabolic rate 144
    and bronchitis incidence 73
    and cancer risk 82, 93
    defined 136
    and degenerative diseases 9
    and dietary requirements 59, 61
    and driving after drinking 103
    and heart disease 81, 143, 144
    and mental illness 8
    and nervous system 144–6
    signs of 138–9
        cellular 137–8
    and skeletal system 139–43
    and stroke incidence 143, 144
    theories of 136–7
    and vulnerability to
    hypothermia 140
    see also menopause
agglutinins 31, 32–3
agglutinogens 31, 32
AID see artificial insemination by
    donor
AIDS (acquired immune deficiency
    syndrome) 3–5, 25, 34
alcohol 86, 108
    abuse of 99, 100–1
    effects of
        on body 96–9
        on society 102–5
allergic reactions 56
    asthma as 69
    and vaccinations 47
alpha-fetoprotein 124
alveoli 70
Alzheimer's disease 145–6
amino acids 58
amniocentesis 123
amoebic dysentery 24
anabolic steroids 86
anaemia 58, 115
aneuploidy 122
aneurysm 78
angina 79

angiotensin-converting enzyme
    inhibitors 77
Anopheles 2
anorexia nervosa 67
anthrax 34
antibiotics 38–40
    bacteriostatic or bactericidal
        action 40
    broad- and narrow-spectrum 39
    effect on microorganisms 39
    resistance to 22, 39, 40–1
    sensitivity to 39, 40
    stomach cancer treatment 63
    tuberculosis treatment 49
antibodies 29, 30, 31
    detection by ELISA 11–12
    monoclonal 36–7
anti-D injections 33
antidiuretic hormone (ADH) 98
antigens 29, 30, 31
    detection by ELISA 11–12
    frequent change in 34
antioxidants (food preservatives) 64
antiseptics 39
arthritis 141
artificial insemination by donor
    (AID) 118, 120
ascorbic acid (food preservative) 64
asthma 9
    monitoring with peak flow
        meter 69, 71
    and tobacco smoke 94
    and vaccinations 47
atheroma 78
atherosclerosis 76, 78, 79
    smoking and 91
athlete's foot 23
    fungus causing 19
atrioventricular node (AVN) 75
autosome abnormalities 122–4

B-cells 29, 30, 36
babies
    defences against disease 30
    fetal alcohol syndrome 102, 105
bacteria 9, 19, 21–2
bactericidal antibiotics 40
bacteriostatic antibiotics 40
balanced diet 57–8
barbiturates 86
barium meal 12
Barnard, Christiaan 80
Barr bodies 125, 126
basal metabolic rate 59
    age-related changes 144
BCG vaccine 50
benzopyrene 93
beta agonists 69
beta blockers 77–8, 79
beta receptors 77–8
biochemical testing 11
biosensor 11
blood
    clotting 27–8
    effects of carbon monoxide
        in 90–1

blood alcohol level 96–7, 97–8
blood groups
    ABO system 31–2
    rhesus system 32–3
blood pressure 75–8, 83
    smoking and 89, 91
blood transfusions 31–2
    HIV transmission 3–4
    for rhesus-affected babies 33
body weight 66–7
bones, effects of ageing 141–2
botulism 35
brain
    CAT scan 13
    damage by alcohol 100
    effects of Alzheimer's disease 145
    see also hypothalamus
breast examination 83
breast feeding
    and dietary requirements 59, 61
    HIV transmission in 4
    ovulation suppression by 116
breathalyser 103
bronchi 70
bronchioles 70
bronchitis 71–3, 92
bulimia 67

caffeine 87, 88–9
calcium, in diet 58, 61
calcium antagonists 77, 79
cancer 10, 14, 82–3
    and alcohol consumption 100–1
    causes 82–3, 92
    of colon 62–3
    diagnosis 13
    and hormone replacement
        therapy 139
    of lung 14, 92
    screening for 83
    smoking and 14, 92–3
    of stomach 64
    see also Kaposi's sarcoma
Candida albicans 23
carbohydrates, in diet 58, 62
carbon monoxide, in cigarette
    smoke 90–1
carcinogens
    in cigarette smoke 92
    Helicobacter pylori as 64
cardiovascular system
    diseases 74–82
    effects of ageing 138, 143–4
    see also heart
care in old age 148–9
cascade system (blood clotting
    mechanism) 28
CAT scanners 13
CD4 glycoprotein 4
cell-mediated immune response
    29, 30
cells, ageing 137–8
cervical smears 83
Chain, Ernst 38, 39
chemotherapy 36
cholera 25, 42, 51

cholesterol 68, 83
chorionic villus sampling 123
chromosomes
    abnormal numbers 122
    and meiosis 121
    karyotypes 124
    nondisjunction 122, 125
    sex, abnormalities 125–7
    see also autosome abnormalities
chronic diseases 71
circulatory diseases, and social
    class 17
cirrhosis of the liver 100
clomiphene 118
Clostridium botulinum 35
Clostridium tetani 27
clotting of blood 27–8
colon cancer 62–3
colourings for foods 64–5
columnar epithelium 70
COMA report 60
Committee on Medical Aspects of
    Food Policy (COMA) 60
common cold virus 19
common-source oubreaks of
    disease 25, 27
computer-assisted tomography 13
constipation 62, 63
contact tracing 50
contraception
    methods 112–15
    social issues 115–16
contraceptive pill 113, 114–15
coronary heart disease see heart
    disease
costal cartilage 141
cot death 94
crime, alcohol and 104
cuboidal epithelium 70
cystic fibrosis 127–8, 131, 132–3

D and C (dilatation and
    curettage) 116
death 146–7, 149
defences against disease
    non-specific 27–9
    see also immune system
deficiency diseases 9–10, 58–9, 67
degenerative diseases 9
delirium tremens 101
dementia 8
dermophytes 23
diabetes
    biochemical test 11
    treatment by genetic
        manipulation 133
diagnosis
    use of monoclonal antibodies 37
    see also disease, detecting
diamorphine see heroin
diaphragm 70
diarrhoeal illnesses 51, 52, 57
diastole 75
diastolic blood pressure 76

diet 57–67
  deficiencies in *see* deficiency
    diseases
  nutritional guidelines 60–2
  role in heart disease 67–8
  'slimming' 67
dietary reference values
  (DRVs) 60
diphtheria vaccine 44
direct contact, disease
  transmission by 25, 26
disease 6–7
  causes 8–10, 14
  detecting 10–14
  diet and 55–68
  studying (epidemiology)
    14–18, 93
  types 7–8
disinfectants 39
disposable soma theory 137
diuretics 77
diverticulitis 62
DNA–RNA hybridisation 129–30
doctor–patient relationship 10–11
Doll, Richard 14, 92
Down's syndrome 122–4, 127
driving, drinking and 103–4
drugs 86–108
  addiction 86, 107–8
  angina treatment 79
  antihistamine 56
  antiviral 5, 41
  asthma therapy 69
  defined 86
  HIV therapy 5
  hypertension treatment 77–8
  illegal 105–8
  immunosuppressant 33, 80
  ovulation-stimulating 118–19
  recreational 86–8
  sulphonamide 38
  tolerance 88, 97
  tuberculosis treatment 49
  see also antibiotics
Duchenne muscular
  dystrophy 127
duodenal ulcers 63–4
dysentery, amoebic 24

E-numbers 64
ecstasy 87, 105–6
Edwards, Robert 120
electrocardiogram 79
elimination of disease 42
ELISA (enzyme-linked
  immunosorbent assay) 11–12
emphysema 73, 92
endemic diseases 25
endocarditis 107
endometrium 114
endorphins 81, 106–7
endoscopy 13–14
energy requirements 59
  age-related changes 144
  nutrients supplying 60, 62
enzyme-linked immunosorbent
  assay (ELISA) 11–12
epidemics 25
  influenza 20
epidemiology 14–18, 93
epithelia 28, 70
eradication of disease 42
Escherichia coli 9, 34
  Scottish food poisoning
    outbreak 56–7
essential amino acids 58

essential fatty acids 58
estimated average requirements
  (EARs) 59, 60
ethanol *see* alcohol
ethical issues
  concerning abortion 116
  concerning genetic
    manipulation 133
  concerning infertility
    treatment 120
  concerning treatment of brain
    dead patients 146–7
ethnic origin
  and blood group 31
  and blood pressure 76
  and health 15–16
eukaryotic organisms 21
exercise 81–2, 140, 142, 144
expiratory reserve volume 71, 72
eyesight, age-related changes 144

Fallopian tubes 117, 118
fats
  in diet 58, 62, 81
  and heart disease 67–8
Feingold diet 65
fertility drugs 118
fetal alcohol syndrome 102, 105
fetoscopy 124
fever 35–6
fibre, dietary 59, 62–3
fibrin 27–8
fibrinogen 27, 28
fitness *see* physical fitness
flagellae (bacteria) 21
flavour enhancers 65
flavourings 65
Fleming, Alexander 38, 39
flora of body
  normal 8–9, 27
  of skin 27
Florey, Howard 38, 39
follicle stimulating hormone
  (FSH) 114, 118, 117.
fomites 26
food additives 64–5
food allergies 56
food-borne infections 56–7
  see also Salmonella
food hygiene regulations 22
fungi 19, 23

gamete intra-fallopian transfer
  (GIFT) 120
gaseous exchange in lung 70
gastric ulcers 63–4
gender differences
  alcohol metabolism 98
  arthritis incidence 141
  blood alcohol levels 97
  causes of death 15
  dietary requirements 59, 61
  GP consultations 8
  heart disease incidence 15, 81
  heart disease mortality 68
  life expectation 148
  lung volumes 72
  multiple sclerosis incidence 129
  and perceptions of ageing 136
gene probes 129–30
genetic counselling 133–4
genetic diseases 9, 14, 121–34
genetic screening 130–2
genetic testing 130
German measles (rubella) 45–6
glucose, measurement of urine
  level 11

glyceryl trinitrate 79
Graham, Hilary 95
Gruinard Island 34
Gusella, James 128–9
gut, defences against disease 29

haemophilia 3, 28
Haemophilus influenzae 19
haemorrhoids 62
hallucinogens 87
health, defined 6
health education
  on cardiovascular disease 81
  on smoking 92
hearing, age-related changes 145
heart
  action of healthy 74–5
  variations in rate 77
heart attack (myocardial
  infarction) 79
heart bypass 80
heart disease 7, 78, 79, 80
  ageing and 143, 144
  alcohol and 99
  and ethnic origin 15–16
  gender differences in 15
  risk factors 81–2
  role of diet in 67–8
  smoking and 80, 81, 91
heart transplants 80
heartburn 98
Helicobacter pylori 63, 64
helminthes 24
helper T-cells 4
hepatitis B vaccine 44
herd effect (vaccination
  programmes) 45
heroin 87, 106–8
heterotrophic organisms 23
hip joint, effect of
  osteoarthritis 141
histamine 56, 69
HIV (human immunodeficiency
  virus) 3–5, 131
horizontal transmission of
  disease 25
hormone replacement therapy
  (HRT) 139, 142
hospices 147
Human Genome Project 130, 131
human immunodeficiency virus
  see HIV
humoral immune response 29, 30
Huntington's disease (chorea)
  128–9, 130
hybridomas 36–7
hyperactivity 65
hypertension 75–8, 83
hypothalamus
  body temperature
    maintenance 35
  body water content
    regulation 98
hypothermia 140

illness 6
  mental 8
  minor 7
  physical 7–8
immune response 4
  pathogen defence against 34
immune system 29–31
  failure with ageing 138
  suspension in pregnancy 32, 33
  temperature sensitivity 36
  and transplant surgery 33

immunoglobulins 30, 56
immunological memory 29, 30
immunosorbent assay *see* enzyme-
  linked immuno sorbent assay
immunosuppressant drugs 33, 80
immunosuppressant pathogens 34
in vitro fertilisation (IVF)
  119–20, 132
infant mortality
  in different countries 16
  and social class 17
infectious diseases 8–9, 19–52
  controlling 36–49
    by vaccination 42–8
    use of antiseptics 39
    use of antiviral drugs 41
    use of monoclonal antibodies
      36–7
  eradicating or eliminating 42
  natural defences
    immune system 29–31
    nonspecific 27–9
  pathogens 33–5
    adaptations for success 33–5
    types 19–24
    virulence 24
  prevention 48–9
  symptoms 35–6
  transmission 24–7
  see also names of specific diseases
infertility 112, 117–21
inflammatory response 28, 36, 45
influenza 20, 25
  changing surface antigens 34
  vaccine 44
  varying virulence of virus 24
ingestion, disease transmission
  by 26
inhalation, disease transmission
  by 26
inherited diseases *see* genetic
  diseases
inoculation, disease transmission
  by 26
inspiratory capacity 72
inspiratory reserve volume 72
intercostal muscles 70
interferons 41
intrauterine device (IUD) 113, 115
ionising radiation 12
iron 115
  in diet 58, 60, 61
  'iron lung' 43
irritable bowel syndrome 62
isoniazid 49

Jenner, Edward 42
joints, effect of arthritis 141

Kaposi's sarcoma 3
keyhole surgery 14
Klinefelter's syndrome 125–6, 127

lactase 55
lactation *see* breast feeding
lactose intolerance 55
laudanum 106
leucocytes (white blood cells) 29–30
libido 111
life expectation 148
lifestyle diseases 10, 55–83
lipofuscin 137, 144
Lister, Joseph 39
listeriosis 56
live vaccines 42–3, 44, 47

liver
  alcohol metabolism in 98–9
  alcohol-related diseases of 100
lower reference nutrient intake
    (LRNI) 60
LSD 87
lung cancer 14, 92
lungs 70
  changes with ageing 138
  components of volume 71, 72
  measurement of capacity 69
luteinising hormone (LH) 114, 117
lymph nodes 29
lymphocytes 29, 30
  killer 29
lysosomes 137
lysozymes 28

macrophages 36
magnetic resonance imaging
    (MRI) 13
malaria 2–3, 42
malnutrition 66–7
marijuana 87, 105
marital status, and health 15
Marshall, Barry 63, 64
mast cells 56, 69
measles 7, 8, 42, 46
  in developing countries 17
  signs and symptoms 7
meiosis 121, 122
memory cells 29, 30
menopause 139
menstrual cycle 114
menstruation
  end at menopause 139
  iron loss in 60
mental illness 8
  and marital status 15
metafemales 125, 126, 127
metronidazole 24
microorganisms in body 8–9
milk 55
mineral salts, in diet 58, 61
miscarriage 116
monoclonal antibodies 36–7
monocytes 29
monogamous sexual
    relationships 111
monosodium glutamate 65
monosomies 122
morbidity 14
morphine 87, 106
mortality 14
  and social class 17–18
mortality ratios 17, 18
MRI (magnetic resonance
    imaging) 13
mucus
  produced by epithelia 28
  produced in lung 70
multicellular parasites 24
multifactorial diseases 130
multiple sclerosis 129
muscle fibres, loss with ageing
    139–40
muscular dystrophy 127
mutations 30, 40
mycelium 23
Mycobacterium bovis 49
Mycobacterium tuberculosis 34, 49
myeloma cells 36–7
myocardial infarction 79

natural killer cells 31
natural (rhythm) method of
    contraception 112, 113

Neisseria gonorrhoeae 34
neutrophils 36
nicotine 87, 89–90, 91, 95
nondisjunction of chromosomes
    122, 125
nutritional guidelines 60–62

obesity 66, 67, 81, 142–3
oestrogen 81, 114–15, 117,
    139, 142
oncogenes 82
opiates 106–8
opioids 106
opium 87, 106
osteoarthritis 7, 141
osteoporosis 141–2
outbreaks of disease 25, 27

p53 gene 93
pacemaker 75, 77
  artificial 80
painkillers 87
palliative care 147
pandemics 25
  influenza 20
parasites 9
  multicellular 24
  worms 19, 24
parasitic diseases 9
  see also malaria
passive smoking 93–4
Pasteur, Louis 42
pathogenicity 34
pathogens 8–9
  adaptations for success 33–5
  defences against *see* defences
      against disease
  mutations 30
  types 19–24
  virulence 24
peak flow meter 69, 71
penicillin 38, 41
Pfeifer, Gerd 93
phagocytes 28, 29–30, 36
phenol 39
phenylketonuria 132
physical fitness 81–2
  in older people 143, 144
physical illness 7–8
pili (bacteria) 21, 34
pituitary hormones 114, 117
plague 25
plaque (deposits in blood vessels)
    77, 78
plasmids 21
Plasmodium (malaria parasite) 2, 34
pleural membranes 70
pointsource oubreaks of disease
    25, 27
polio 42, 43–4
polygamous sexual
    relationships 111
population trends 149
pregnancy
  and dietary requirements 59, 61
  HIV transmission in 4
  monitoring by ultrasound
      13, 124
  risks in
    from alcohol consumption 102
    from herointaking 108
    from *Listeria* 56
    from rhesus incompatibility
        32–3
    from rubella 45
    from smoking 90–1

pregnancy tests 37
preservatives (food) 64
primary immune response 30
progesterone 114, 115, 117
prokaryotic organisms 21
prolactin 116
Prontosil 38
propranolol 77
proteins, in diet 58, 61, 62
prothrombin 27, 28
protooncogenes 82
protozoans 19, 23–4
psychiatric disorders *see* mental
    illness
Purkyne tissue 75

qualitative measures of health 6
quantitative descriptions of
    health 6

rashes 36
recommended daily amounts *see*
    reference nutrient intakes
reference nutrient intakes (RNIs)
    60, 61
reflux oesophagitis *see* heartburn
rehydration therapy 51, 52
rejection of transplants 33
relationships, role of alcohol in
    104–5
reproductive health 111–34
  fertility problems 112, 117–21
  genetic diseases 9, 14, 121–34
  sexually transmitted diseases 9,
      34, 111–12
reserve capacity 137
  decline with ageing 137, 138
residual volume 72
respiratory system 70
  changes with ageing 138
  changes due to arthritis 141
  diseases 69–73
    and influenza epidemics 20
    and social class 17
    see also tuberculosis
  effects of ageing 138, 143–4
  mucus production in 28
  see also lungs
rhesus factor 32–3
rheumatoid arthritis 141
rhythm method of contraception
    112, 113
rickets 58
rifampicin 49
road traffic accidents, and alcohol
    103–4
Röntgen, Wilhelm 12
roughage *see* fibre, dietary
rubella (German measles) 45–6

safe intake 60
Salmonella 21–2
Salmonella typhi 51
saturated fat 67–8
Saunders, Cicely 147
schistosomiasis 24
  parasite causing 19
screening 83
sebum 27
secondary immune response 30
sedatives 86
  alcohol as 96
selective toxicity 38
self-inflicted diseases 10
serotonin 27
set point 66

sex chromosomes, abnormalities
    125–7
sexual relationships 111
sexually transmitted diseases 9,
    34, 111–12
sickness 6
signs of disease 7
sinoatrial node (SAN) 75
skin
  defence against disease 27
  rashes 36
sleeping sickness
    (trypanosomiasis) 34
smallpox, vaccination against
    42, 48
smoking 10, 89–95
  and bronchitis 73
  and cancer 14, 92–3
  and damage to blood vessels
      77, 138–9
  economics 94–5
  and emphysema 73
  and heart disease 80, 81, 91
  passive 93–4
  reasons for 95
  and sudden infant death
      syndrome 94
social class and health 17–18,
    72–3
social diseases *see* sexually
    transmitted diseases
sodium cromoglycate 69
spermatogenesis 118
sphygmomanometer 75
spina bifida 124
spirometer 72
spores 34
sports sponsorship 95
squamous epithelium 70
standardised mortality ratios 17, 18
Staphylococcus aureus, resistance to
    penicillin 41
Steptoe, Patrick 120
sterilisation 112, 113
steroids 69
  anabolic 86
stillbirths
  smoking and 91
  and social class 17, 18
stimulants 87
stomach cancer 64
stomach ulcers 63–4
stroke 76, 78, 79
  ageing and 143
  and ethnic origin 15–16
  smoking and 91
sudden infant death syndrome 94
sulphonamide drugs 38
'superbugs' 40, 41
superovulation 119, 120
surrogate mothers 120–21
sympathetic nervous system 77
symptoms of disease 7
  varying causes 10
systole 75
systolic blood pressure 76

T4 cells 4
T-cells 4, 29, 30
tar, in cigarette smoke 92
Tay-Sachs disease 131, 132
'test tube babies' *see in vitro*
    fertilisation
testes 118
  examination 83

testosterone 86
tetanus 27
thalassaemia 131–2
threadworms 24
thrombin 27, 28
thromboplastin 27, 28
thrombosis 78, 91
throughput time 62
thrush 23
tidal volume 72
tobacco smoking *see* smoking
tocopherol (food preservative) 64
total lung capacity 72
toxins, microbial 34, 44
Toxoplasma gondii 34
trachea 70
transplant surgery 33
Trichomonas vaginalis 19
trisomies 122
trypanosomiasis (sleeping
 sickness) 34

tuberculosis 42, 49–50
 changes in mortality 48
tumours 82–3
Turner's syndrome 125, 126, 127
typhoid 51

ultrasound 13, 124
'universal donors/recipients'
 (blood groups) 31
urinary system, mucus production
 in 28

vaccination 42–8
vaccines
 adjuvants in 44–5
 BCG 50
 British scheme 45
 cholera 51
 hepatitis B 44
 HIV 5
 influenza 20, 44
 live 42–3, 44, 47

measles 8, 46
polio 43, 44
risks 46, 47–8
rubella 45
smallpox 42
typhoid 51
whooping cough 47
vasectomy 113
vectors 2, 26
vertical transmission of disease 25
Vibrio cholerae 51
virulence of pathogens 24
viruses 19–20, 21
 drugs against 41
 mutations 30
 see also HIV
vital capacity 71, 72
vitamins 58, 61
 vitamin A 58
 vitamin C 64
 vitamin D 58–9, 142
 vitamin E 64
vomiting 10

water 59
white blood cells (leucocytes)
 29–30
 phagocytic *see* phagocytes
whooping cough
 changes in mortality 48
 vaccination against 47
withdrawal symptoms 88
 alcohol 101
 heroin 107
worms, parasitic 19

X-chromosomerelated diseases 15
X-rays 12–13

zinc, in diet 58, 61
zoonosis 25